POLITICS & CLIMATE CHANGE

A HISTORY

We the People

Bill of Rights

The SCIENTIFIC METHOD

SKEPTICS

AL GORE

ACADEMIA

Union of Concerned Scientists

GREENPEACE

ALARMISTS

ANDY MAY

Politics and Climate Change: A History

By Andy May

American Freedom Publications LLC

www.americanfreedompublications.com

2638 E. Wildwood Road

Springfield 65804

978-1-63625-261-2 Hardback Version

978-1-63625-262-9 Paperback Version

978-1-63625-263-6 eBook Version

Cover Design: Christopher. M. Capages

www.capagescreative.com

Manuscript Editor: Martin Capages Jr. PhD

First Edition- October 31, 2020

Printed in the United States of America

Dedication

To my fellow skeptics

Other Works by The Author

Climate Catastrophe! Science or Science Fiction?
Blood and Honor: The People of Bleeding Kansas

Acknowledgements

To my wife Aurelia for her patience during the preparation of another book by her husband.

Table of Contents

Foreword

Andy May has done a great service by compiling the actual recent history of climate change science. He ably dissects the distortions, errors and perhaps even, intentional deceptions in the political/scientific debate now embroiling this previously uncontroversial branch of earth and atmospheric science. The key descriptor is that term "political/scientific" that I mentioned. It shouldn't exist. There should be no political influence on science. It should always be the other way around. Science should help to define policy, but today, that is not the case. The Scientific Method as applied to climate change is in shambles.

When I was a kid, my dad gave me a simple radiometer as a birthday gift. It was a marvelous glass bulb with a rotor that had four triangular vanes painted black on one side and white on the other. The device was called a Crookes "light mill." My dad explained that that the black side of the vanes absorbed the light and the white reflected light making the rotor turn. He said it had to be in a vacuum to reduce drag. That was the theory according to Dad and even Crookes himself. Years later, I bought a Crookes radiometer as a desk ornament. I noticed that the rotor turned in the opposite direction than my dad's statement of the theory. So that theory had to be wrong by observation. In 1879 Osborne Reynolds would prove that the mechanics involved related to the transfer of heat rather than the direct effect of photons and that having just the right degree of vacuum was vital. The actual process is called Thermal transpiration (or thermal diffusion) and refers to the thermal force on a gas due to a temperature difference. This effect is historically famous as being an explanation for the rotation of the Crookes radiometer. But, in defense of my dad, the internal politics in the world of famous scientists, in this case Maxwell and Reynolds, would keep the actual correct theory from the public.

The actual observations of changes in the climate caused by human activity will play out in a geological timeframe. Setting government policy, in particular energy policy, on dubious computer models is not rational. It is particularly unwise to make quality of life decisions for billons of people on the range of the standard deviation of a set of statistical models that lack any sense of peer review. But then, favorable peer reviews do not make a wrong theory correct either. In just means there are more wrong experts than we thought. And all the government funding in the world will not make an incorrect hypothesis a correct theory, but, unfortunately, it may make it seem like it is. Thanks for laying it all out for us Andy.

Martin Capages, Jr. PhD PE

Author of *The Moral Case for American Freedom* and *OF OSTRICHES AND LEMMINGS: The Silliness of Climate Change Hysteria*

Preface

This book is a brief history of the human-caused climate change debate from its origins in the 19th century until today. The goal is to put the political drama of the debate into a proper scientific context. The drama is widely reported, but the background scientific debate is usually ignored.

There are thousands of scientists who believe humans control the climate and are heading us into a climate disaster; these are the climate alarmists. There are also thousands of scientists who are unconvinced that recent warming, whether natural or human-caused, is dangerous, these are the climate skeptics.

Nearly everyone agrees that humans have some influence on climate through our greenhouse gas emissions, so only very few, if any, "deny" the human contribution to climate. Thus, the commonly used epithet "denier" seems inappropriate. We don't know any deniers.

We write about the scientists and the debate between the climate alarmists and the skeptics. We also write about the politicians, government bureaucrats and news media who write and speak about climate change. Some are honest and provide the public with clear unbiased reporting of the science, Matt Ridley, Bjorn Lomborg, Rasmus Benestad, and James Delingpole come to mind. Others are agenda driven, they ignore the science and attempt to suppress opposing views with ridicule or intimidation. These are the "science is settled" (Al Gore, et al.) or the "We're not going to debate climate change" (Chuck Todd, et al.) people. We discuss many of these commenters in the first three chapters of the book.

This book is organized around the people. The science is brought in for context. The book is not organized around the science, those that wish to read about the science in a more organized fashion without all the politics and fighting (more euphemistically: "debate") should read my first book, *Climate Catastrophe! Science or Science Fiction?* (May, 2018).

The connection between greenhouse gases and surface temperature was proposed in the 19th century by Irish researcher John Tyndall and the Swedish scientist Svante Arrhenius. An Englishman, Guy Callendar, provided some measurements of the possible effect. Many researchers discounted their ideas until Guy Callendar provided convincing measurements of the effect during the early 20th century as the world warmed from 1900 to 1944. But then the world began to cool, and it cooled until 1977. Emissions were still increasing, but the world was cooling, so skepticism grew. Even many of Callendar's friends and supporters quickly abandoned him.

The idea that global warming might be dangerous did not really appear until the 1980s, after the world began to warm again. This was immediately on the heels of the "global cooling" scare of the 1970s. Because the public had been told we were all going to freeze in the 1970s and now they were being told we will burn in the 1980s, everyone was skeptical.

The alarmists allied themselves with politicians, the news media, and government bureaucrats around the world and, with billions of dollars from the United Nations, western governments, and liberal "foundations," they started a campaign to convince people that the world was coming to an end due to dangerous man-made global warming. The weather cooperated, and, until 1998, the world warmed dramatically. Then the warming suddenly stopped. By 2009 the winters were very cold, this led Kevin Trenberth, a leading man-made climate change alarmist at NCAR (National Center for Atmospheric Research) to write, in a now famous 2009 *climategate* email:

> "I have my own article on "where the heck is global warming?" We are asking that here in Boulder where we have broken records the past two days for the coldest days on record. ... The fact is that we can't account for the lack of warming at the moment and it is a travesty that we can't." (Costella, 2010, p. 164)

John Costella has collected the *climategate* emails, which were hacked by someone from the U.K. Met Hadley Centre or, possibly, the Climatic Research Unit at the University of East Anglia in 2009 (Costella, 2010). The emails provide us with a look inside the small circle of climate alarmist scientists, often referred to as Michael Mann's "Hockey Team."

While the alarmists have yet to convince the public that climate change is an imminent danger that must be addressed by eliminating or curtailing fossil fuels, the campaign to persuade them otherwise continues. It is a political campaign, so the campaigners try to keep science out of the discussion. A new political phrase enters the lexicon, *an existential threat*. It sounds so ominous. Education weakens political campaigns since it leads to understanding. We discuss this campaigning concept in Chapter 3.

Science is a process or methodology used to discover the way the world and the universe work. The term can also be used to describe the collective knowledge uncovered about the world and universe to date. Science is not a belief, we cannot "believe in science." Science is not subject to a "consensus." If the consensus determined scientific truth, we would still believe the Sun revolved around Earth and Nicolaus Copernicus and Galileo Galilei would be forgotten cranks. The scientific process is discussed in Chapter 6.

Politics is about reaching consensus by persuasion or intimidation, science is about upsetting the consensus with detailed measurements, logic, and reason. When politics gets deeply into science, it corrupts it. We will present many examples of this.

Science has never proven anything. Science is a method of disproving ideas. A scientist presents an idea to his or her colleagues and they might challenge it. The advocate must counter every challenge. If he or she succeeds, the idea becomes a hypothesis.

The scientists may then publish the idea, the supporting data, and reasoning. Every valid and credible challenge to the paper must be dealt with. One person with one successful challenge can destroy the hypothesis or force it to be changed. When the challenges die down, a surviving hypothesis may become an established theory. It still isn't proven and can still be challenged.

We will examine the intersection of politics and climate science. In chapter 3 we have a section on the Union of Concerned Scientists. This political organization claims to have scientific roots. Yet, they call a difference of opinion on what causes climate change, an attack on science. Opinions are not facts, no matter who utters them.

In Chapter 8 we ask if government funding of research is a good idea. Are government bureaucrats and politicians the right people to decide what topics are researched? Is the government corrupting science?

---Andy May

Author of *Climate Catastrophe! Science or Science Fiction?*

And *Blood and Honor: The People of Bleeding Kansas*

Chapter 1: Politicians and Climate Change

"At the present time, it is very difficult to obtain funding, either from U.S. governmental sources or from private foundations, for research that does not presuppose impending environmental doom. Suggestions that moderate global warming may actually be a good thing for humanity are treated with ridicule and hostility." William Happer. (Gough, 2003, Ch. 1)

"The whole aim of practical politics is to keep the populace alarmed (and hence clamorous to be led to safety) by menacing it with a series of hobgoblins, all of them imaginary." H. L. Mencken, *In Defense of Women*, 1918

"the world has never before suffered from deception on such a scale." Tim Ball (Ball, 2014)

Politicians want to forge a consensus opinion on critical issues of the day. Once the consensus is formed, the public votes, laws are passed, regulations issued, the minority concedes, and conflict is avoided. Scientists exist to challenge consensus opinion. They require no one else, they use facts, observations, and analysis to show the consensus is wrong. Politicians and scientists don't mix. They are like fire and water, opposites. But, what about when no one trusts the politician and he needs a scientist to back up his story? What happens when the government becomes the sole source of research money?

We will address the attempt by politicians to control scientific research and research outcomes. They do this by selectively funding projects that look for potential disasters, ideally global disasters. People love disaster stories, journalists love disaster stories, scientists love to be quoted in newspapers and on television. So, it is not surprising that as government has taken over funding scientific research, scientists have migrated from research that helps people, to researching possible catastrophes, no matter how remote the possibility. Science has devolved from improving human lives to developing plots for disaster movies.

And, if humans can be blamed for the catastrophe, it is even better, then the politicians can mandate people change their lives "for the greater good." The politician's power increases because exercising power increases it and people will give up their freedoms in exchange for security, whether the danger is real or not.

Simultaneously, the politicians, the scientists, and the journalists, try to discredit privately funded research. If government completely controls scientific research funding, science becomes a powerful political tool. We will see how non-profit organizations and the federal bureaucracy cooperate to make this happen.

Dr. Roger Revelle

Roger Revelle was an outstanding and famous oceanographer. He met Al Gore, in the late 1960s, when Gore was a student in one of his classes at Harvard University. Revelle was unsure about the eventual impact of human carbon dioxide emissions on climate, but he did show that all carbon dioxide emitted by man would not be absorbed by the oceans. For an interesting discussion of Revelle's work in this area see this post on "The Discovery of Global Warming," by Spencer Weart (Weart, 2007). The original paper, on CO_2 absorption by the oceans, published in 1957 by Roger Revelle and Hans Suess, is entitled: "Carbon Dioxide Exchange Between Atmosphere and Ocean and the Question of an Increase of Atmospheric CO_2, during the Past Decades" (Revelle & Suess, 1957). This meant that carbon dioxide would accumulate in the atmosphere and that the CO_2 atmospheric concentration would increase, probably causing Earth's surface to warm at some unknown rate. This is not an alarming conclusion, as Revelle well knew, but Al Gore turned it into one.

One of Revelle's good friends was Dr. S. Fred Singer. Singer was a professor of environmental science at the University of Virginia and both Revelle and Singer had been science advisors in the U.S. Department of the Interior. They first met in 1957 and were more than professional colleagues, they were personal friends (Singer, 2003). Unfortunately, Revelle passed away in July 1991 and Singer passed away in April 2020, so we will refer to them and their friendship in the past tense. Both were leading Earth scientists and at the top of their fields, it was natural they would become friends. They also shared an interest in climate change and chose to write an article together near the end of Revelle's life.

The article was published in *Cosmos* and entitled "What To Do about Greenhouse Warming: Look before You Leap" (Singer, Revelle, & Starr, 1991). Singer and Revelle had already written a first draft of the article, when they invited the third author, Chauncey Starr, to help them complete it. Starr was an expert in energy research and policy. He holds the National Medal of Technology and was the director of the Electrical Power Research Institute in Palo Alto, California. As leading scientists, Starr, Singer and Revelle understood how uncertain the possible dangers of global warming were and they did not want the government to go off half-cocked, they wrote:

> "We can sum up our conclusions in a simple message: The scientific [basis] for a greenhouse warming is too uncertain to justify drastic action at this [time]. There is little risk in delaying policy responses to this century old problem since there is every expectation that scientific understanding will be substantially improved within the next decade." (Singer, Revelle, & Starr, 1991)

Revelle had studied the growth of carbon dioxide in the atmosphere and concluded that it might cause some warming, but he was unsure if it would be a problem. Al Gore, who had little training in science, suffered no such doubts. He was sure that burning fossil fuels was causing carbon dioxide to rise to "dangerous" levels in the atmosphere and convinced this was a problem for civilization through rising sea levels and extreme weather. There was no evidence to support these assumptions, but Al Gore didn't need evidence, he could always rely on climate models and he did. Revelle distrusted the models.

Al Gore and Climate Change

In 1992, after Singer, Revelle and Starr published their *Cosmos* article, their statements caused Al Gore, who was running for Vice-President at the time, some problems. Gore had just published *The Earth in the Balance* (Gore, 1992) and in it he credited Revelle with discovering that human emissions of carbon dioxide were causing Earth to warm and this could be very dangerous. Yet, Singer, Revelle and Starr's paper said:

"Drastic, precipitous—and, especially, unilateral—steps to delay the putative greenhouse impacts can cost jobs and prosperity and increase the human costs of global poverty, without being effective. Stringent economic controls [on CO_2 emissions] now would be economically devastating particularly for developing countries..." (Singer, Revelle, & Starr, 1991)

They also quote Yale economist William Nordhaus, who wrote:

"...those who argue for strong measures to slow greenhouse warming have reached their conclusion without any discernible analysis of the cost and benefits..." (Nordhaus, 1990)

Nordhaus has studied both the costs of reducing CO_2 and the benefits of doing so, his analysis shows there is little to be gained, economically, from reducing emissions (Nordhaus W. , 2007, p. 236). While Nordhaus supports a "carbon tax," he acknowledges that the "pace and extent of warming is highly uncertain." Contrast this with how Al Gore characterizes Roger Revelle's view in his book:

"Professor Revelle explained that higher levels of CO_2 would create what he called the greenhouse effect, which would cause the earth to grow warmer. The implications of his words were startling; we were looking at only eight years of information, but if this trend continued, human civilization *would be forcing* a profound and disruptive change in the entire global climate." (Gore, 1992, p. 5) *italics* added.

The differences between what Nordhaus and Revelle are saying and what Al Gore is saying are stark. All three believe human emissions of CO_2 might cause Earth to warm. But Gore naively assumes that is a bad thing. Revelle and Nordhaus acknowledge it might be, but they recognize that we don't know that. Further, they understand destroying our fossil fuel-based economy may not alleviate the warming and may cause more harm than good. To quote Bertrand Russell:

> "The whole problem with the world is that fools and fanatics are always so certain of themselves, and wiser people so full of doubts."
> Bertrand Russell

To a scientist, like Roger Revelle, the uncertainty was obvious. Politicians, like Al Gore and most of the news media do not do uncertainty, everything must be black and white and false dichotomies are how they think. Notice Al Gore presumptively writes "would be forcing" when Revelle would clearly write "could be forcing." This illustrates the difference between a politician with an agenda and a scientist who understands uncertainty.

The incompatibility between Revelle's true views and the way they were presented in Gore's book was noticed by Gregg Easterbrook, a *Newsweek* editor, who wrote about it in the July 6, 1992 issue of *New Republic* (Easterbrook, 1992). This article angered Al Gore and his supporters. Walter Munk and Edward Frieman published a short note in *Oceanography* in 1992 objecting to Easterbrook's article and claimed that the late Revelle had been worried about global warming, but probably did not want "drastic" action taken at that time (Munk & Frieman, 1992). Revelle's views were clear and well known. The following is from a letter Revelle sent Senator Tim Wirth, an ally of Gore's and a member of the Clinton/Gore administration in July 1988:

> "we should be careful not to arouse too much alarm until the rate and amount of warming becomes clearer. It is not yet obvious that this summer's hot weather and drought are the result of a global climatic change or simply an example of the uncertainties of climate variability. My own feeling is that we had better wait another 10 years before making confident predictions." Written by Roger Revelle as reported by (Booker, 2013, p. 59)

Unlike Senators Al Gore and Tim Wirth, Revelle understood global warming computer models and did not trust them. He argued with Singer about this very issue and Singer convinced Revelle that the models were getting better (Singer, Revelle, & Starr, 1991). However, regardless of the accuracy of the models, Revelle was not convinced global warming was a problem and he knew the natural rate of warming and the additional amount expected from human greenhouse emissions was unknown. His caution was warranted, because just ten years later it became apparent that warming was slowing down (Met Office, 2013). The slowdown continued until the strong El Niño of 2016. The following reflects Revelle's own views, it is from the "Look before you Leap" article:

> "The models used to calculate future climate are not yet good enough because the climate balancing processes are not sufficiently understood, nor are they likely to be good enough until we gain more understanding through observations and experiments. As a consequence, we cannot be sure whether the next century will bring a warming that is negligible or a warming that is significant. Finally, even if there are a global warming and associated climate changes, it is debatable whether the consequences will be good or bad; likely some places on the planet would benefit, some would suffer." (Singer, Revelle, & Starr, 1991)

Revelle's views were clear and well documented, but Al Gore and his supporters were humiliated by Easterbrook's article and follow up articles by George Will and others. Dr. Justin Lancaster was Revelle's graduate student and teaching assistant at the Scripps Institution of Oceanography from 1981 until Revelle's sudden death in July 1991. He was also an Al Gore supporter. Lancaster claimed that Revelle was "hoodwinked" by Singer into adding his name to the *Cosmos* article. He also claimed that Revelle was "intensely embarrassed that his name was associated" with it. Lancaster further claimed that Singer's actions were "unethical" and specifically designed to undercut Senator Al Gore's global warming policy position. Lancaster harassed Singer in 1992, accusing him of putting Revelle's name on the article over his objections and demanding that Singer have it removed. He even demanded that the publisher of a volume that was to include the article (Geyer, 1993) remove it.

Professor Singer, the *Cosmos* publisher of the "Look before you Leap" article and the publisher (CRC Press) of Richard Geyer's book, objected to these demands and charges. Then Singer sued Lancaster for libel with the help of the Center for Individual Rights in Washington, D.C. Professor Singer and the Center won the lawsuit and forced Lancaster to issue an apology.

The discovery process during the lawsuit revealed that Lancaster was working closely with Al Gore and his staff. In fact, Al Gore personally called

Lancaster after the Easterbrook article appeared and asked him about Revelle's mental capacity in the months before his death in July of 1991. Friends and family of Revelle recall that he was sharp and active right up to the moment when he passed away from a sudden heart attack. But this did not stop Al Gore and Lancaster from claiming Revelle was suffering from senility or dementia and that was why the account in Gore's book was so different from what Revelle wrote elsewhere, including in the "Look before you leap" article. Lancaster had even written in a draft of a letter to Al Gore that Revelle was "mentally sharp to the end" and was "not casual about his integrity" (Singer, 2003).

During the discovery process, Singer and his lawyers found that Lancaster knew everything in the "Look before you leap" article was true and that Revelle agreed with everything in it. The article even included a lot of material that Revelle had previously presented to a 1990 AAAS (American Academy for the Advancement of Science) meeting. More details can be seen in Fred Singer's deposition (Jones D. , 1993).

Roger Revelle's daughter, Carolyn Revelle Hufbaurer, wrote that Revelle was concerned about global warming (Hufbauer, 1992). But his concern lessened later in life and he knew the problem, if there was a problem, was not urgent. He thought more study was required before anything was done. As usual, and we will see this time and time again in this book, the news media and politicians have no sense of the complexity and uncertainty that surrounds the scientific debate about human-caused climate change. When Revelle argued against "drastic" action, he meant measures that would cost trillions of dollars and cripple the fossil fuel industry and developing countries. Up until his death, he thought extreme measures were premature. He clearly believed that we should look before we leap.

Al Gore tried to get Ted Koppel to trash Singer on his TV show and it failed spectacularly. He asked Koppel to investigate the "antienvironmental movement" and in particular "expose the fact" that Singer and other skeptical scientists were receiving financial support from the coal industry and the wacky Lyndon LaRouche organization. Rather than do Al Gore's bidding Ted Koppel said the following on his *Nightline* television program, on February 24, 1994:

"There is some irony in the fact that Vice President Gore, one of the most scientifically literate men to sit in the White House in this century, [is] resorting to political means to achieve what should ultimately be resolved on a purely scientific basis. The measure of good science is neither the politics of the scientist nor the people with whom the scientist associates. It is the immersion of hypotheses into the acid of truth. That's the hard way to do it, but it's the only way that works." Ted Koppel as reported in (Singer, 2003)

Calling Gore "scientifically literate" is debatable, but Koppel has the rest of it right. He has integrity that is lacking in journalism today, further he understands the scientific process. The attempt to use Koppel to tar Singer, brought a huge amount of well-deserved criticism down on Gore.

Given this, it is not surprising that Lancaster agreed to issue an apology only two months later, on April 29, 1994. Lancaster's retraction was specific:

"I retract as being unwarranted any and all statements, oral or written, I have made which state or imply that Professor Revelle was not a true and voluntary coauthor of the *Cosmos* article, or which in any other way impugn or malign the conduct or motives of Professor Singer with regard to the *Cosmos* article (including but not limited to its drafting, editing, publication, republication, and circulation). I agree not to make any such statements in future. ... I apologize to Professor Singer" (Singer, 2003)

So, in his court affidavit Lancaster admitted he lied about Singer. Then afterward, Lancaster withdrew his court-ordered retraction and reiterated his charges (Lancaster, 2006). He admits he lied under oath in a courtroom and in writing, then tells us he didn't lie. He admits that Professor Revelle was a true coauthor of the paper, then he states "Revelle did not write it" and "Revelle cannot be an author" (Lancaster, 2006). What some people are willing do to their reputations, in the name of catastrophic climate change is hard to believe. He retracted his retraction despite documentary evidence in Revelle's own handwriting, and numerous testimonials from others that Revelle did contribute to the article.

Some of Revelle's other papers, letters and presentations have nearly identical language to that in the paper, for example compare the quote from his letter to Senator Tim Wirth above with the first page of the "Look before you Leap" paper. In the paper, they say we need to wait because "scientific understanding will be substantially improved within the next decade" (Singer, Revelle, & Starr, 1991). In the letter to Wirth, quoted above, he says "10 years," but the meaning is the same. He, and many other climate scientists, did not feel we knew enough in the early nineties to do anything significant. He was right about this, warming slowed to a crawl after 1998. It even went negative for a time.

The issue was raised in the televised vice-presidential debate that year. Gore's response was to protest that Revelle's views in the article had been taken out of context. We can clearly see that it was Al Gore's book that took Revelle's comments out of context.

Al Gore's web site

In 2017 the author obtained a ticket to Al Gore's global warming lecture at Rice University in Houston on October 23 and planned to attend. The announcement said he will take questions, so an examination of his web site to look for ideas was warranted.

Gore's scientific credentials are thin, *The Washington Times*, after viewing Al Gore's Harvard transcript (Inside Politics, 2005) as released by the *Washington Post*, concluded that Al Gore was a slow learner in college, especially in science. Notably, he received a D and C- in his natural science college courses and avoided all math and logic courses. So, he would seem poorly prepared to lecture on climate science.

Al Gore founded "The Climate Reality Project" in 2005. It is a non-profit organization "devoted to solving the climate crisis." So, what is the "climate crisis?" Documents on his web site, including "The 12 Questions" and "Climate 101," gave the following reasons in 2017.

What is the climate crisis?

Global temperatures are rising.

More frequent and more devastating storms, floods, droughts, etc.

Glaciers melting at a "record" pace.

Rising sea level.

What is the cause of climate change?

Al Gore believes it is primarily man-made carbon dioxide due to burning fossil fuels, although methane emissions and deforestation play a role. He offers no evidence, other than "Scientists are crystal clear about the relationship between carbon [dioxide] pollution and climate change."

These ideas are asserted in his documents and he claims oil and gas companies and their minions are "attacking" the science of climate. He seems to say science is a thing that can be attacked, like an opinion, rather than a process and a method of learning the truth. A critical part of science is actively trying to disprove any proposed idea or theory, regardless of its popularity. Thus, "attacks," if we may use this word, are an essential element of the scientific method. It is unscientific to claim that man-made climate change is an unassailable, pristine, and perfect law of nature, sanctified by a political "consensus."

But Al Gore is not a scientist, either by training, experience, or education. When Al Gore went to college, climate was studied by geologists and meteorologists, it was a sleepy field in those days. It appears that the field now called "climate science" was invented to exclude geologists and meteorologists from it, since they used to be the only scientists who knew anything about it.

How certain are scientists that climate change is man-made and dangerous?

The evidence according to Al Gore's website

"Over 97 percent of climate scientists ..."

"18 different major scientific associations wrote ..."

"Climate scientists have estimated the planet has previously taken around 5,000 years to recover – by warming between 4-7 degrees Celsius – after an ice age has ended."

"In the twentieth century alone, the average surface temperature increased by 0.8 degrees Celsius – a rate eight times faster than a typical post-ice-age-recovery. And this cycle is rapidly accelerating."

The first two are "appeals to authority" and easily dismissed as irrelevant. The usual reference for the first is an article by John Cook and colleagues in

Environmental Research Letters (Cook, et al., 2013). There are many refutations of the so-called 97% consensus, and we will discuss some of them in later chapters, but here we will discuss an early refutation by David Legates and co-authors, published online by *Science and Education* in 2015 (Legates, Soon, Briggs, & Monckton, 2015). We will also discuss an article by Joseph Bast and Roy Spencer in the *Wall Street Journal* (Bast & Spencer, 2014). David Legates, Willie Soon, William Briggs, and Christopher Monckton of Brenchley make the following point that is important here:

> "Cook et al. (2013), after a subjective review of only the abstracts of 11,944 papers on climate change [that] matched the topics 'global climate change' or 'global warming', conclude that 97.1% of those that expressed an opinion endorsed the hypothesis [that anthropogenic greenhouse gases are responsible for most of Earth's warming in the second half of the twentieth century.] ... However, 66.4% percent ... expressed no position. Thus, 32.6% of the entire sample, or 97.1% of the 33.6% ..., [agreed with the hypothesis.] However, ... the authors' own dataset showed that they had categorized only 64 abstracts, just 0.5 % of the sample, as endorsing the [hypothesis.] ... 41 of the 64 papers, or 0.3 % of the sample of 11,944 papers [endorsed the hypothesis.] (Legates, Soon, Briggs, & Monckton, 2015)

So, we see that Cook, et al. surveyed abstracts of papers, not scientists. Then they cleverly reduced their sample to get to the desired 97%. There are other claims that some high percentage of scientists agree that humans are causing climate change and it is dangerous, some are listed in the *Wall Street Journal* article by Joseph Bast and Roy Spencer, but they are all easily refuted (Bast & Spencer, 2014). Regardless of the percentage, there are thousands of scientists who are skeptical that human greenhouse gas emissions are dangerous (petitionproject.org, 2009). It only takes one scientist to disprove a consensus view, just ask Galileo or Copernicus.

Legates and colleagues were accused of spreading misinformation about climate science (Bedford & Cook, 2013) after they published an earlier paper in *Science and Education* in 2013 (Legates, Soon, & Briggs, 2013). The Legates paper argues that using "consensus science" to decide what to teach students is not a good idea. It is one-sided. Legates and his colleagues want the students to understand complex scientific issues, like climate, not just be taught a belief. From the paper:

> Their [Bedford and Cook's] definition of climate 'misinformation'
> was contingent upon the post-modernist assumptions that scientific truth
> is discernible by measuring a consensus among experts, and that a near
> unanimous consensus exists. (Legates, Soon, Briggs, & Monckton, 2015)

This is essentially what Gore is doing. He is confusing the political idea of "consensus science" with the true scientific process. So, the first two items in Al Gore's list can be dismissed.

The next item about recovering from an ice age can be checked. Technically we are still in an ice age. The geological definition of an ice age is the presence of significant year-round ice caps on one or both poles. This state is unusual in Earth's history (Scotese, 2015). Cold periods, with major glacial advances and the formation of, at least one, year-round polar ice cap, have only occurred four times in the past 600 million years. These ice ages usually last 20-40 million years and the current one has lasted over 30 million years so far (May, Earth's Ice Ages, 2020a). In the current ice age, significant modern year-round ice caps first formed on Antarctica about 30 million years ago and then on the North Pole about 2.6 million years ago (Knies, et al., 2014) and have remained since then.

Gore appears to be defining "ice age" as a major glacial advance within a conventionally defined ice age. The most recent major glacial advance, generally called a "glacial period," ended about 12,000 years ago at the beginning of the Holocene Epoch. He might also be referring to the last glacial maximum within the current ice age. This most recent glacial maximum was reached around 19,000 years ago (May, 2015b). Temperatures, in Greenland, were about 16°C (29°F) cooler than today at the time of the last glacial maximum (LGM).

Figure 1 is a global temperature reconstruction, starting 12,000 years ago (May, 2017h). We start 12,000 years ago because temperatures before then were so much colder, especially at the poles, that little detail can be seen in the last 12,000 years if we include the earlier temperatures (May, 2015b).

The temperature reconstruction in Figure 1 relies mostly on marine temperature proxies, thus it mostly reflects shallow global ocean temperatures. Since 99.9% of the Earth's surface thermal energy (aka "heat") is in the oceans and less than 0.1% is in the atmosphere ocean temperatures are a good way to track long-range global temperature changes.

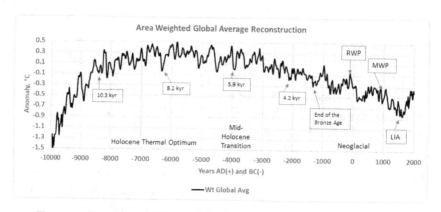

Figure 1. Estimated global temperatures from ice cores, ocean floor cores and lake sediments. The 10.3 kyr, 8.2 kyr, 5.9 kyr climatic events are labeled. Also, the end of the Bronze age, the Roman Warm Period (RWP), the Medieval Warm Period (MWP), and the Little Ice Age (LIA) are marked. Source: After (May, Climate Catastrophe! Science or Science Fiction?, 2018, p. 123).

Figure 1 starts on the left-hand side at the beginning of the Holocene with a temperature anomaly of -1.5°C (2.7°F) and reaches a peak of +0.5°C (0.9°F) about 4,000 years later. This increase of 2°C (3.6°F) occurs near the middle of the warm Holocene Thermal Optimum (HTO). After the 5.9 kyr event (3,900 BC) temperatures begin a long decline. This change from the warming trend in the HTO to the Neoglacial temperature decline is called the Mid-Holocene Transition. The coldest point, since the beginning of the Holocene, is reached in the Little Ice Age (LIA) around 300-400 years ago. Global temperatures were bitterly cold from about 1640 to 1715AD, especially in the Northern Hemisphere.

The bitter cold led to a collapse of Chinese agriculture and mass starvation, as well as the end of the Ming Dynasty. The last Ming Chinese Emperor hanged himself in 1644AD. Colder weather brings droughts and less precipitation. Often people assume droughts are accompanied by warmer weather, but the opposite is usually true, historically. The combination of cold and drought brought famine to China between 1618 and 1643. Numerous records in China show that the mid-1600s were the coldest time in China in the past 1,000 years (Soon, Baliunas, Idso, Idso, & Legates, 2003b).

Records from this time show many very cold winters, some cold summers, famines and plagues in Thailand, Indonesia and in Europe (Behringer, 2010, pp. 113-114). The winter of 1683-84 was one of the coldest in English history, the Thames River was frozen down to London Bridge by the second of January and stayed frozen for months. During this time the Baltic Sea repeatedly froze over, sea ice surrounded Iceland and glaciers all over Europe advanced (Oosthoek, 2015).

George Denton and Wibjörn Karlén (Denton & Karlén, 1973) show that the maximum glacial advance, due to Little Ice Age cooling, was reached between 1600 and 1750AD. The *Mer de glace* glacier in France advanced rapidly in 1601 and engulfed two villages and nearly a third (Behringer, 2010, pp. 89-90). The canals of Venice froze so solidly in 1684 and 1709 that heavy goods could be transported on the ice without breaking through.

Besides noting the major periods in the Holocene, we've also labeled the Medieval Warm Period (MWP), the Roman Warm Period (RWP), the end of Bronze Age cold period, the 4.2 kyr (kyr = 1,000 years ago) cold period, the 5.9 kyr cold period, the 8.2 kyr cold event (a time of great human migration), and the 10.3 kyr cold event. The Sahara changes from a savannah to a desert during the Mid-Holocene Transition. Thus, Earth recovered from the most recent major glacial advance in about 4,000 to 5,000 years by warming over 2°C (3.6°F), on average, if we start at the beginning of the Holocene. The Earth's average surface temperature during the LGM is not known accurately but was less than the 16°C (29°F) drop in Greenland. Gore's estimate of 4-7°C (7.2°F–12.6°F) is reasonable.

The warming is somewhat jerky and unevenly distributed. There are periods where the global average shallow ocean temperature rises or falls nearly 0.6°C (1°F) in less than 100 years, which is comparable to the sea surface warming in the 20th century of about 0.9°C (1.6°F) according to the HadSST4 dataset (Met Office Hadley Centre datasets, 2020).

The reconstruction shown in Figure 1 is based upon averages of noisy proxies that have considerable dating uncertainties. Averaging or otherwise combining multiple noisy and poorly dated proxies will cause the reconstruction to show less variability than modern thermometer or satellite records. Figure 1 is a reconstruction by the author, it uses proxies collected by Marcott, et al. (Marcott, Shakun, Clark, & Mix, 2013). Shaun Marcott, et al. estimate their reconstruction, using the same proxies, preserves variability for 2,000-year periods, but only 50% of the variability for 1,000-year periods. Most importantly, they conclude it preserves "essentially no variability" for less than

300 years. These figures also apply to Figure 1, except our reconstruction might show slightly more variability over 300 years, perhaps 25%. Figure 1 uses simple averages, rather than regression, to retain more variability, but at 150 years no variability is left. When one considers that the entire global temperature record is only 170 years, this makes comparisons of modern temperatures to paleo-temperatures problematic.

Both modern temperature measurements and proxies have some uncertainty. Modern global temperatures have about ±0.05°C (0.09°F) of uncertainty according to the U.K. Met Office (Met Office Hadley Centre datasets, 2020). The proxy reconstruction in Figure 1 has an uncertainty about 10x larger, roughly ±0.5°C (0.9°F) during the last few thousand years, more for earlier millennia, using estimates from Bo Christiansen (Christiansen & Ljungqvist, 2011). Using Shaun Marcott's error analysis, as shown in his supplemental materials, for the proxies used to make Figure 1, we also get approximately ±0.5°C (Marcott S. , Shakun, Clark, & Mix, 2013c). Therefore, short-term century-scale increases or decreases of 0.6°C can be considered statistically comparable to modern day, thermometer measured, increases, or decreases of 0.9°C (1.6°F). Not taking uncertainty in measuring or reconstructing global temperatures into account can, and has, led to serious problems interpreting the significance of recent global warming.

Antarctic and Greenland ice core data, which are proxies of surface air temperatures, show several periods of roughly 100 years where temperatures rose between one and 2.4°C (4.3°F) (May, 2018, p. 94). At the beginning of the Holocene, the Central Greenland ice core record shows 10°C (18°F) of warming in 144 years, from 11,755 BP to 11,611 BP. BP means before 1950. Jeffery Severinghaus and colleagues present evidence that at the beginning of the Holocene, approximately 11,600 years ago, Northern Hemisphere temperatures rose over 5-10°C (9°F-18°F) in "several decades or less" (Severinghaus, Sowers, Brook, Alley, & Bender, 1998).

Several Holocene temperature reconstructions have shown that the Northern Hemisphere has the greatest climate variability (May, 2017h). Global average temperature is a poor metric for the impact on people, regional average temperatures are more appropriate.

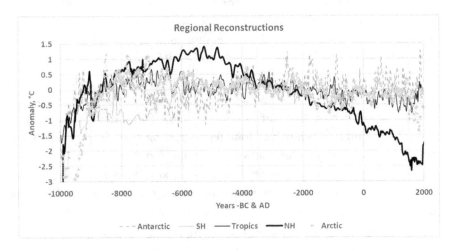

Figure 2. Temperature reconstructions by latitude slices. The Antarctic and Arctic slices are greater than 60° South and North latitude. The Northern Hemisphere (NH) and Southern Hemisphere (SH) slices are between 60° and 30° latitude. The tropics are between 30°N and 30°S. The main point is that the Northern Hemisphere is an outlier and has greater variability than the other latitude slices. Source: (May, 2017b).

The heavy black line in Figure 2 is a Northern Hemisphere temperature anomaly reconstruction for 30°N to 60°N, it stands in stark contrast to other parts of Earth. All the reconstructions show a LIA, but the LIA in the Northern Hemisphere is much colder. No one knows precisely why the Northern Hemisphere is so different, but Javier Vinós has speculated it is mostly because Northern Hemisphere summer solar insolation peaked about 8000BC (-8000 in Figure 2). At that time, Earth's orbital precession and obliquity caused Northern Hemisphere insolation to reach its maximum (Vinós, 2017). Javier Vinós is a microbiologist and biochemist in Madrid but has written extensively on paleoclimate and climate history.

We remember that Mann's hockey stick was a Northern Hemisphere temperature reconstruction but has often been viewed as though it were a global reconstruction. Figure 2 shows this not necessarily correct. Averaging the Arctic changes and the northern part of the Tropics with the Northern Hemisphere slice in Figure 2, as Mann did, helps, but even then, the result is quite different from the Southern Hemisphere and Antarctic.

Renee Hannon did an analysis of temperature variability and concluded that modern warming is well within the range of normal, natural climate (aka temperature) variability (Hannon, 2018). Hannon carefully separates climate variability from climate change and argues that only changes over 500 years or more can be characterized as "climate change." Changes of 500 years or less are simply climate variability. Our current instrumental record of 170 years is too short to be called climate change using her definition.

So, Al Gore is in the ballpark when he says it took 5,000 years to "recover" from the most recent major glacial advance (or glacial period) with a rise in surface temperatures of 4-7°C (7°F-12.6°F). But his next statement is false. The world has seen natural long-term warming of 0.7°C or more in less than 100 years many times, particularly in the Northern Hemisphere. His description ignores the complexity of the data used to build paleo-temperature reconstructions and modern instrumental temperature records. He also vastly underestimates the difficulty of comparing the two.

There are many more misleading, or simply false statements on Al Gore's web site, but these stood out. We have avoided the "economics of climate change" statements since that always devolves to arguing whose "fantasy" numbers are correct. Economic predictions are shaky enough without making them using shaky climate predictions as input, we will not move one more dimension from reality.

An Al Gore Lecture

The author attended Al Gore's climate change lecture at Houston's Rice University October 23rd, 2017. Rice University has a beautiful campus and it was a lovely walk from the parking lot to the Tudor Fieldhouse which seats 5,750. By the time the Rice University Provost was introducing Al Gore, there were no empty seats.

A couple of minutes later, Al Gore came on stage and received a standing ovation. About 40% of Texans vote Democratic and these voters are concentrated in Houston, San Antonio and Austin. As an example, Houston went for Hillary Clinton by over 160,000 votes. This was very apparent in Tudor Fieldhouse. The crowd even cheered when Gore railed against the fossil fuel industry and called for dismantling it. Although, lots of people, including the couple sitting next to the author, got up and walked out at that point. When the lights came up for questions, there were many empty seats, perhaps a quarter or more, had walked out during the speech.

As some predicted, prior to the speech, questions were pre-screened by the provost (Professor of statistics Marie Lynn Miranda). She is an unquestioning true believer in catastrophic man-made global warming (CAGW) just like Al Gore, so the three hand-picked questions she asked were softballs that merely prompted more vitriol about "deniers." Yes, he used the word a few times. Once he said, "I know I'm being dismissive of them, but what can I do?" This was accompanied with an irritatingly smug and superior smile, like those that lost him the election in 2000.

The first question is the only one we will discuss here. It was (paraphrasing): "Why is the media ignoring climate change?" Al Gore's answer was very long and rambling, but he essentially said, even though climate change is the most important issue facing human civilization ever, the media ignores it because too many people turn off their TV's or radios or change the channel whenever it comes up. He believes the news media are not informing any more but, are for entertainment only. Then he went on to say the internet and social media are not a positive thing today, they are divisive; but he had hopes for the future. The news media is toast, since both the right and left think it has devolved into vacuous entertainment.

Points made in the lecture

The lecture was in two parts. In the first Gore asserted that humans are causing "dangerous" climate change, without offering any proof. He further asserted that 16 of the 17 warmest years "on record" were in this century, asserted that greenhouse gases ("mainly carbon dioxide") were the cause since they "trap" 400,000 Hiroshima bombs worth of heat (he means thermal energy) on Earth every year. He presented no evidence that greenhouse gases are related to the warming or that thermal energy is "trapped."

The "evidence" that man's emissions cause climate change comes from computer climate models, and not observations, as we will discuss in more detail in Chapters 6 and 7. The popular concept of greenhouse gases "trapping" heat like a "blanket" is misleading and "unrealistic" according to Rasmus Benestad (Benestad, 2016). Both greenhouses and blankets work by restricting air circulation, CO_2 works to warm Earth's surface in a completely different way. Benestad has a PhD in physics from Oxford University and falls into the climate alarmist camp, but he does very good work at the Norwegian Meteorological Institute and explains the poorly named greenhouse effect very clearly. Unlike many alarmists, Benestad understands uncertainty and tries to stay within the bounds of his data. Gore's idea of CO_2 acting like a "blanket" and "trapping" "heat" is annoying to the scientifically literate, Benestad's description of the greenhouse effect makes more sense.

The Greenhouse Effect

Benestad explains that as the concentration of greenhouse gases in the atmosphere increases, the lower atmosphere becomes opaquer to infrared radiation. Infrared radiation is thermal energy or "IR." Thermal energy is colloquially called "heat," but heat is not, strictly speaking, energy. Heat is the transfer of thermal energy or the flow of energy from a warmer object to a cooler object. Thermal energy is emitted by Earth's surface to rid itself of the absorbed incoming radiation from the Sun. Greenhouse gases do not just absorb infrared radiation from the Sun and Earth's surface, they also emit it very quickly (a few milliseconds to a few tenths of a second) afterward. The absorbed IR or thermal energy excites the greenhouse gas molecules, causing them to collide with other molecules millions of times before the absorbed energy is re-emitted, these collisions raise the atmospheric temperature according to Raymond Pierrehumbert at the University of Chicago (Pierrehumbert, 2011).

On average the infrared radiation (IR) emitted to outer space from Earth, is from an altitude where the temperature is 254K, or -19°C (-2°F) according to satellite spectroscopic data. Air temperature decreases about 6.5°C per kilometer (~20°F per mile) of altitude and the average surface temperature of the Earth is about 15°C (59°F). This means, again on average, that the IR emitted to space from the Earth is emitted from an altitude of about 5 kilometers or 3 miles. As greenhouse gases are added to the lower atmosphere, it takes longer for IR to escape the surface and reach a height where it can be radiated to space without encountering a greenhouse gas molecule. Each bit of IR is captured, emitted, and captured again many times on its way to space and when greenhouse gases increase, it takes longer and the height at which the IR is emitted gets higher.

Satellite radiation measurements have shown that the "emission level" of the earth is rising about 23 meters or 75 feet per decade. As the level rises, the temperature gets colder, so the amount of emitted radiation goes down. This, combined with the increasing opacity of the lower atmosphere to IR, works to increase surface temperatures. Increased convection (basically latent heat carried in evaporated water vapor) compensates for this and works to warm the poles and the higher latitudes, as it cools the tropics. One major mechanism for cooling the tropics are thunderstorms. Increased evaporation ultimately leads to increased cloudiness, which has a cooling effect, at least during the daytime. Clouds probably have a warming effect at night. Increased convection causes warming to be more intense at the poles than in the tropics.

This is still an oversimplified picture, but at least the physics of the process makes sense, unlike the usual "atmospheric blanket" or "heat trapping" nonsense. Radiation is emitted to outer space from all altitudes, including directly from the surface. Surface to space radiation is more common at the poles and in the Sahara and other deserts, where the humidity is low. Water vapor is, by far, the most powerful greenhouse gas, so humidity and cloud cover largely determine how quickly radiation can transport thermal energy to outer space.

The Warmest Years

The idea that 16 of the 17 warmest years "on record" are in this century is debatable and depends upon which surface temperature record one chooses to use and the estimated measurement error (Frank, 2016). Patrick Frank explains that both the rate and magnitude of the change in global temperatures from 1850 to 1980 cannot be known to within ±1°C (1.8°F), which is about how much warming we currently estimate for the period. Patrick Frank is a scientist at the Stanford Synchrotron Radiation Lightsource, which is part of the Stanford Linear Accelerator Center in California. We do know the warming since 1980 more accurately, but the error is still ±0.6°C (1.1°F), which is the estimated warming over that short period. It has warmed over the past century, but by how much is not known to any degree of accuracy, thus claiming any 16 years is the warmest on record is statistically absurd. Gore is talking about hundredths or tenths of a degree and we cannot accurately measure differences that small.

As already discussed, historical records show that the world has warmed since the cold and miserable Little Ice Age. We don't know by how much, but it has warmed. Do we want to go back to that time and those temperatures? It is safe to say, most people like the world warmer than that.

So, most of Gore's assertions are contestable, yet he moves on undeterred, and describes cherry-picked catastrophes all over the world, with emotional pictures. According to him, all are linked to man's supposed influence on global climate. He asserts that hurricanes Harvey, Irma, and Maria were all made worse by global warming. He acknowledges "some say no link of climate change to extreme weather can be shown." He doesn't mention a source, but I suspect he was referring to the excellent work by Roger Pielke Jr. (Pielke Jr. R. , 2017) and Cliff Mass (Mass, 2017). Judith Curry, a hurricane expert, has also discussed global warming and hurricanes (Curry J. , 2017). Curry, in the cited post, says:

"Thinking that reducing fossil fuels is going to help with extreme events on the timescale of the 21st century is a pipe dream. Even if you believe the climate models, and we are able to drastically reduce fossil fuel emissions by 2050, we're going to see miniscule impacts on the climate and the weather by the end of the 21st century. Any benefits would be realized in the 22nd and 23rd centuries. If we think we have enough wisdom and knowledge to [know] what might happen in the 22nd and 23rd Century — personally I'd rather see us deal with here and now, and maybe focus on what we might be facing out to 2050. That seems a more practical and realistic goal, for what we should be trying to do. That's my opinion." (Curry J. , 2017)

Gore moves on to blame global warming (or climate change) for "record breaking" precipitation, droughts, wildfires, etc. Sea level rise will flood Miami and other low-lying cities. "Rain bombs" are the new scary monster. He says CO_2, through warming, supposedly increases water use by plants, ignoring evidence that CO_2 decreases water use per pound of plant (May, 2016d). Further, he claims climate change also caused the "Arab Spring," destabilizes governments, and we are in the sixth great extinction event. Fifty percent of all species will be wiped out, and on and on. If it's in the news, global warming did it. All these claims are obvious nonsense as we show in our book, *Climate Catastrophe! Science or Science Fiction?* (May, 2018)

Al Gore believes that fossil fuels receive $700 billion in subsidies. He didn't supply a period of time, but this was just for the U.S. According to a 2015 report by the EIA, exclusive of welfare programs like LIHEAP (Low Income Home Energy Assistance), the U.S. fossil fuel industry received $3.4 billion in subsidies in 2013. Our blog post, "The Economist, Fossil Fuel Subsidies and Climate Disaster," shows that even the $3.4 billion number is probably too high (May, 2016h). By way of contrast, renewables, from the same report, received over $29 billion dollars in subsidies in 2013 to produce far less energy. To put this in perspective, fossil fuels produced 80% of the world's energy in 2019 (EIA, 2020). Renewables (excluding nuclear and hydro) provided 9%. Per unit (1%) of energy produced, the fossil fuel subsidy is 0.043 billion dollars and the renewable subsidy is 3.2 billion dollars, 75 times higher.

Gore also believes that solar and wind are at grid parity (cost of producing electricity) with coal and other fossil fuels and soon will be cheaper. This is sheer fantasy as Larry Hamlin explains (Hamlin, 2017). Christopher Clack and colleagues go into more detail in an article and supplementary materials in *PNAS (Proceedings of the National Academy of Sciences)*. They examined studies that claim a transition to renewables can be done at low cost. One study by Mark Jacobson, et al. (Jacobson, Delucchi, Cameron, & Frew, 2015) claimed 100% of the U.S. energy needs can be met with wind, water and solar energy sources at low cost. Clack, et al. found the study had serious problems. They concluded:

> In this paper, we ... find significant shortcomings in the analysis. In particular, we point out that this work used invalid modeling tools, contained modeling errors, and made implausible and inadequately supported assumptions. Policy makers should treat with caution any visions of a rapid, reliable, and low-cost transition to entire energy systems that [rely] almost exclusively on wind, solar, and hydroelectric power. (Clack, et al., 2017)

Wind, solar and hydroelectric sources of power have their place in our system, but the technology to power the United States only from these sources does not exist, nor will it in the foreseeable future. Even if the technical challenges of using such unreliable sources as wind and solar could be met, it would be far too expensive. The land necessary for more hydroelectric dams precludes the expansion of this energy resource.

At the end of his speech Gore received a standing ovation.

The speech was all over the place, many scary photos of floods, droughts, rising sea level, wildfires, etc. There is always a flood, a drought or a very high tide somewhere, they don't have to be caused by the same thing. As a skeptical scientist, with some knowledge in the area, this author was unconvinced, but others in the audience seemed happy with what he had to say.

Gore's speech was more anti-fossil-fuels than pro-Catastrophic-Anthropogenic-Global-Warming (CAGW). He stated that he wanted to completely replace fossil fuels with other sources of energy. He is also pro-nuclear, which unlike hydroelectric, wind, and solar, is a viable, if not quite politically correct, alternative.

Al Gore was called "one of the most ruthless and determined politicians of his generation" by Henry I. Miller (Gough, 2003, Ch. 2). Dr. Miller started work at the Food and Drug Administration (FDA) in 1979 where he reviewed the first genetically engineered drugs approved by the FDA. Later he was the founding director of the FDA's Office of Biotechnology. After he retired from the FDA he became the Robert Wesson Fellow in Scientific Philosophy and Public Policy at the Hoover Institution (Gough, 2003).

Raúl Grijalva

As we will discuss in the next chapter, Greenpeace and Kert Davies' so-called Climate Investigations Center persuaded the *New York Times* to publish a wildly incorrect story about Willie Soon, an astrophysicist who works for the Harvard-Smithsonian Center for Astrophysics. The story was published February 21, 2015 by Justin Gillis and John Schwartz (Gillis & Schwartz, 2015). It claims, incorrectly, that Soon received over $1.2 million dollars from the fossil fuel industry and did not properly disclose the funding in his published papers. The money they are referring to was donated to the Smithsonian, there was nothing for Soon to disclose. We will have much more on this story in Chapter 2.

In the middle of the uproar caused by all of this, U.S. Representative Raúl Grijalva, who is also connected to Greenpeace and the Climate Investigations Center (Schleeter, 2020), sent letters to numerous universities where climate skeptics work, asking for information on their funding.

Soon and the targets of Grijalva's investigation had appeared numerous times before Congress and questioned the scientific basis behind the co-called "need" to limit greenhouse gas emissions.

These letters were widely criticized as an affront to academic freedom and an unwarranted invasion of privacy. Further, why were the letters sent only to academics who were skeptical of the consensus view that humans have caused climate change or global warming?

This sort of investigation is reserved for criminal investigations or FBI background checks for a sensitive appointment, in which the potential appointee signs a disclosure form and gives permission for such an inquiry. None of these scientists gave Grijalva permission to do this. And, if disclosure is important, shouldn't it be important for the climate alarmist scientists to disclose their sources of funding and salaries as well?

A portion of the form letter is shown below, the symbol "X" refers to various climate skeptics. Some of the recipients are listed below the form letter.

"Companies with a direct financial interest in climate and air quality standards are funding environmental research that influences state and federal regulations and shapes public understanding of climate science. ...

3. Please provide information on Prof. [X] sources of external funding. "External funding" refers to consulting fees, promotional considerations, speaking fees, honoraria, travel expenses, salary, compensation, and other monies given to Prof. [X] that did not originate from the institution itself. Please include:

a) The source of funding;
b) The amount of funding;
c) The reason for receiving the funding;
d) For grants, a description of the research proposal and copy of the funded grant;
e) Communications regarding the funding.

4. Please provide all financial disclosure forms filed by Prof [X] in which [your university] is listed as his professional affiliation, even if it is only stated for purposes of identification.

5. Please provide Prof [X]'s total annual compensation for each year covered here. Thank you for your attention to this issue. Please provide a full response no later than March 16, 2015." (Watts, 2015)

Seven professors whose institutions received these letters were:

David Legates, Department of Agricultural Economics & Statistics, University of Delaware climatologist

John Christy, University of Alabama, atmospheric scientist

Judith Curry, Georgia Institute of Technology, climatologist

Richard Lindzen, Massachusetts Institute of Technology, atmospheric physicist

Robert C Balling Jr., Arizona State University, geographer

Roger Pielke Jr., University of Colorado, political scientist

Steven Hayward, School of Public Policy, Pepperdine University historian

These letters sound like persecution for one's beliefs and are close to a violation of the first amendment rights of free speech and religion. It is also probably a violation of 18 U.S. Code § 241 which makes it a crime to threaten or intimidate a person in order to prevent them from exercising their constitutional rights (Columbia Law School, 2020).

One recalls that Socrates was sentenced to death for the crime of questioning the consensus view that the Greek gods existed. Was this what Grijalva had in mind?

The letter and the list of recipients, reeks of political bias and intimidation. Professor Roger Pielke Jr. wrote:

> "I know with complete certainty that this investigation is a politically-motivated "witch hunt" designed to intimidate me (and others) and to smear my name." (Pielke Jr. R. , 2015)

Professor Pielke Jr. writes that he has no funding, declared or undeclared, from any fossil fuel company or interest, as if it matters. If he had received funding from a fossil fuel company, what difference would it make? His work either stands on its own and is reproducible or it isn't, the source of funding is irrelevant. If Grijalva suspected the scientific work that Pielke Jr., or any of the others had published was incorrect, the proper way to approach the problem is to request their data and code and show what's wrong with their conclusions.

We will discuss many examples of the scientific process in this book. In the next chapter and in Chapter 5 we use the National Academy of Sciences investigation (National Research Council, 2006), the Wegman Investigation (Wegman, Scott, & Said, 2010), and the private investigations by McIntyre and McKitrick (McIntyre & McKitrick, 2005) of Michael Mann's hockey stick temperature reconstruction as examples of the proper way to dispute a scientific hypothesis. Attack their conclusions, methods, or their assumptions; don't attack the person, harass them, intimidate them, or send the law after them.

Dr. Rasmus Benestad was annoyed by people calling the greenhouse effect a "blanket." So, he wrote a paper that we summarized above (Benestad, 2016). He explained the greenhouse effect in a more physically meaningful way. This is another good example of how to challenge scientific ideas or publications you disagree with.

Oddly, while Pielke Jr. is not an alarmist, he does support a carbon tax. This is in full agreement with climate alarmists, like Grijalva. But he does not toe the party line adequately. Accepting part of their position is not sufficient, they want him to blindly accept, with unquestioning faith, all their assertions about the dangers of human-caused climate change. His careful research shows that the increasing nominal cost of natural disasters is not due to an increase in storm severity, and probably has nothing to do with human greenhouse gas emissions. That was his "sin." As Pielke Jr. states:

"Congressman Grijalva doesn't have any evidence of any wrongdoing on my part, either ethical or legal, because there is none. He simply disagrees with the substance of my testimony – which is based on peer-reviewed research funded by the US taxpayer, and which also happens to be the consensus of the IPCC." (Pielke Jr. R. , 2015)

The malicious and untrue attack on Willie Soon, described in the next chapter, had some wide-ranging consequences as described by Richard Lindzen in the *Wall Street Journal* (Lindzen, 2015). Dr. Lindzen notes:

[Now the dialog has moved] from "global warming" to "climate change" indicat[ing] the silliness of this issue. The climate has been changing since the Earth was formed. This normal course is now taken to be evidence of doom.

Mr. Grijalva's letters convey an unstated but perfectly clear threat: Research disputing alarm over the climate should cease lest universities that employ such individuals incur massive inconvenience and expense—and scientists holding such views should not offer testimony to Congress. After the *[New York] Times* article [about Willie Soon], Sens. Edward Markey (D., Mass.), Sheldon Whitehouse (D., R.I.) and Barbara Boxer (D., Calif.) also sent letters to numerous energy companies, industrial organizations and, strangely, many right-of-center think tanks (including the Cato Institute, with which I have an association) to unearth their alleged influence peddling. (Lindzen, 2015)

Lindzen explains in his 2015 op-ed in the *Wall Street Journal* that variations in solar radiation are much more important than admitted by the climate "consensus." He goes on to show that there has been no increase in extreme weather and that the additional atmospheric CO_2 has contributed to the increase in agricultural productivity we are enjoying today. He notes that billions of dollars have been spent to spread false stories of an impending climate disaster and to overthrow our fossil fuel-based energy economy.

The blatant political persecution of David Legates, John Christy, Judith Curry, Robert Balling, Roger Pielke Jr., Steven Hayward and Richard Lindzen by Rep Raúl Grijalva and Senators Sheldon Whitehouse, Barbara Boxer and Edward Markey for their scientific opinions is appalling. These famous and well-respected scientists simply did their job and challenged a poorly supported scientific hypothesis with data and proper scientific analysis. You cannot even say they were persecuted for their beliefs; they were persecuted for doing a good job and pointing out serious flaws in the "consensus hypothesis," something all scientists have an obligation to do.

This highlights a problem with many, if not most, climate alarmists, like Grijalva or Al Gore. They have not taken the time to read and understand climate science. Someone told them that humans control the climate, that global warming is occurring, and it is dangerous. Every hurricane, every heavy snowfall, every flood, and drought are caused or "enhanced" by human greenhouse emissions and they accept these assertions without any understanding of the topic. Because they are radical political figures, anyone who disagrees with them is evil, in their view. All the fine scientists listed above have written excellent papers and books on climate. Their works are well written and easy to understand, their conclusions are reproducible, as any proper scientific study must be. The papers stand on their own. But I doubt Grijalva or Gore ever bothered to read any of them, after all, the science is "settled," why should they?

Senator Sheldon Whitehouse

Whitehouse has the reputation of being the most obsessed with climate change of any senator (Freedman, 2018). Between 2012 and 2018 Whitehouse gave 200 speeches on global warming on the Senate floor, generally by himself.

He likes to boast that he has studied the "science" of climate change, but his statements on the subject tend to be assertions, with no analysis or observations to back them up. He is a lawyer that equates what he calls "climate failure" to "dark money." By climate failure, he means the lack of legislation reducing or banning the use of fossil fuels and by dark money, he means money donated secretly to a nonprofit organization. He does not want to debate, or even discuss, climate science, after all that is "settled." He wants to discuss destroying the fossil fuel industry, this is what "climate science" means to him.

Alex Epstein, the author of *The Moral Case for Fossil Fuels* (Epstein, 2014), commented in Senate testimony that Whitehouse is harming people and companies by immorally damning people by association. He believes that what Whitehouse is doing to the free speech of fossil fuel companies and those associated with them is unconstitutional and that he should apologize or resign for these acts (Epstein, 2016).

Whitehouse introduced a bill in the Senate, in 2019, that would require all nonprofits to disclose their donations and donors, if they spend money on elections (Whitehouse, 2019b). He claims that fossil fuel companies are supplying "dark money" to conservative organizations to block climate change legislation (McDermott, 2019). However, dark money is common in organizations on all sides of the climate debate. Far left climate alarmist organizations, like Kert Davies' Climate Investigations Center or CIC do not disclose where their funds come from. Then they use the money to complain about dark money donated to conservative organizations. Or, in the case of Willie Soon, they complain about him not disclosing open and public donations to the Smithsonian Institution.

Spencer Walrath reported in 2019, that the Climate Investigations Center receives its funding from the Our Next Economy organization, which is a pass-through organization for the Sustainable Markets Foundation (Walrath, 2019b). The Sustainable Markets Foundation exists only on paper. It receives money from what the Senate Committee on Environment and Public Works calls "The Billionaires Club" (Bolar & Steel, 2014). The Sustainable Markets Foundation distributes money to many activist organizations, such as 350.org. In addition, the Sustainable Markets Foundation funds other pass-through organizations, such as Our Next Economy, which then funds secretive activist organizations, like the CIC, that harass climate scientists, like Willie Soon. Our Next Economy received $1.5 million from the Sustainable Markets Foundation in 2018, a substantial portion of that apparently went to the CIC.

The Billionaire's Club, the Senate Minority report refers to includes many liberal foundations, including the Rockefeller Brother's Fund, the William and Flora Hewlett Foundation, the David and Lucile Packard Foundation, the Schmidt Family Foundation, the Sea Change Foundation, the Park

Foundation and the Marisla Foundation. Their goal seems to be, in the words of Nat Simons, President of the Sea Change Foundation:

> "it's not really a question of whether we move to a low carbon economy. I think it's clear we're moving there... the question is how quickly. The role of philanthropy is really to facilitate that process." (Bolar & Steel, 2014, p. 2)

Obviously, the Sea Change Foundation, The Billionaire's Club, and Senator Whitehouse have decided that burning fossil fuels is causing global warming, despite the lack of evidence. It seems Whitehouse believes anyone who disagrees with him is a criminal. Therefore in 2015 he proposed using RICO (Racketeer Influenced and Corrupt Organizations Act) laws against any climate scientists and fossil fuel companies that challenge the consensus view of climate change (Whitehouse, 2015). Of course, this is followed, as you might expect, by a comparison to tobacco company lawsuits. In fact, most of Whitehouse's op-ed is an attempt to show that the "fossil fuel industry's denial operation" is the same as the tobacco industry's campaign to deny the health dangers of smoking.

The link between smoking and cancer is direct, the link between greenhouse gases and some unknown amount of warming is also direct. Where this analogy fails, is that cancer is often deadly, people die from it every day. The link between smoking and cancer can be quantified, we know that smoking increases the risk of cancer and by how much. The cost of smoking, to the government and to the population, can be calculated. No one has died from human-caused climate change, increasing greenhouse gases, or global warming. The costs and benefits of warming are unknown (eelegal, 2016). People have died from extreme weather, but as Professor Roger Pielke Jr. and the IPCC (Intergovernmental Panel on Climate Change) have shown, there is no connection between greenhouse gas emissions and any extreme weather event (Pielke Jr., 2017). Absent a crime and a cost, RICO laws are meaningless and inapplicable.

Using RICO statutes against any scientist or scientific study seems a bit extreme, whether the research is attempting to show smoking is safe or man-made climate change is not dangerous. If one questions a scientific study, as discussed above, the proper way to address it, is to request the data and code behind the study and try and replicate the results and reach the same conclusions. There is no need to bring the law into it. It is a lot cheaper and less trouble to simply show the study is flawed, if indeed that is the result of your work. Why tie up the courts and law enforcement over a difference of opinion on what the data are showing? This sort of dispute can be resolved using the scientific process.

No one can show how much warming is due to greenhouse gas emissions (human or natural), it could be a small amount. No one can even show how much warming is due to natural causes. Willie Soon and others have shown we do not understand what normal, natural climate variability is. Finally, there is considerable doubt that global warming, whether human-caused or natural, will ever pose a danger to humans or the planet.

As evidence that the "evil" fossil fuel industry is conspiring to deceive the public like the tobacco industry apparently did, Sheldon Whitehouse offers a memo written to the members of the American Petroleum Institute (API) Global Climate Science Team by Joe Walker of the API (Walker, 1998). He also references an article entitled, "Industrial Group Plans to Battle Climate Treaty," in the *New York Times* discussing the content of the API memo (Cushman Jr., 1998).

The 1998 API memo is professionally written and reinforces many important points about the climate debate that are still valid today. The news media, in 1998 and today, did not understand the uncertainties in various projections of future climate change due to human activities. This memo was written while the Clinton Administration and many other governments were pushing the Kyoto Climate Change Treaty. The treaty was killed by the Bush Administration's EPA leader, Christine Todd Whitman March 28, 2001 (Borger, 2001) and the treaty was never ratified in the Senate, even though Al Gore signed it in December 1997.

To the Bush Administration, the fatal flaw in the treaty was that the United States was to cut greenhouse gas emissions by 7% before 2012 because it exempted developing countries, hurting the U.S. economy. As Walker's memo says, the Kyoto Treaty would "place the U.S. at a competitive disadvantage with most other nations and will be extremely expensive to implement." This cost would be borne by American consumers.

Joe Walker's memo points out that the supporters of the treaty have been able to avoid defending their shaky projections of future climate change and have convinced the news media and much of the public that human-caused global warming is a fact, rather than a hypothesis that many reasonable

43

scientists disagree with. He cites Tom Wathen of the National Environmental Trust, who writes,

> "Most stories described predictions of global warming as the position of the overwhelming number of mainstream scientists. That the environmental community had, to a great extent, settled the scientific issue with the U.S. media is the other great success that ... became apparent during Kyoto." Tom Wathen, as reported by (Walker, 1998)

So, the "consensus" argument was effective, even in 1997. Walker believed, in 1998, that the science underpinning the man-made climate change hypothesis had not been effectively challenged. For this reason, the climate change alarmists could bypass that weakness in their case and move onto the political issue of what should be done. This is often true of news media organizations, as we will see in the next chapter.

By, not challenging the scientific issues, the skeptics were only left with arguing the economic issues surrounding the elimination or curtailment of fossil fuels. Walker did not believe that economic issues, versus stories of an impending climate disaster, was a winning argument. As Walker notes, in 1998, most true climate scientists did not think the Kyoto Treaty was supported by climate science. Nothing much has changed in that regard since 1998.

The goals established in Walker's memo were to help the average citizen and the news media understand the uncertainty in climate projections. They wanted the news media to be more balanced in their coverage of climate predictions. They also wanted industry leaders themselves to be more informed on the issues. Lastly, they wanted the Kyoto treaty to die.

They made progress, the Kyoto Treaty was not approved, and the public did gain some appreciation of the uncertainty in climate projections. The public also learned that scientists were more divided than they had been told by the press. In a *Climate Change* journal article by Robert Brulle he cites a Pew Research poll from 2012 that shows only 43% of the public believe that human activity is causing Earth to become warmer, versus 45% who said it's not (Brulle, 2013). Thus, at that time, the country was evenly divided.

Today, most are aware that humans contribute to global warming to some extent, the key question is how much and is it dangerous. A Pew Research poll reported November 25, 2019 (Funk & Hefferon, 2019) that 49%

of U.S. adults think that human activity contributes a "great deal" to climate change, which is a slight increase. On the same question, 14% of conservative Republicans and 84% of liberal Democrats said yes. So overall it did not change very much between 2012 and 2019, but the issue became much more political.

The most important question is, "Do you think global warming will pose a serious threat to your way of life?" On this question in 1998, 25% said yes. In answer to the same question in 2014, 35% said yes. It goes up and down over the years, but the public are not convinced global warming is a problem (Dennis, Mufson, & Clement, 2019).

Mark Hemingway of the *Washington Examiner* (Hemingway, 2015) wrote this about Senator Whitehouse's RICO idea:

> "[Senator Whitehouse] wrote this opinion in the Washington Post on Friday, and no one much noticed or batted an eye at the consequences of what he's advocating here. Such calls for draconian restrictions on speech are becoming alarmingly regular. And if more people don't start speaking out against it, sooner or later we're actually going to end up in a place where people are being hauled into court for having an opinion that differs from politicians such as Senator Whitehouse. (Hemingway, 2015)

Senator Whitehouse's proposal to use the RICO statute against the "climate denial network" that is "undermining climate science" is largely based on the *Climate Change* journal article by Robert Brulle (Brulle, 2013) cited above. Brulle used IRS data to find out who was funding conservative non-profit organizations, such as the Competitive Enterprise Institute and the Heartland Institute, which he classified as the "Climate Change Counter-Movement." According to Brulle, these organizations lobby and contribute to political candidates and run a "large number of communications and media efforts that aim" to undermine climate science. A quick check of the first amendment to the constitution verifies that all these activities are protected as free speech, freedom of the press, and the freedom to petition the government. So, exactly how does RICO apply to these activities?

The *Washington Examiner's* Mark Hemingway calls both Whitehouse and Raúl Grijalva cranks, we agree. But we would add that they are dangerous and ignorant cranks. Legitimate scientific disagreements on how to interpret climate change data is not something that can be called racketeering, RICO is not applicable in this situation. It is surprising that a sitting senator, with a law degree, no less, would even suggest something like this. The scientific process is designed explicitly to address this sort of disagreement, RICO is no substitute, nor will it ever be.

Next, we will discuss the news media and climate change. Over most of U.S. history the news media was biased. Often, they put "Democrat" or "Republican" on their mast head to advertise which way they leaned. The *Arkansas Democrat-Gazette* still exists. There was a brief period after World War II when journalists made an attempt to be unbiased and tell the full story. But that noble generation is gone now. The press is mostly a tool for the Democratic Party now, with a few notable exceptions, like *FOX News* or the *Washington Times*. We will discuss examples of the press lying by omission and being used by environmental activists in the next chapter.

Chapter 2: The News Media and Climate Change

There are laws to protect the freedom of the press's speech, but none that are worth anything to protect the people from the press.

…

It seems to me that just in the ratio that our newspapers increase, our morals decay. The more newspapers the worse morals. Where we have one newspaper that does good, I think we have fifty that do harm. We ought to look upon the establishment of a newspaper of the average pattern in a virtuous village as a calamity. Mark Twain, March 31, 1873 at the Monday Evening Club at Hartford, Connecticut. (Twain, 1880, pp. 46-47)

It is clear these days that political bias exists in the news media. According to a Gallup poll in 2017, 62% of the public believes that the news media favors one party or the other, the highest number ever recorded (Swift, 2017). Only 32% say the news media are careful to separate fact from opinion and only 44% can think of an objective news source (Jones & Ritter, 2018). According to a November 14, 2019 Rasmussen poll only 32% believe most reporters are interested in reporting the news in an unbiased manner (Rasmussen, 2019). For a very long time, the *New York Times* was the definitive source for news, yet in 2019 a Rasmussen poll found that only 33% of the population thought it was usually accurate (Rasmussen, 2019).

A 2005 multi-University study by Tim Groseclose and Jeffrey Milyo found most of the news media are biased strongly to the left of the general population and even tilt to the left of the average member of Congress (Groseclose & Milyo, 2005). It is notable that the that *CBS Evening News* and the *New York Times* received scores that were far left of center. This is important to understand in a discussion of climate change. What causes climate change is no longer a scientific debate, but a political debate. Eighty-four percent of U.S. liberal Democrats think humans contribute a great deal to climate change and only fourteen percent of conservative Republicans think the same according to Pew Research in 2019 (Funk & Hefferon, 2019). Overall, the country is divided 50/50.

A scientific debate revolves around the accuracy of observations, what the observations mean for the future and how to analyze them properly. Most

47

importantly, observations contrary to a scientific hypothesis, invalidate the hypothesis. But, in a political debate, contrary data are ignored. A politician creates a consensus with persuasion, intimidation and by suppressing opposing views. A scientist challenges the consensus with observations, analysis, and reasoning.

The liberal bias of the news media affects their coverage of climate science and climate scientists. They do not consider the data or the analysis of it by scientists, only the opinions of the scientists they choose to interview, and they only choose to interview climate alarmists. The primary alternative hypothesis is that variations in the Sun are the primary cause of climate change and humans have a minor impact. Skeptical scientists accept the solar cause hypothesis or simply don't know what causes climate to change.

Climate models suggest that humans could have a large and dominant influence on climate, but there are no data or observations supporting this idea. Further, the models suggesting that human activities cause climate change have never been validated. This will be discussed more thoroughly in Chapters 6 and 7.

Since the 1990s one of the leading experts on the relationship between the Sun and Earth's weather and climate has been Dr. Willie Soon of the Harvard-Smithsonian Center for Astrophysics. Soon is both an astrophysicist and a geoscientist and is well suited to study this interaction. He has received numerous awards and written or co-authored over 200 peer-reviewed papers that have been cited more than 6,111 times according to Google Scholar as of May 10th, 2020.

Willie Soon was born in Kangar, a city in northernmost Malaysia as Wei-Hock Soon in 1966. He now prefers the name Willie. He is one of the most accomplished American scientists alive today, so it is quite surprising that he has had to endure vicious and unjustified political attacks from Greenpeace and the *New York Times*. The late physicist and mathematician, Dr. Freeman Dyson, wrote the following about Dr. Soon:

"The whole point of science is to question accepted dogmas. For that reason, I respect Willie Soon as a good scientist and a courageous citizen." Dr. Freeman Dyson, to the *Boston Globe*, Nov. 5, 2013

The brilliant Dyson hit the nail on the head. Science is not a belief. The scientific process exists to challenge the consensus view. It is the way one person can show the overwhelming majority is mistaken.

Soon began studying the relationship between the Sun and climate change in 1992 immediately after receiving his PhD from the University of Southern California.

Kert Davies started harassing Soon in 1997 when Soon had just started as an astrophysicist at the Harvard-Smithsonian Center for Astrophysics and worked for Sallie Baliunas. Exactly why Davies decided to attack Soon, is not clear. But, in late 1998, when he worked for the Environmental Working Group, he helped produce a Clearinghouse on Environmental Advocacy and Research (CLEAR) report, or "hit list" titled "Affiliations of Selected Global Warming Skeptics" (CLEAR, 1998). Willie Soon is listed as having received "Suspected fossil fuel funding." He is in good company, thirteen of the top climate scientists of the day are also on Davies' hit list.

Davies and his friend John Passacantando were running an organization called Ozone Action, which they merged into Greenpeace in 2000. Davies had left the Environmental Working Group and joined Passacantando at Ozone Action around October of 1998 (Cook R. , 2015).

Kert Davies became the Greenpeace U.S. Research Director and Passacantando, became an executive director of Greenpeace U.S. While at Greenpeace, Kert Davies was the chief architect of the notorious "ExxonSecrets" campaign, launched in 2004. This campaign, described in more detail later, attempted to label the Smithsonian Institution, Willie Soon's employer, a radical "Climate Denial Machine." Davies is a verbal bully who attacks anyone who believes differently than he does, even scientists doing legitimate inquiries.

Two Prominent 2003 Papers

Willie Soon's classic *Energy and Environment* paper "Reconstructing climatic and environmental changes of the past 1000 years: a reappraisal," (Soon, Baliunas, Idso, Idso, & Legates, 2003b), and the earlier companion *Climate Research* paper, "Proxy climatic and environmental changes of the past 1000 years" (Soon & Baliunas, 2003) presented summaries of decades of published evidence that the Medieval Warm Period (abbreviated MWP, roughly 900AD to 1200AD) and the Little Ice Age (abbreviated LIA, roughly 1500AD to 1800AD) were global events. They also showed that recent warming is probably not unusual in the past 1,000 years.

The *Climate Research* paper has been cited 258 times and the *Energy and Environment* paper has been cited 159 times according to Google Scholar on June 23, 2020. The number of citations put these papers into the top 1.8% of all academic peer-reviewed papers (Beaulieu, 2015). To put the number into perspective, about half of all published papers have fewer than four citations and the average paper has about eight (Weingart, 2012). The *Energy and Environment* paper was written with Soon's supervisor at the Harvard-Smithsonian Center for Astrophysics, Sallie Baliunas and their colleagues, Craig Idso and Sherwood Idso of the Center for the Study of Carbon Dioxide and Global Change, and David Legates, a professor of climatology and geography at the University of Delaware.

These papers were the first to challenge the, now infamous, hockey stick graph of Northern Hemisphere average temperature for the past 1,000 years by Michael Mann and his co-author Raymond Bradley (Mann & Bradley, 1999). Their graph was displayed prominently as Figure 1 on page 3 of the IPCC *Third Assessment Report* (IPCC, 2001). The third assessment report is often abbreviated as "TAR." It is also Figure 28 in Chapter 7 and prominently displayed in Al Gore's 2006 movie, *An Inconvenient Truth*.

The graph shows the period from 1000AD to 1900AD as very flat, so it becomes the handle of a hockey stick shape, then the 20th century becomes the blade with temperatures that shoot upward. Mann and Bradley, Gore's movie, and TAR present the hockey stick as evidence that human emissions of CO_2 and other greenhouse gases are warming Earth's atmosphere. They claim that the long flat handle from 1000AD to 1900AD is the "normal climate" and the 20th century, the 1990s and 1998 are 1,000-year anomalies. These anomalies are not coincidence, they say, they exist only because we are emitting greenhouse gases, mainly carbon dioxide (CO_2), into the atmosphere which is warming the planet. Pretty scary stuff.

The problem with the hockey stick graph is that it shows no sign of either the Medieval Warm Period or the Little Ice Age. The two papers Soon and his colleagues published show that these events are well established in history and in the climate literature. Further, the data available suggests the Medieval Warm Period was just as warm as today, or warmer. According to historical and geological records, especially records of mountain glacier advances and retreats, these should be prominent climatic anomalies, yet they are not detectable in the hockey stick graph.

The discrepancy between Mann's hockey stick and the Soon, et al. papers caused an uproar in the news media, as one might imagine, but the news media did not present the scientific debate or the evidence, only the conflict. The news media also took sides.

Irene Sanchez wrote about the controversy on September 12, 2003 in *The Harvard Crimson*. She briefly mentions that Soon and Baliunas concluded that the weather in the 20th century was not unusual, then spends 18 paragraphs listing comments from their critics. Only at the end of the article, does she state that Willie "Soon would only discuss the science – not the politics – of the report for this article." Soon did explain his scientific position, but she didn't print any of it. *The Harvard Crimson* was obviously not interested in educating their readers. Soon told her, "I don't want to say any harsh words," he just wanted to encourage more research. Apparently, even to the *Harvard Crimson*, the scientific debate wasn't important. They just wanted to trash anyone with a view different from their chosen sources (Sanchez, 2003). The *New York Times* and other publications treated the dispute in the same way. After all, the science is settled, right?

Figure 3. Willie Soon in 2003. This is from an interview published by CEI in December 2003, in the Monthly Planet newsletter, about his papers that establish the existance of the Medieval Warming Period and the Little Ice Age. Source: Willie Soon, used with permission.

Willie Soon's papers attracted White House and national attention. A few people even read them. The Bush White House and the Senate Environment and Public Works Committee studied them closely. This and the uproar in the liberal media and the climate alarmist community made Willie Soon a national figure. His national prominence caused Greenpeace and Kert Davies to step up their attacks. Davies created a page, devoted to Willie Soon, on his ExxonSecrets.org web site. The 2003 papers are listed as his "key deeds." Soon's employer, the Smithsonian Astrophysical Observatory, is listed on the web site as a recipient of donations from (gasp!) ExxonMobil.

We will dissect Mann's hockey stick in later chapters, especially Chapters 5 and 7, but for now we will just point out that various investigations of the hockey stick, including a National Research Council investigation (National Research Council, 2006) and a Congressional Investigation led by Dr. Edward Wegman (Wegman, Scott, & Said, 2010), concluded the hockey stick and the conclusions Mann, his co-authors, and the IPCC drew from it, were incorrect. These investigations, and others, concluded the statistical methodology and the data used by Mann and Bradley were inappropriate.

The MWP existed and is a prominent anomaly on all modern temperature reconstructions, except for Mann's hockey stick and reconstructions that use similar methods. They show that peak MWP warming occurred around 950-1000AD when the Vikings colonized Greenland and Newfoundland, Canada (see Figures 19 to 21 in Chapter 5). The LIA is also well established in history and was clearly much colder than the hockey stick showed. Even Mann's later temperature reconstructions (Mann M. , et al., 2008) show the MWP was as warm as today, although he tries to claim otherwise in the conclusions by invalidly comparing modern instrumental temperatures to ancient temperature proxies.

The papers, published in January and May of 2003, summarized over 240 published peer-review papers on past temperature and climate proxies. They examined glacier records, ice core data, borehole temperature surveys, historical records, tree-ring data, sea floor sediment cores and many other climate proxies that cover the past 1,000 years.

As Baliunas and Soon pointed out there are many natural phenomena that influence climate and none of them have been disproven by modern research. Most of them revolve, to some extent, around changing the amount of solar radiation that is absorbed by the Earth's surface or changing where it is absorbed. This can be due to Earth's orbital changes, as in the Milankovitch cycles (May, 2016k), or due to changes in the Sun itself (May, 2020b). They think the narrow focus that modern climate science has on average global temperature is myopic, and misguided. When an outside perturbation is applied to Earth's climate system, more than just temperature changes. To understand climate change, it is better to examine a "broader scope of changes." (Competitive Enterprise Institute, 2003).

As Soon and Baliunas explain in their 2003 papers, the LIA is defined as the most recent period when glaciers reached their maximum extent within the past millennium, and perhaps in the last 11,000 years. Glacier extent fluctuates from year to year, but during the LIA, records show they remained significantly extended for hundreds of years. The maximum glacier extent was not synchronous around the world but was reached most places, at least in the Northern Hemisphere, within a defined period called the Little Ice Age. The earliest cooling started around 1300AD and did not completely end until nearly 1900AD. At peak cooling, sometime between 1600 and 1715, according to most proxies and reconstructions, it was at least one degree Celsius or 1.8°F cooler than today, in the Northern Hemisphere.

Paul Mayewski, a professor at the University of Maine, showed that the maximum global glacier advance occurred between 1600 to 1800AD in an article in *Quaternary Research* (Mayewski, et al., 2004, his Figs. 1 and 4). Glacial advances and retreats only respond to long-term changes in regional average temperature, and they leave both historical and geographic markers of where they have been. For these reasons they are one of the best indicators of past climate changes. Other significant hemisphere-wide data that show the Little Ice Age and the Medieval Warm Period, by Peter deMenocal, et al. in *Science*, are shown in Chapter 5, Figure 21 (deMenocal, Ortiz, Guilderson, & Sarnthein, 2000).

Temperature proxies, including glacier advances and retreat records, suggest that the period from 1600AD to 1750AD was the coldest time in the last millennium in the Czech Republic, Japan, New Zealand, parts of Antarctica and Chile (Soon, Baliunas, Idso, Idso, & Legates, 2003b). Severe cold and drought also brought down the Ming dynasty in 1644AD in China according to Wolfgang Behringer (Behringer, 2010, pp. 114-115). The cooling appears to have been worldwide, except for some portions of Antarctica.

Likewise, the MWP is usually defined as the greatest recent retreat of glaciers worldwide for an extended period. The greatest retreat in the Northern Hemisphere and possibly in the Southern Hemisphere as well, occurred from roughly 950 to 1100AD (Mayewski, et al., 2004, Fig. 1 and 4). Evidence of an unusually warm period from 900 to 1100AD exists in New Zealand, South

Africa, Chile, North America, Greenland, Antarctica, China, and Europe. Evidence of Atlantic Ocean and Greenland warming is presented by Peter deMenocal and colleagues in their paper in *Science*, cited above.

Climate changes in Antarctica, or at least in part of Antarctica, are often out of sync with the rest of the world. This tendency for Antarctica to change independently of the rest of the world can be observed historically, for the LIA and MWP, and for today, as pointed out by Renee Hannon (Hannon, 2020).

Besides looking for evidence supporting the MWP and LIA, Soon and Baliunas looked for evidence that the 20th century was the warmest time in the past millennium or had the most extreme precipitation or drought. Long-term cold weather is often associated with dryness and long-term warm weather with higher precipitation, but it can go the other way in some areas, such as deserts. Soon and Baliunas did not try and associate dryness or high precipitation rates with either higher or lower temperatures, but were looking for significant changes in climate. They note that local and regional climate changes are more important to people than global changes, global changes are almost an abstraction (Competitive Enterprise Institute, 2003). It is common these days to equate "climate change" to warmer or cooler weather, but climate incorporates more than just surface temperature.

All their comparisons were from a proxy to itself; they did not compare proxy reconstructions to the modern instrumental temperature record like Mann and Bradley did. Also, unlike Mann and Bradley, they did not combine proxies into one temperature record. Proxies contain a lot of noise, which masks detail. Further, combining noisy proxies via statistical regression, like Mann and Bradley did, smooths through peaks and valleys, reducing variability, as noise cancels noise. Calibrating proxies to local temperature records, which is done via linear regression, also reduces temperature variability.

Thus, proxy derived high and low temperatures will always show much less variability than more precise instrumental records. We discuss this problem in more detail in Chapter 5, but it should be clear that to establish that the 20th century is warmer or cooler than the MWP, we must compare the periods directly with the same units of measure. Neither modern thermometers, nor temperature proxies are accurate enough, we are talking about differences of less than one-tenth of a degree C over 1,000 years, when comparing recent warming to the MWP. This is easily seen in Figures 19-21.

Soon and Baliunas looked for climate extremes, as defined above, that were 50 years long or longer and compared them to the 20th century. In all they looked at 105 proxies that had a 50-year climate anomaly in the 20th century. There were 12 proxies that had an overall maximum (either maximum temperature or most extreme precipitation or drought) in the late 20th century, 10 with an overall maximum in the early 20th century (pre-1970). This left 83 with a 50-year 20th century anomaly that was not the highest in the last 1,000 years. In other words, most of the worldwide proxies, with a 20th century anomaly, did not show a maximum temperature or precipitation extreme in the 20th century.

The Soon and Baliunas Controversy

Once the 2003 papers were published, they immediately created a stir. The papers caught the eye of Philip Cooney, President George W. Bush administration's Council on Environmental Quality chief of staff. Cooney was in the process of reviewing the first EPA *Report on the Environment* (EPA, 2003). On April 21, 2003, about three months after Soon and Baliunas' first paper came out, Cooney wrote, in a memo to Vice Presidential aide Kevin O'Donovan:

"The recent paper of Soon-Baliunas contradicts a dogmatic view held by many in the climate science community that the past century was the warmest in the past millennium and signals human induced "global warming." (U.S. House of Representatives, 2007, p. 23)

Cooney's statement is very reasonable. There is a serious problem with Mann and Bradley's hockey stick and their conclusion that it shows 20th century warming to be unusual. The MWP is nowhere to be found on the hockey stick. Thus, the hockey stick attempts to overturn decades of research showing the MWP existed and was probably as warm as today. All Soon and Baliunas did was compile and summarize this research with the help of Craig Idso, Sherwood Idso and David Legates. As David Legates said, it was Mann's hockey stick that was the "scientific outlier," Soon and Baliunas work is and was in the scientific mainstream (Legates D. , 2003).

The research was funded by NASA, the Air Force, and the American Petroleum Institute. However, everyone at NASA was not happy with the work. Dr. Drew Shindell, a NASA climate scientist, in congressional testimony before Henry Waxman's Committee on Oversight and Government Reform, tied himself in knots trying to discredit the paper, by saying that Soon and Baliunas did no original research and collected other climate scientists work. Collecting papers on a specific topic and summarizing them is called a literature review paper and such papers are common and valuable. Literature review books are called textbooks. Shindell then says, they used this data from the papers to assess the uncertainties in estimating ancient temperatures and concluded that we really can't say modern warming is unusual.

It is a matter of opinion whether Soon and Baliunas' assessment of proxy uncertainty, relative to the variation in temperature over the past 1,000 years, is appropriate or not. Shindell appears to think it isn't. This author and many others believe Soon and Baliunas did a good job of putting the proxies into perspective, relative to recent warming. Then he says that in his view this is not representative of the "views of nearly every expert in climate science" (U.S. House of Representatives, 2007, p. 24). He goes on to say, "I would not say that one alternative paper undermines the thousands of papers that go into a document like the IPCC report."

He ignores the fact that the thousands of papers in an IPCC report generally deal with other topics. However, Soon and Baliunas' paper summarizes the work of hundreds of scientists, going back as far as Hubert H. Lamb's classic paper, that specifically describe the MWP and LIA (Lamb, 1965). Lamb and hundreds of other papers present abundant evidence that the climate anomalies existed and that there was between 1.2 and 1.4°C (2.2°F to 2.5°F) difference between them in England and around the Northern Hemisphere.

Lamb also estimates that the much of the world was over one degree Celsius warmer from 1000 to 1200AD than today. The rather vain Shindell seems to think only his friends matter and that the two-hundred-plus researchers that wrote the papers Soon and Baliunas summarized do not. Dr. Lamb is undoubtedly rolling over in his grave at the thought. This is somewhat common among the small, vain, and insular community of self-described "climate scientists," they only consider themselves and their colleagues to be intelligent and worthwhile. As David Legates cogently said, it is the hockey stick that is the scientific outlier.

Once the White House became involved, the Congress was quick to follow. Then there were investigations, such as Henry Waxman's, already cited (U.S. House of Representatives, 2007).

Mann, Shindell, Bradley, and the rest of "Mann's Hockey Team" are trying to overturn decades of work by hundreds of scientists with their hockey stick and they say trust us, we are the real climate scientists. No other scientific opinions matter.

The uproar was not over. Even though the Soon and Baliunas 2003 *Climate Research* paper had been reviewed by four reviewers, who approved it for publication unanimously, the journal was attacked. Michael Mann and his Hockey Team penned a rebuttal to Soon and Baliunas (Mann, Amman, Bradley, & Briffa, 2003).

The Mann rebuttal, in the journal *Eos*, signed by twelve Hockey Team members, states explicitly, that they consider the hockey stick graph and similar temperature reconstructions to be a "compelling basis for concern over future climate changes, including increases in global-mean surface temperatures, due to increased concentrations of greenhouse gases, primarily from fossil fuel burning" (Mann, Amman, Bradley, & Briffa, 2003). The Wegman Congressional Report on the hockey stick graph (Wegman, Scott, & Said, 2010) presents an analysis of the entire "Hockey Team," a group of some 42 self-appointed "climate experts." One of the conclusions of the Wegman Report was:

> "we were struck by the isolation of communities such as the paleoclimate community that rely heavily on statistical methods, yet do not seem to be interacting with the mainstream statistical community. The public policy implications of this debate are financially staggering and yet apparently no independent statistical expertise was sought or used." (Wegman, Scott, & Said, 2010)

Billions of dollars are being spent around the world on climate change research and mitigation and millions of fossil fuel jobs hang on these policy decisions. Yet, the statistical methods and data that went into the hockey stick, a key bit of evidence, perhaps the only direct evidence, that humans control the climate, have not been checked. The FDA expects statisticians to review clinical trials of new drugs and medical devices. The same sort of review is certainly warranted for scientific studies used to justify spending billions of public dollars and throwing millions out of work.

It is interesting and amusing to view Mann's criticism of the Soon and Baliunas paper with 20/20 hindsight. We now know the 1999 hockey stick is wrong because the statistical methods Mann used to create it were inappropriate for the task of merging numerous, incompatible, and noisy temperature proxies into one reconstruction. These were serious flaws, as we will discuss in more detail in Chapter 5. But these very flaws are what he uses to criticize Soon and Baliunas' work.

Soon and Baliunas specifically did not calibrate, quantitatively, their climate proxies. They simply noted if it had a temperature signal or not (according to the original author of the proxy) and then compared the proxy to itself, was the highest 50-year temperature or precipitation signal in the 20th century or not? By not merging the proxies statistically, as Mann and Bradley did, they avoided much of the serious reduction in early (pre-instrumental) variability that Mann's reconstruction suffered.

Willie Soon, Sallie Baliunas and David Legates responded to Mann's comment in the same issue of *Eos* (Soon, Baliunas, & Legates, 2003c). They did not address the serious statistical problems in Mann's reconstruction, and given how poorly Mann described his methods and how secretive he was with his data, they may not have been aware of them. They did point out one serious flaw though. The early part of Mann's hockey stick (pre-1400AD) relies almost exclusively on a few bristlecone tree ring series in western North America. These tree rings do not correlate well to temperature in the 20th century, in fact they decline, as temperatures go up.

This is the origin of the famous "hide the decline" scandal that would embarrass the Hockey Team in 2009 (McIntyre, 2014). Soon and Baliunas do point out that there are great uncertainties in Mann's hockey stick graph, regardless of the methods used to create it, and this was also the point of their two 2003 papers. David Legates points out that Mann comparing his reconstruction to modern instrumental temperatures to draw his conclusions is an invalid "apples-to-oranges comparison" (Legates D. , 2003).

It was hard to see in 2003, but since then we have come to understand that the hockey stick graph was an elaborate fiction, created in a haze of complex statistics and computer code. Later investigators, including the National Research Council and the Wegman Congressional Committee, would speculate that even Mann did not understand what he had done. Had Mann been more forthcoming with his data and code, the errors would have been found much more quickly, but he didn't. Others took Mann's secrecy to mean he did know what he had done and was trying to hide his duplicity. We may never know which is true, but it doesn't matter. There is no proof that Mann deceived us and absent proof, he is innocent.

Soon and Baliunas presented the proxies in a way that clearly showed the hockey stick did not reflect them. There was a serious disconnect between the underlying data and the result, but the public, the politicians and many of the scientists who commented on the debate didn't see it or didn't want to see it. It wasn't until years later, when Mann was finally forced to give up most of his code and data that the flaws that allowed him to concoct the hockey stick, from data that said the opposite, were uncovered. Two Canadian scientists, Stephen McIntyre and Ross McKitrick eventually were able to explain how it all happened. Their first paper was published in *Energy and Environment*, in November 2003 (McIntyre & McKitrick, 2003). But their most devastating analysis of the hockey stick would not come out until 2005. We will cover the details in Chapter 5.

In 2003, most of the public and the media sided with Mann's Hockey Team and their various fictional hockey sticks. Philip Cooney and the Bush administration were correct that the hockey stick was very uncertain and the preponderance of the climate science literature supported the existence of the MWP and the LIA. But they could not convince the public and the news media. The hockey stick was "quantitative," it came out of a computer, it was statistical, it was simple, it had to be correct. Soon and Baliunas' papers were vague and didn't have numbers. In those days, if you wanted people to believe you, you had to have numbers, especially numbers with lots of decimal places. Now, it is easy to see how absurd computer models can be, but then we were in awe of them, if it came from a computer it had to be right.

Philip Cooney had been a lobbyist for the American Petroleum Institute, which was also one of the organizations that sponsored Soon and Baliunas' research. This was all it took for the news media to concoct a "vast right-wing conspiracy" by the "evil" oil companies to suppress "climate science." Andrew Revkin, of the *New York Times*, ominously noted that Cooney added the word "extremely" to this sentence: "The attribution of the causes ... to climate change ... is *extremely* difficult" (Revkin, 2005). The emphasis is added. The edit was made to a draft of the regularly published government document, "Our Changing Planet." Cooney's addition is obviously correct, thousands of scientists have spent billions of dollars trying to identify the causes of climate change and have come up with nothing. "Extremely" is very appropriate in that sentence (Climate Change Science Program, 2003). Revkin and the *New York Times* are hopeless.

Cooney tried to highlight the uncertainty in the attribution of climate change to human activities. This was part of his White House job, but he was vilified for doing it because he was supposedly politically interfering with government climate change science (U.S. House of Representatives, 2007, p. i). Apparently an official, appointed by the elected president, is not allowed to question the scientists he supervises? There are dangers when government-run science is unchecked, the bureaucrats begin to believe their speculation.

How quickly Democrats forget that government scientists work for elected officials and their appointees, not the other way round when a Republican president is elected. That is also correct when the political parties are reversed. This is the main reason to keep the government and politics out of science. When scientific studies must be used to help set policy, especially in the EPA, then the data and code from the studies must be publicly available and the studies' conclusions replicated independently before the new policy is put in place. If a study passes peer-review and the conclusions can be replicated, then the funding for the study, and the political party in charge, doesn't matter. Transparency is our only protection from scientists and bureaucrats with agendas running amuck.

Revkin's article also points out that Cooney changed the sentence, "Many scientific observations indicate that Earth is undergoing a period of relatively rapid change" to "… *may be* undergoing a period of relatively rapid change." The emphasis is added. Unlike his earlier edit, quoted above, this edit did make it into the final draft and today we know that Cooney's version is far more accurate than the original. We now know that the hockey stick was dampened significantly by the statistical methods used by Mann and Bradley. Cooney simply acknowledged the appropriate level of uncertainty with his corrections.

There were other repercussions as well. While Soon and Baliunas' work was very good and later shown to be correct, a portion of the climate change community thought the paper was very poor, mainly because it contradicted the saintly hockey stick. In other words, the hypothesis is correct; thus, the data displayed by Soon and Baliunas are bad.

Many members of Mann's Hockey Team reside at the University of East Anglia in the U.K. One of them is Clare Goodess, who wrote about how publishing the Soon and Baliunas' paper in *Climate Research* caused half of the journal's editorial board to resign (Goodess, 2003). She calls the paper a "poor paper," but acknowledges that all four reviewers of the paper and the journal editor recommended publication. An investigation, by the journal, concluded that the review process had been properly conducted and many of the staff supported the paper. But some were opposed and half of them resigned over the controversy. This was not a scientific dispute, but a political one. The people that resigned had done nothing wrong, as alleged by Mann's Hockey Team, they simply had the "wrong" opinion about the paper. Stalin could not have done better.

Soon and Baliunas' 2003 papers were thoroughly researched and showed the MWP and LIA are "widespread and near-synchronous phenomena." Their second conclusion that the "20th century does not contain the warmest anomaly of the past millennium in most of the proxy records" is also clearly supported by their data. Over the course of time these conclusions were shown to be correct by the National Research Council, the Wegman Congressional Report and even by Michael Mann's 2008 temperature reconstruction in which the MWP and LIA magically reappear (see Chapter 5 for details, especially Figure 22). The same investigations also found that Mann's conclusions in his hockey stick papers are not supported by the data and analysis he presents in them.

Soon and Baliunas' papers were solid scientific work, good science is not always correct, but these papers were, as far as we know in 2020. Even so, they were vilified in the press and dismissed by politicians like Henry Waxman. An article in *Science* reports that Henry Waxman and some scientists have accused the Bush administration of distorting and suppressing science to advance their policies (Malakoff, 2003). However, the resignations at *Climate Research* suggest it was Mann's Hockey Team, a compliant news media, and Congressional Democrats who were suppressing and distorting science.

Performance Review in 2010

Soon was attacked within the Smithsonian Institution due to his numerous publications on the relationship between solar activity and Earth's climate. The attacks were due to political pressure from outside the organization and Soon's 2010 performance review was put in danger because of them. The attack on Soon had nothing to do with his performance, he is a widely cited and famous researcher.

Simply put, he had embarrassed the climate change establishment with his 2003 papers on climate change over the past 1,000 years. These papers inflamed the humiliation caused by the "*climategate*" scandal of 2009. The release of the hacked *climategate* emails (Costella, 2010), during the very cold winter of 2009-2010 required a response and the alarmists found Willie Soon vulnerable.

Professor Christopher Essex, who is the Associate Chair of the Department of Applied Mathematics at the University of Western Ontario, wrote to Professor Charles Alcock at the Harvard-Smithsonian Center for Astrophysics and Soon's superior. An excerpt from his email to Alcock:

"the theme is one of academic freedom, if you have not been personally targeted by the mischief of environmental activism, its scope or even its very existence can seem a bit fantastic. But be assured that such activism not only exists, it is organized, influential, and well-funded. ...

Singling out and targeting dissenting scientists personally instead of their scientific arguments is their standard operating procedure. ...

The activist's goal is to depict skepticism about climate change ... as being driven by actionable corruption rather than something that is a simple expression of honest scientific doubt. ... But attacking the person is no way to find the truth of Nature as you well know. We in science go on the scientific credibility of the ideas rather than the political credibility of the source for very good reasons. ...

I ask you to begin to repair the science by simply standing up for scientific skepticism ... Singling out [Dr. Willie Soon] at the behest of sworn enemies with mischief in mind to offer publicly what has never been provided since the inception of email is not fair by any measure." (Prof. Christopher Essex, an email to Dr. Charles Alcock, June 7, 2010)

The *climategate* scandal revealed how the climate alarmists were manipulating the peer-review process and using ad hominem attacks to squash opinions, even the opinions of very prominent scientists, like Soon and Baliunas, that were different from their own. It showed how political climate science had become. One of the *climategate* emails contained one of the most anti-scientific statements we've ever seen, it is from Phil Jones, a director of the University of East Anglia Climate Research Unit (CRU) on Nov. 16, 1999:

I've just completed Mike's Nature trick of adding in the real temperatures to each series for the last 20 years (i.e. from 1981 onwards) and from 1961 for Keith's to hide the decline. (Costella, 2010, p. 17)

The second most anti-scientific email was also sent by Phil Jones. He sent it to Warwick Hughes in 2005:

> "Why should I make the data available to you, when your aim is to try and find something wrong with it." (Wall Street Journal Editorial Board, 2009)

The whole idea of science is to examine and re-examine data and ideas *to find something wrong*. After the humiliation of *climategate* and the very cold winters of 2008-2009 and 2009-2010, it was natural to try and shift attention to someone else by attacking Soon and Baliunas. Soon was demonstrating that solar variability was more important to climate change than the IPCC was willing to admit, further he had participated in the extensive criticism of Michael Mann's hockey stick. So, Willie Soon became their target.

Besides Soon's 2003 papers, the later papers by Stephen McIntyre and Ross McKitrick, discussed in Chapter 5, also showed the hockey stick was wrong. Even later, two entire books were devoted to listing and explaining all the criticisms of the hockey stick. The first was *The Hockey Stick Illusion* by Andrew Montford, which details the numerous data problems and the flawed statistical methodology (Montford, 2010). Second was Mark Steyn's *A Disgrace to the Profession* (Steyn, 2015).

Steyn's book reports that Professor Jonathan A. Jones at Oxford University said the "Hockey Stick is obviously wrong. Everybody knows it is obviously wrong" (Steyn, 2015, Ch. 11). McIntyre and McKitrick demonstrated that the statistical methodology used to create the hockey stick, created the same shape from random red noise 99% of the time. McIntyre and McKitrick's finding was supported by the National Academy of Sciences and reproduced by the Wegman Congressional investigation (Wegman, Scott, & Said, 2010, pp. 29-33). Even so, in April 2020 Michael Mann was elected to the National Academy of Sciences, which is odd.

Professor Christopher Essex also believes the humiliation caused by the *climategate* email release, by an unknown hacker, motivated Greenpeace to attack Soon in 2010 and wrote:

"Regardless of how and why the communications from the University of East Anglia were released and whether the release was appropriate or not, this does not justify the demand by Greenpeace for access to all correspondence from or to any particular scientist. ...

We are extremely concerned that the possibility exists that the Smithsonian Institution may accede to Greenpeace's demand. We understand that the Smithsonian Institution is not subject to the Freedom of Information Act [FOIA] and therefore has the discretion to weigh the appropriateness of the request for Dr. Soon's correspondence. ... It is difficult to see how the Smithsonian's interests are served by subjecting its employees to the intimidation tactics of advocacy groups and setting a precedent that any scientist at the Smithsonian can be subjected to the same threat in the future." (Prof. Christopher Essex, in a letter of support that was signed by 56 noted climate scientists and addressed to Dr. Charles Alcock) (Essex, 2010)

Greenpeace sent an FOIA (Freedom of Information Act) request to the Smithsonian Institution in late 2009, asking for all correspondence by Soon relating to his work on climate issues. Once they found they could get away with this, due to the weak management at the Smithsonian, they continued to do this every few years in a pattern of harassment against Soon that the Smithsonian should have never allowed.

The Smithsonian is a government institution, but as a government trust, the Smithsonian is not required to respond to an FOIA, and it could have denied the request, as Essex mentions in the quote above. FOIA are only mandatory for executive branch agencies of the government (Smithsonian Institution, 2020). As Professor Essex and the other 56 signatories of the letter to Director Alcock wrote:

"The worst of all worlds for the Smithsonian would be if it were seen as playing favorites in making discretionary FOIA choices so as to favor one or another in scientific and/or policy debates." (Prof. Christopher Essex, in a letter of support that was signed by 56 noted climate scientists and addressed to Dr. Charles Alcock) (Essex, 2010)

The original purpose of the FOIA was to help the public understand the workings of government, it was not intended to allow organizations, like Greenpeace, to harass and intimidate individuals for their opinions and writings. Even though it was clear that the FOIA request was a personal attack on Soon and was simply over a difference in opinion regarding the causes of climate change, Alcock, against all advice and common decency, conceded to the request and ordered Soon to comply. Since Greenpeace is a registered non-profit, Soon and the Smithsonian had to do the record search for free.

The response from the world's scientists to this attack on Soon was tremendous and they immediately sent a barrage of letters supporting him to his superiors at the Harvard-Smithsonian Center for Astrophysics. A sampling of quotes follows:

Professor, emeritus Dr. Eugene Parker, University of Chicago:

> "I am appalled by the attacks on his integrity. I understand that Greenpeace has demanded to see his private memos, etc. clearly with the intent of attacking him as they have attacked others with whom they disagree. If organizations such as Greenpeace disapprove of Dr. Soon's conclusions, let them attack him with published scientific evidence, so that Dr. Soon can defend his views on a scientific level. Locking down his computer [shutting off his Smithsonian email] disgraces the concept of scientific inquiry. Dr. Soon represents a bright spot of independent thought. That independence may be troublesome, but it is essential if we are ever to see the issue of global warming in perspective." Letters of support, (andymaypetrophysicist.com, 2020)

Parker refers to a time when the Smithsonian Institute shut down Soon's Harvard-Smithsonian email, which was disgraceful. Notice the importance that Parker assigns to Soon's independent thinking.

Next, we see that Dr. Harry Van Loon of the National Center for Atmospheric Research has written:

"Among those few scientists who have contributed significantly to the understanding of the climate problem is Dr. Willie Soon, who during the past 16 years has published a series of important papers on the sun-climate problem. Dr. Soon has a solid background in the physics of the sun and other sun-like stars, which is more than can be said of many who deal with climate change; and his knowledge has added to [our] understanding of the sun-climate problem. He has indeed advanced the cumulative knowledge of the solar relationship immensely." Letters of support, (andymaypetrophysicist.com, 2020)

Dr. Christopher Essex writes the following directly to Professor Gary Melnick, Chairman of the Smithsonian Professional Accomplishments Evaluation Committee regarding Willie Soon:

"Wealthy organizations like Greenpeace, for example, have enormous budgets aimed at going after people and organizations that don't go along with their worldview. There are many people working full time thinking of ways to confound the lives of scientists like Dr. Soon with ad hominem reasoning and such petty torments as they can dream up. They care little that what he does is legitimate science and fair comment. Here is a recent quotation hastily removed by Greenpeace from its blog directed at non-conforming scientists among others, 'We know who you are. We know where you live. We know where you work. And we be many, but you be few." Letters of support, (andymaypetrophysicist.com, 2020)

Professor Essex also notes that one of Greenpeace's subsidiary organizations, had requested all of Soon's emails. As we will see, Greenpeace supports numerous small organizations that can act more freely because they do not have to disclose their sources of funds or their financials.

The MIT atmospheric physicist Professor Richard Lindzen writes:

"Dr. Soon is one of the leading experts in relating solar phenomena to the earth's climate. [He] has suffered considerably and clearly unjustly for taking a politically incorrect position." Letters of support, (andymaypetrophysicist.com, 2020)

There are other testimonials and recommendations from the late Dr. Robert Carter (James Cook University), Professor Eric Posmentier (Dartmouth College), Professor Joseph Kunc (University of Southern California), Professor William Gray (Colorado State University) Professor William Happer (Princeton University) and many others. Professor Happer writes:

> "[Dr. Soon] is convinced that the Sun has a very major influence on Earth's climate. This has not been a popular view during much of Willie's career, when an implacable Cult of CO_2 has acquired monstrous power. According to the dogma of the Cult, the "pollutant" CO_2 is the only important influence on Earth's climate. Willie has shown in many ways, observational facts do not fit the CO_2 dogma." Letters of support,
>
> (andymaypetrophysicist.com, 2020)

Soon survived his performance review and is still employed at the Harvard-Smithsonian Center for Astrophysics. Due to the lies and harassment from Kert Davies and the *New York Times*, Soon was ostracized by some at the Center for Astrophysics. While he is popular with his co-workers, many of whom quietly cheer him on, he was moved out of the main office to a remote location in 2009. Sallie Baliunas was also moved to the remote location.

Soon has reduced his hours at the Center and changed his status to part-time. His friend and former supervisor Dr. Sallie Baliunas retired around 2009, in the midst of all of this, largely due to the harassment. Soon's health has suffered. This sort of harassment does have its consequences, but people like Kert Davies don't care, they think they are "saving the world" and every injustice is justified. After all everyone should think just like them, no dissent is allowed.

Kert Davies, John Passacantando, and Greenpeace

Kert Davies and John Passacantando eventually left Greenpeace and formed a group to discredit ExxonMobil and other fossil fuel companies. They became involved with the ExxonKnew campaign described in the next chapter. They were given $5 million dollars for this effort by Greenpeace.

Some of the money was used by Kert Davies to start the Climate Investigations Center (or "CIC") in 2014 (Cook R. , 2020). The rest of the money went into the secretive "Our Next Economy, LLC" organization, located in Alexandria, Virginia, next to Washington, D.C. Neither the Climate Investigations Center (Johnson, 2019) or Our Next Economy are registered as non-profits with the IRS (IRS, 2020), but they describe themselves as non-profits (Climate Investigations Center, 2016). Sources conflict, but it appears that Davies has Greenpeace file their FOIA requests since they are a registered non-profit and can do so for free.

Where the money comes from for the ongoing operations and salaries at CIC is unclear. Davies and his allies, like Senator Sheldon Whitehouse, like to complain about secret funds and so-called dark money when it finances their opponents, but they do not disclose the source of funds for some of their own organizations. Besides the Climate Investigations Center, Davies also directs the Climate Communications and Law (CCL) organization in Maryland.

CCL has a Maryland address, but they claim to do no business there and, for this reason, did not register there. Cleta Mitchell, an attorney with Foley and Lardner LLP, has filed a complaint with Judge John Wobensmith, the Secretary of State for Maryland about CCL. Her complaint, filed August 20, 2019, claims that CCL is operating as a non-profit without registering with the state (Mitchell, 2019). The disclosure laws in Maryland are minimal, but CCL has not complied with them (Cato, 2019).

The Paper that blew it up

In late February 2015, Soon was accused by Kert Davies of failing to disclose conflicts of interest to an academic journal, *Science Bulletin*. The article in question is "Why Models run hot: results from an irreducibly simple climate model" (Monckton, Soon, Legates, & Briggs, 2015). We will abbreviate this paper as MSLB15 here. Besides Soon, the other authors of the paper are Christopher Monckton (Lord Monckton, Viscount of Brenchley), David Legates (Professor of Geography and Climatology, University of Delaware), and William Briggs (Mathematician and statistician, former professor of statistics at Cornell Medical School). In the article, the authors "declare that they have no conflict of interest." The definition of a conflict of interest is:

"A conflict of interest is "a set of circumstances that creates a risk that professional judgment or actions regarding a primary interest will be unduly influenced by a secondary interest (Lo and Field, 2009)." (Vian & Crable, 2017)

MSLB15 was instantly popular and devastating to the climate alarmist cause and to the IPCC *Fifth Assessment Report* (IPCC, 2013). The IPCC is the Intergovernmental Panel on Climate Change, a research organization set up by the United Nations in 1988. MSLB15 was published online January 8th, 2015 and downloaded 22,000 times in less than two months, an outstanding number of downloads.

The paper caused a stir because it explained that the IPCC's *Fifth Assessment Report* or "AR5" reduced its near-term warming projections substantially, but left its long-term, higher, projections alone. This was because the IPCC central estimate of the climate sensitivity to CO_2 was reduced from 3.2°C (5.8°F) to 2.2°C (4°F) per doubling of CO_2 concentration. The sensitivity to CO_2 is often abbreviated "ECS" for equilibrium climate sensitivity. The MSLB15 calculation was done the way the IPCC used in their *Fourth Assessment Report*, abbreviated "AR4."

If the new estimate is correct, the projected rise in temperature for the 21st century is less than one-degree C. Another implication of the change is that the combustion of all fossil fuels estimated to exist would only cause a temperature increase of 2.2°C (4°F). This amount of warming is trivial, good for humanity, but bad for the climate alarmists.

The organization that models climate projections for the IPCC is the CMIP, or the Coupled Model Intercomparison Project. It was created in 1995 to consolidate climate models from around the world into a set of projections that could form the basis for the IPCC reports. As we will see in Chapter 6, the CMIP climate models used for the IPCC fourth and fifth assessment reports overestimate global warming by a substantial amount (see Figure 24).

AR5 was essentially a repeat of AR4 with respect to the computation of human influence on climate. Yet, MSLB15 tells us that deep in AR5 a dramatic change was made in the model calculations that lowers the computed climate impact of CO_2. But the change was not reflected in the long-term climate projections in AR5.

Modern computer climate models are expensive "general circulation" models that model thermal energy moving through the atmosphere and the upper part of the oceans. The models break the atmosphere into 3D grid boxes that are assumed to be in local thermodynamic equilibrium and only change at their edges where they contact neighboring boxes. The older models, such as the 1979 Charney model (Charney, et al., 1979), were simpler and modeled the whole atmosphere and the upper ocean conceptually.

The complexity of modern models has not changed the estimated climate sensitivity to CO_2 or made it more accurate. The earlier models, like the Charney Report model, computed the same range of sensitivity to CO_2 that the new models compute. Except for AR4, they all say doubling the CO_2 concentration in the atmosphere will cause a change of 1.5°C (2.7°F) to 4.5°C (8.1°F) as shown in Table 1. This range has survived intact for forty years despite the efforts of thousands of U.S. researchers spending over one-hundred billion 2014 dollars between 1993 and 2015 (U.S. Government Accountability Office (GAO), 2016).

So, when MSLB15 showed up online, explaining that the AR5 model's feedback estimates suggested an ECS of 2.2°C (4°F), rather than the AR4 estimate of 3.26°C (5.9°F) (IPCC, 2007, p. 798) it caused a huge uproar. The feedback they are speaking of is due to the direct warming from the additional CO_2. The direct warming is small, around one-degree Celsius for a doubling of CO_2. This slight warming will cause a feedback, generally assumed to be due to an increase in absolute humidity, caused by warmer temperatures. Water vapor is a much stronger greenhouse gas than CO_2, so this feedback is what the climate alarmists are worried about. In the AR4 models, the estimated feedback was large, but it was revised downward in AR5. This reduction is what MSLB15 reported.

Adding fuel to the fire was the fact that no best estimate of ECS was given in AR5. There are many ways to compute ECS and they disagree so much in the AR5 models, that the IPCC did not feel they could give a best estimate. Both TAR (the IPCC third assessment report) and AR4 provided a best estimate of 3°C (5.4°F), so if AR5 had stated their implied ECS of 2.2°C (4°F), the precipitous decline would have been obvious and politically damaging. So, they were silent. The obvious question is why? Did they think no one would notice?

Because the IPCC supplied no best estimate of ECS in AR5, the implied central ECS estimate became the average of the upper and lower bounding temperature estimates. Figure 4 shows why this assumption is an error. The critical value in ECS is the additional radiative forcing supplied by the extra greenhouse gases emitted by humans. This value is denoted as f_∞ in the figure. The relationship of ECS and the forcing is linear, but the relationship with temperature is a power function. Therefore, when f_∞ varies from 1.3 to 2.9, temperature varies from 2 to over 12 degrees. Because the object of study is human influence, it is more appropriate to average the extra radiative forcing than the temperature. Both AR4 and MSLB15 average the forcing. The average of the additional CO_2 radiative forcing is not the mid-point of the temperatures, but well below it as shown in Figure 4. The graph shown in Figure 4 does not represent actual numbers from AR4 or AR5, it is just an illustration of the physical principles.

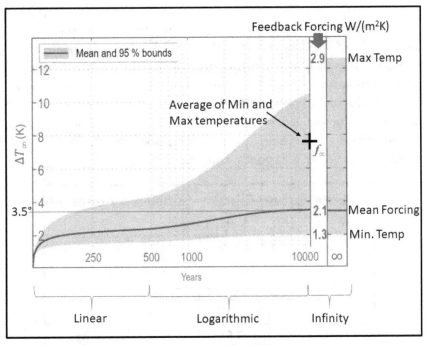

Figure 4. The feedback forcing in the middle column is closely related to ECS, the equilibrium climate sensitivity. It is the input energy that causes the temperature change on the left-hand axis. See the text for a full explanation. Note this example is not from either AR4 or AR5, just an illustration of the principles. Source: after (Monckton, Soon, Legates, & Briggs, 2015). Used with permission.

Equilibrium climate sensitivity is the ultimate change in temperature (left-hand vertical axis). Therefore, infinity is shown on the graph and the time scale changes from linear to logarithmic to infinity on the horizontal axis. In this illustration, the potential feedback to additional CO_2 is 1.3 W/(m²K) to 2.9 W/(m²K) and the average is 2.1. A forcing of 2.1, in this model, causes a temperature change, at infinity, of 3.5°C (6.3°F). Using this method with data from AR5 the ECS is only 2.2°C (4°F). Perhaps for this reason, the IPCC decided not to provide a central estimate of ECS, they said:

"In contrast to AR4, no best estimate for ECS is given because of a lack of agreement on the best estimate across lines of evidence and studies and an improved understanding of the uncertainties in estimates based on the observed warming." (IPCC, 2013, p. 85)

There are many ways to estimate ECS. One can use climate model results, analysis of feedbacks (like in AR4 or MSLB15), observed temperature and CO_2 changes (Lewis & Curry, 2018), or paleoclimate studies. The dilemma the IPCC faced in AR5 was that these estimates did not agree and many of them were far below those given in AR4 and previous assessment reports, as shown in Table 1. One wonders why the IPCC is so sure that humans control the climate with their greenhouse gas emissions, when the impact of the main greenhouse gas, CO_2, is so poorly understood?

Equilibrium Climate Sensitivity Best Estimates			
Report	Best or central estimate	Overall range	Page in Assessment Report
	$°C/2xCO_2$	$°C/2xCO_2$	
Charney, 1979	3.0	1.5 to 4.5	page 2
FAR, 1990/1992	2.5 to 4.0	1.5 to 4.5	page 75
SAR, 1995	2.5	1.5 to 4.5	page 34
TAR, 2001	3.0	1.5 to 4.5	page 67
AR4, 2007	3.0	2 to 4.5	page 727
AR5, 2013	NA	1.5 to 4.5	page 16
MSLB15, 2015	2.2		AR5 data
Lewis & Curry 2018	1.5	1.1 to 2.45	page 6068

Table 1. Various central or "best estimates" of ECS, which is denoted by $°C/2xCO_2$ or the temperature change due to a doubling of CO_2. The MSLB15 estimate uses AR5 data, but their simple model uses the AR4 method. The Lewis and Curry estimate uses historical temperature and CO_2 data.

Once Christopher Monckton and his co-authors, including Willie Soon, noticed that the CO_2 feedback forcing was lowered in AR5, they created a simple model to investigate this difference and then published their assessment. It is virtually impossible to attack the "Irreducibly simple climate model" presented in the paper, it is too basic. So, the alarmist cabal initially said that *Science Bulletin* was an obscure journal, therefore the paper cannot be any good. Predictably, that didn't work, besides, the *Science Bulletin* is the Chinese version of *Nature* or *Science* (Istvan, 2015).

Next, the alarmists, possibly including John Holdren, senior advisor to President Obama, began to attack Willie Soon through his employer, the Harvard-Smithsonian Center for Astrophysics. John Holdren had already attacked Willie Soon and Sallie Baliunas' 2003 papers when he was still at Harvard according to *The Harvard Crimson* article described previously (Sanchez, 2003). He claimed it was a "flawed analysis." The analysis was not flawed, it was quite good, and it embarrassed the Obama administration.

Unable to attack the science, they wanted the skeptics in the Center for Astrophysics silenced. The Smithsonian responded with new directives on conduct that contained a "loyalty to the Smithsonian" clause. The Smithsonian's Inspector General investigated Soon and found no wrongdoing on his part, but this simply enraged the critics and didn't settle anything (Arnold, 2016). Attacks on climate skeptics were very common in 2015 and 2016 and the Obama administration was not alone, some of the harassment came from Congress as discussed in Chapter 1.

The *New York Times* and the other news organizations covering the story should have written about what MSLB15 said, the story isn't that complicated. But they didn't. The fact they didn't speaks volumes, as stated in the web site "Bishop Hill" by Andrew Montford (Montford, 2015). The news media wanted to attack the people; they didn't care what they had to say about climate science or what evidence they had.

The 2015 Attack

As mentioned briefly in Chapter 1, the *New York Times* published an article by Justin Gillis and John Schwartz (Gillis & Schwartz, 2015) on February 21, 2015 attacking Willie Soon personally. They relied upon false information from Kert Davies (Davies, 2020), the founder of the secretive Climate Investigations Center or CIC.

Most of what is in the *New York Times* article is either wrong or misleading and we will address each of their accusations in more detail below. But, the basis for the attack was a Freedom of Information Act request (FOIA) to obtain internal documents from the Harvard-Smithsonian Center for Astrophysics, where Soon is employed as an astrophysicist. The FOIA was filed by Davies and Greenpeace.

As he did in 2010, the director, Charles Alcock, made a mistake and ordered Willie Soon to comply with the request. These documents (*New York Times*, 2015) include research proposals from the Smithsonian Astrophysical Observatory and written by Soon, to The Southern Company (NYSE: SO) a leading natural gas and electric utility company, ExxonMobil, the Charles Koch Charitable Foundation, and Donor's Trust.

We have established that science is a process of challenging the consensus view and that science cannot prove anything. Albert Einstein is widely reported to have said:

> "No amount of experimentation can ever prove me right; a single experiment can prove me wrong."

Exactly where and when he said this is lost to history, but Einstein was a scientist and any experienced working scientist would say the same thing. Scientists are forever challenging assumptions, hypotheses, and theories. Yet, the *New York Times* article asserts that:

> "The documents shed light on the role of scientists like Dr. Soon in fostering public debate over whether human activity is causing global warming. The vast majority of experts have concluded that it is, and that greenhouse emissions pose long-term risks to civilization." (Gillis & Schwartz, 2015)

This unsupported assertion is laughably anti-scientific. As we have seen, "the vast majority" or a consensus of scientists is a political thing. A scientist looks at the conclusion of the "vast majority" and asks, "Is that true? How can I test that idea?" Challenging the consensus view is the whole idea of science. A true scientist wants to foster "public debate."

Prior to the new popular idea that humans control the climate with our greenhouse gas emissions, the "consensus" view was that the Sun controlled

Earth's climate. We hypothesize that solar internal variability, as illustrated by the number and type of sunspots, is one significant factor. The Sun also has a dynamic and constantly changing magnetic field that affects Earth's climate. Some of the factors are discussed in more detail in a blog post by the author here: (May, 2018).

Over longer periods of time, variations in Earth's surface, Earth's orbit, and its axial tilt influence climate. Long-term changes in incoming solar radiation or "insolation," influence ocean currents, which affect weather and climate. This is summarized in a blog post by the author (May, 2016k). Soon's research supports the classic view that solar variability, both internal and due to Earth's orbit, largely control climate (Soon, Connolly, & Connolly, 2015).

The premise of the *New York Times* article is quite disturbing for several reasons. Firstly, they assume the so-called "consensus" view that climate is controlled by humans is true, even though no direct evidence supporting it exists. The computer model projections relied upon by the IPCC are not direct evidence. Secondly, they assume that privately funded research, by an established and very credible astrophysicist, working for the Harvard-Smithsonian Center for Astrophysics, is somehow tainted by donations to the Smithsonian. Thirdly, they seem to think that since Soon "has received little federal research money over the past decade" that this somehow makes him inferior to other researchers. All three assumptions are horrible. Do they really think that private companies should not be allowed to fund scientific research? Or, if they do, that the research should be discounted based only on the source of funding?

These views are not only juvenile, they are anti-scientific and possibly violate the free speech portion of the first amendment of the U.S Constitution. It is illegal to attempt to take away a person's constitutional rights through intimidation or other means (Columbia Law School, 2020).

One of the Smithsonian studies, partially funded, by ExxonMobil, Donor's Trust and the Southern Company was "Understanding Solar Variability and Climate Change: Signals from Temperature Records of the United States." For one interested in climate change this would seem to be an important topic to investigate. The checks from these organizations were made out to the Smithsonian Astrophysical Observatory or the Smithsonian Institution. No money was paid to Willie Soon, who is a government employee and paid a salary. He wrote the proposals for the Smithsonian because that is one of his duties as their employee (Arnold, 2016).

Science stands on its own, the conclusions either follow from the evidence and analysis presented, or they do not. The study can be replicated, or it cannot. Funding has nothing to do with it. Just because the *New York Times* reporters cannot understand Soon's papers, does not mean no one can. Other scientists will read his papers with a properly skeptical eye and let him, or others, know if there is a problem. The papers survive or fail on their own merits.

The first amendment grants people, and through them corporations, the right to free speech and the right to petition the government for a redress of grievances. This concept is supported by the Supreme Court in rulings like Citizens United (Smith B. , 2020). The *New York Times* article complains that Soon presented his research, funded through the Smithsonian, by the Southern Company, ExxonMobil and the Donor's Trust, to Congress. Are they saying that Soon and the people who funded some of his research should have their first amendment rights taken away because they disagree with "most" scientists or the *New York Times*? That is not the way science, or the United States works. In general, the article was anti-science and anti-American, but beyond the possible constitutional violations and the clearly fascist attitude toward dissent, there were many factual errors in the article. We will discuss these next.

The Undisclosed Conflict-of-Interest

The factual errors in the *New York Times* article are numerous and egregious and they show that the reporters relied heavily upon Greenpeace and Kert Davies without thoroughly checking what they wrote. The central lie in the article came directly from Greenpeace and Kert Davies, who asserted that Dr. Soon did not disclose a conflict-of-interest. Taking Greenpeace at its word was a mistake. The founders of Greenpeace often said:

> "It does not matter what is true, it only matters what people believe is true." (May, 2016j)

Greenpeace believes that "You are what the media define you to be" (Spencer, Bollwerk, & Morais, 1991). These concepts are discussed in detail in a Heartland Institute report on the Greenpeace business model (Connolly, Connolly, Soon, Moore, & Connolly, 2018) by Michael Connolly, Ronan

Connolly Imelda Connolly, Willie Soon and Patrick Moore, one of the founders of Greenpeace.

In court, Greenpeace once used their habit of lying as a defense in a defamation and false claims lawsuit against them by Resolute, a Canadian forest products company. They admitted they lied in court, claim it was rhetoric and never meant to be taken literally.

> "The [Greenpeace] publications' use of the word "Forest Destroyer," for example, is obvious rhetoric," Greenpeace writes in its motion to dismiss the Resolute lawsuit. "Resolute did not literally destroy an entire forest. ... The "Forest Destroyer" statement cannot be proven true or false, it is merely an opinion." (Thompson, 2017)

And then there is this quote from Richard Garneau, the chief executive of Resolute. The quote is from a *National Review* op-ed he wrote:

> "They were lying about our forestry practices, so we did something that none of the group's other targets have yet found the wherewithal to do: We sued them, in Canada, for defamation and intentional interference with economic relations, and in the United States under RICO statutes." (Garneau, 2017)

Unfortunately, the lawsuits that Resolute brought against Greenpeace are still tied up in the courts after six years (Rinne, 2019). The wheels of justice turn very slowly.

Professor of Ecology, Peter Reich, of the University of Minnesota, has said that Greenpeace has "a fundamental disregard for scientific reality." Yet, Greenpeace and their affiliate, the Climate Investigations Center, are the source for nearly all the *New York Times* allegations against Soon.

The most egregious lie by Justin Gillis and John Schwartz, straight from Greenpeace, was the following statement early in the *New York Times* article:

> "He has accepted more than $1.2 million in money from the fossil-fuel industry over the last decade while failing to disclose that conflict of interest in most of his scientific papers. At least 11 papers he has published since 2008 omitted such a disclosure, and in at least eight of those cases, he appears to have violated ethical guidelines of the journals that published his work." (Gillis & Schwartz, 2015)

As described above, the money was requested by the Smithsonian Astrophysical Observatory and paid to the Smithsonian. Soon was listed in the request only as the principal investigator. One of the requests for funds is shown below as Figure 5, it is not from Soon, but from Amanda Preston of the Astrophysical Observatory where he works. Soon is paid a salary, none of the money goes directly to him. Part of his job is raising money for the Smithsonian Trust, but he receives no commission or other compensation for any resulting donations.

 Smithsonian Astrophysical Observatory

c/o Amanda Preston
60 Garden Street
MS-45
Cambridge, MA 02138-1516

Phone: 617-495-7321
Fax: 617-495-7105
E-mail:
apreston@cfa.harvard.edu

Request for Payment

To:

Attention: Mark Boudreaux
ExxonMobil Corporation
2008 K. Street, NW
Suite 710
Washington, DC 20006

Please make check payable to:
Smithsonian Astrophysical Observatory

Mail check to:
Amanda Preston
Advancement and External Affairs Officer
Smithsonian Astrophysical Observatory
60 Garden Street, MS 45
Cambridge, MA 02138-1516

December 2, 2008

Request for contribution to support Year Two of the research project: "Understanding Solar Variability and Climate Change: Signals from Temperature Records of the United States", Dr. Willie Soon, Principal Investigator

Figure 5. The Smithsonian Astrophysical Observatory request for payment, sent to ExxonMobil. Source: FOIA documents (Smithsonian Astrophysical Observatory, 2012).

The check written by ExxonMobil to the Smithsonian Astrophysical Observatory is shown in Figure 6:

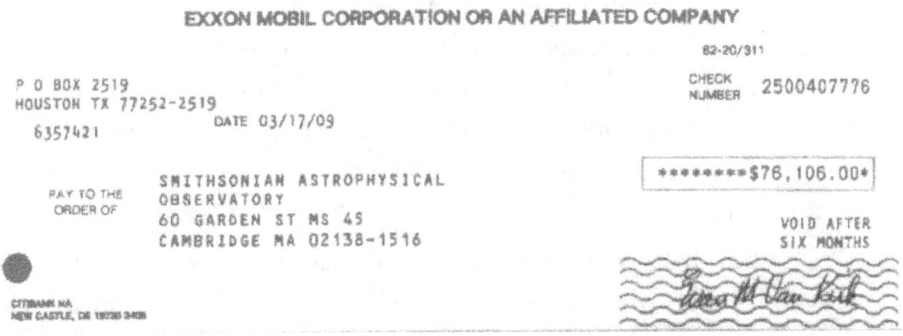
EXXON MOBIL CORPORATION OR AN AFFILIATED COMPANY

82-20/311

P O BOX 2519
HOUSTON TX 77252-2519
6357421

CHECK NUMBER 2500407776

DATE 03/17/09

PAY TO THE ORDER OF
SMITHSONIAN ASTROPHYSICAL
OBSERVATORY
60 GARDEN ST MS 45
CAMBRIDGE MA 02138-1516

********$76,106.00*

VOID AFTER
SIX MONTHS

CITIBANK NA
NEW CASTLE, DE

Figure 6. One of the checks sent to the Smithsonian for their investigation "Understanding Solar variability and Climate Change: Signals from Temperature Records of the United States." Source: FOIA documents (Smithsonian Astrophysical Observatory, 2012).

It is important to understand the Smithsonian procedures. A researcher, like Soon, may suggest a potential project funder. But first the project must be approved by the director. The researcher will write a draft proposal, but the request for funds and the proposal are sent out to the company by the director. In some cases, money may be solicited and received for a project and the researcher does not even know who contributed the funds. His salary comes from the Smithsonian Trust.

The article contains the following quote from Kert Davies, which illustrates the truly insidious motive behind the article and the Climate Investigations Center's FOIA request:

> "What it shows is the continuation of a long-term campaign by specific fossil-fuel companies and interests to undermine the scientific consensus on climate change, said Kert Davies, executive director of the Climate Investigations Center, a group funded by foundations seeking to limit the risks of climate change." (Gillis & Schwartz, 2015)

Undermining the "scientific consensus" *is* the purpose of science. What Davies is promoting is fascism or religious zealotry. He is dictating what we should believe. He is declaring that his "scientific consensus" is truth and we should all fall in line.

When Stalin's Trofim Lysenko rejected Mendelian genetics and executed or imprisoned people who accepted Mendel's ideas (Gough, 2003, Ch. 1), he was doing exactly what Davies is saying, only more harshly. See Chapter 4 for a discussion of Trofim Lysenko. Science is always questioning and challenging ideas. There may be a consensus of some scientists, perhaps even most scientists, that man-made climate change exists and dominates our climate. But it is still a scientific hypothesis and open to challenge, all hypotheses and theories can be challenged.

The idea that variations in solar irradiance dominate long-term climate change is also a hypothesis that can be challenged. These two ideas conflict and will only be resolved by scientific debate. Davies and the *New York Times* are free to challenge the solar irradiance idea with scientific research, but they are not entitled to attack Soon personally for his beliefs and writings.

All the lies in the *New York Times* article were not by the article's authors or Kert Davies. They also quote the director of the Harvard-Smithsonian Center for Astrophysics, Charles Alcock, as saying:

"Alcock … acknowledged on Friday that Dr. Soon had violated the disclosure standards of some journals. 'I think that's inappropriate behavior,' Dr. Alcock said. 'This frankly becomes a personnel matter, which we have to handle with Dr. Soon internally." (Gillis & Schwartz, 2015)

Soon did not violate "the disclosure standards" of any journals, as subsequent investigations, including an investigation by the Smithsonian Institution, later proved. He had nothing to disclose. Probably Alcock was rattled by the phone call from the *New York Times*, but that is not an excuse to lie and say "Soon had violated the disclosure standards," without knowing that was true. The statement was extremely unprofessional, to say the least.

The under-secretary for science at the Smithsonian, John Kress, was more accurate when he said:

"We are checking into this ourselves." (Gillis & Schwartz, 2015)

The Smithsonian did check into it and quickly realized that Soon had violated no journal's disclosure standards or Smithsonian policies. In 2015, mostly in response to the *New York Times* article, the Smithsonian placed a press release on their website stating that their Office of Inspector General was investigating Soon's scientific publications and funding disclosures. The investigation, which Soon fully cooperated with, was concluded in 2016 and no problems were found. Yet the press release announcing it was under way, was not taken down from the website until February of 2020, at Soon's insistence. Again, very unprofessional conduct.

Besides the article in *Science Direct*, Kert Davies and his Climate Investigations Center also accused Soon of violating disclosure policies in an article Willie Soon and David Legates published in *Ecology Law Currents* (Soon & Legates, 2010). But the editors of the journal said it was not true and that Soon had complied with their rules. This was also true for another article Soon co-wrote for *Nature Geoscience* (Yan, et al., 2015). The senior author of the *Science Bulletin* paper (Monckton, Soon, Legates, & Briggs, 2015), Christopher Monckton, said none of the authors of the paper have a conflict of interest because they all worked on the paper on their own time. Monckton calls the allegations by Kert Davies, "manifestly untruthful and malevolent" (Tollefson, 2015). *Science Direct* conducted no investigation and has remained silent on the issue. MSLB15 still states, in June of 2020, that "the authors declare that they have no conflict of interest" (Monckton, Soon, Legates, & Briggs, 2015).

Science Bulletin's current conflict-of-interest policy is quite vague and difficult to understand (Elsevier, 2020). It says: "All submissions must include disclosure of all relationships that could be viewed as presenting a potential conflict of interest." This is overly broad, to the point of being unreasonable. In plain English, it seems to say all sources of funding to the writer or the organization he works for must be disclosed. Presumably, if we are being logical, this would include all government funding as well as all private funding to either entity for anything at all. Government agencies, especially the EPA, also have agendas. It could mean other clients and customers of the company or agency the researcher works for. Presumably, it includes non-profit organizations, which certainly have political agendas. It is so broad, it is absurd.

The single alleged conflict that seems to come up a lot, is the Southern Company, which is an electrical utility in the southern United States. ExxonMobil also comes up a lot, but ExxonMobil has been all over the map about man-made climate change, so it doesn't make a good case. The real issue here is that the Climate Investigations Center and Kert Davies want to condemn and discredit any scientist or organization that disagrees with them on man-made climate change. This isn't about disclosure; this is about suppressing discussion of, and research into, natural climate change.

The CEO of the Southern Company is Tom Fanning and he has said that he doesn't deny that climate change is occurring. He just doesn't believe the evidence proves that CO_2 is the culprit (Belvedere, 2017). This is a very reasonable view, shared by thousands of scientists around the world. Why would a contribution to the Harvard-Smithsonian Center for Astrophysics by the Southern Company mean that Willie Soon should disclose a conflict of interest? Because the CEO holds an extremely popular belief? In any case, Willie Soon had no conflict-of-interest.

What is a Conflict-of-Interest?

Another conflict-of-interest dispute has been raised at *PNAS* (*Proceedings of the National Academy of Sciences*) with respect to a letter, written by David Legates, Willis Eschenbach and Willie Soon (Legates, Eschenbach, & Soon, 2014). Daniel Salsbury, a director at *PNAS*, sent Soon the following in 2015, more than a year after the letter was published:

> Dear Dr. Soon,
>
> We are contacting you regarding your PNAS publication titled "Arctic albedo changes are small compared with changes in cloud cover in the tropics." We have been contacted by a reporter about the conflict of interest disclosure in this Letter. Per PNAS policy, please let us know if a conflict of interest should be disclosed for this publication. (email, June 9, 2015)

Soon, Legates, and Eschenbach, the three authors of the letter to *PNAS*, all replied and affirmed that there was no conflict-of-interest regarding the letter and that the time spent on the letter was their own time and not funded by anyone or any organization.

This dispute occurred at about the same time as the *Science Bulletin* dispute and is instructive. The issue of conflict-of-interest is complicated, because as Professor Roger Pielke Jr. has noted, "Once you tug on the thread of undisclosed financial interests in climate science, you'll find it more a norm than exception" (Curry J. , 2015).

We have already mentioned Michael Mann of the University of Pennsylvania and he will come up many more times in this book. Mann is a member of the Advisory Board of the Climate Change Communication Network (since 2010), Climate Communication (since 2011), OurEarth (since 2008), and 1Sky (since 2008) (Mann M. , Curriculum Vitae, 2020). It isn't clear if he is paid for these posts, but he did not disclose them in any of his publications.

Soon was not paid anything by ExxonMobil, the Southern Company, or Donor's Trust. He was not paid for any publication or compensated in any other way. They merely donated money to the Smithsonian Astrophysical Observatory. Who has donated money to Climate Change Communication Network, OurEarth, and 1Sky? Professor David Legates, of the University of Delaware, saw that *PNAS* requires that any association that can be perceived as posing a competing interest in connection with the manuscript must be disclosed. The exact wording from the *PNAS* web site:

> "Authors must disclose, at submission, any association that poses or could be reasonably perceived as posing a financial or personal competing interest in connection with the manuscript and acknowledge all funding sources supporting the work." (PNAS, 2020)

Legates, on June 17th, 2015 writes, in an email to Salsbury, that Michael Mann has published articles in *PNAS* and declared no conflict of interest (Mann & Gleick, 2015). Another of the authors, Willis Eschenbach, wrote the following to Salsbury:

> "I must admit, however, that because the work was published heading towards a year ago, your sudden interest in this matter is most curious to me.
>
> For what reason have you chosen to focus your attention on our poor submission so long after the fact? I'm serious, Dr. Salsbury. This gives every impression of being a witch-hunt, and I would very much like to believe it is not one."
>
> Willis Eschenbach (email: June 26, 2015)

Daniel Salsbury replied to Legates and the others on June 26th, and said, "We apply the same policy to every submission," however this is clearly not true. He did not demand Michael Mann restate his disclosure.

This was followed by a more detailed email from Professor Legates to Professor Inder Verma, editor-in-chief of *PNAS* on July 27, 2015. Legates points out that he had inquired as to why Soon was accused of misrepresenting his conflict-of-interest, when Michael Mann was not, when the circumstances were the same. Legates email included six additional papers written by Michael Mann that did not declare any conflicts of interest. Legates did not receive a reply, even after a month had passed. He still wanted assurance that the same disclosure standard will be applied to all authors.

Legates sent another email to Professor Verma:

> Professor Verma,
>
> I assume you have chosen not to respond to my question and that Mr. Salsbury has gone back on his word. I still await your replies.
>
> Sincerely,
>
> David R. Legates

After this email and another, Willie Soon, on September 14, 2015 also requested an answer, none was forthcoming, and all was silent. No comment was made in *PNAS* regarding the article by Legates, Eschenbach and Soon and no apology from the journal, for their unjust inquiry, was ever received.

It is worth noting here that Professor Inder Verma was accused of sexual harassment of numerous women and eventually forced out of his positions at *PNAS* and the Salk Institute for Biological Studies in San Diego (Wadman, 2018). His replacement at *PNAS* has still not answered Professor Legates questions, at least not as of May 13, 2020.

Some scientific journals do not require disclosures, some require that sources of funding for the research be disclosed, some require that any potential financial conflicts be disclosed, and some, like *PNAS*, *Science*, and *Science Direct*, require that any possible perception of a conflict be disclosed. The latter is unreasonable. The sources of funding for the paper itself and the research behind it should probably be disclosed. Real conflicts of interest should be disclosed, but anything that might be perceived as a conflict of interest? This seems absurd. Especially since they did not apply to Michael

Mann or any other researcher affiliated with non-profit environmental organizations. Many climate researchers are in management or advisory positions with politically active organizations, such as those that *Science* requires be disclosed:

> "Management/Advisory affiliations: Within the last 3 years, status as an officer, a member of the Board, or a member of an Advisory Committee of any entity engaged in activity related to the subject matter of this contribution. Please disclose the nature of these relationships and the financial arrangements." [Part of the *Science* disclosure rules in 2015. (Curry J. , Conflicts of interest in climate science, 2015)]

For a list of the many climate researchers that this disclosure requirement applies to, see this blog post on Judith Curry's *Climate, Etc.* web site (Curry J. , 2014). If associations with fossil fuel companies and conservative organizations must be disclosed, then the same must be true for environmental and liberal organizations.

More *New York Times* Errors and Lies

Besides asserting that Soon improperly did not disclose a conflict-of-interest, the *New York Times* also claims that "Soon is not an astrophysicist." This is silly, that's his job title at the Harvard-Smithsonian Center for Astrophysics. Further, all his work since joining the Center for Astrophysics has been in astrophysics or geoscience, generally both, since his primary area of research for the past 30 years is the effect of solar variability on climate.

The *Times*, quotes Gavin Schmidt, a climate modeler and Director of the NASA Goddard Institute for Space Studies, as saying:

> "The science that Willie Soon does is almost pointless." (Gillis & Schwartz, 2015)

This quote is obviously not true. Soon, according to Google Scholar, has 6,118 citations of his work and 2,043 from 2015 to 2020. He is a co-author of

"Chromospheric variations in main-sequence stars," (Baliunas, et al., 1995) which has 1,100 citations, a remarkable number for one paper.

The "science" that Soon does is clearly not pointless according to thousands of scientists who cite his work in their papers. It is obvious that Schmidt is either mistaken or lying when he states this opinion and the *New York Times* should have known this. Finding the number of citations of Soon's work takes only a few seconds on "scholar.google.com/citations". There are more lies and mistakes in the *New York Times* article, but they are variations of those already discussed.

PBS

Russell Cook was a regular viewer of PBS in 2002, when he noticed that they rarely showed interviews with global warming skeptics. PBS portrayed itself as a news portal that showed both sides of the story, yet with global warming or climate change they were only showing one side. Years later, he wrote them a letter asking them why this was. He also wrote to the Media Research Center complaining about PBS' lack of balance on the topic (Cook R. , 2009).

Robert MacNeil and Jim Lehrer liked to say, "Assume there is at least one other side or version to every story" (Frazee & Finnegan, 2020). Cook wrote to them in 2009 and asked why climate change was an exception to the rule. PBS delayed mentioning the *climategate* email scandal for a week, when the story created a firestorm of coverage elsewhere. He also wanted to know why news casting doubt on human-caused global warming was not covered on the *NewsHour* and if the *NewsHour* staff had a bias (Getler, 2009).

Both Murrey Jacobson (a senior producer of the *MacNeil/Lehrer NewsHour*) and the PBS Ombudsman (Michael Getler) responded to Russell Cook's letter (Getler, 2009).

The ombudsman agrees the *PBS NewsHour* did a poor job covering the *climategate* email scandal and devoted too little time to it. Then he goes on to cite the "consensus of scientists …" irrelevant nonsense and says, because of that, that the *NewsHour* does not want to set up a "false equivalence." Thus, with his vast knowledge and expertise, he has decided that humans control climate, based on a "vote" of cherry-picked scientists and without understanding the science. This is very typical of news media types. Reporting is always secondary to biases.

Jacobson and Getler's responses are particularly helpful in understanding the news media's problem understanding the true issues in climate science. He says they have focused on what should be done about climate change, rather than on the debate about the science behind it. In other words, he accepts, as fact, that humans are causing climate change, even though there is no direct evidence that this is the case. He wants to debate solutions, without understanding the problem, always a mistake.

The scientific debate is about how much humans are contributing to climate change. The human contribution is either very small or more than half of the total we will discuss in detail in Chapters 6 and 7. If the human contribution is large and dangerous, then reducing or eliminating human greenhouse gas emissions is one possible solution. If the human contribution is small and the natural contribution large, and the change is potentially dangerous; reducing greenhouse gas emissions is foolish. In the latter case we need fossil fuels to build protective sea walls, levees, stronger houses, and buildings. The fuel is needed to power the construction equipment, air conditioning and heating units, etc. So, in a real way, if you have already decided, with no evidence, that humans are controlling the climate, and the resulting changes are dangerous, you have already decided what to do about it. The *Newshour* folks are literally assuming a solution and working backwards from it.

If you frame the question, you can force the answer. The *PBS NewsHour*, by skipping the scientific debate, is advocating for the *political* view that human's control the climate. In reality we don't know what the human contribution to climate change is or if it is dangerous.

Jacobson cites President Bush's statement on climate change:

> "It's now recognized that the surface of the earth is warmer, and that an increase in greenhouse gases caused by humans is contributing to the problem." (Getler, 2009)

This is mostly a reasonable statement, although referring to recent warming as a problem is speculation. Economist's Bjorn Lomborg and Richard Tol believe that warming to date has been beneficial and that future warming will also be beneficial for, at least, several more decades (Ridley, 2013). But Jacobson, like nearly every other journalist, completely misses the point. It isn't whether humans contribute to climate change, it is by how much and if the warming is dangerous.

Jacobson does get one thing right and it is instructive:

> "In each instance, there are different points of view on WHAT should be done about the problem; those are the points of view we have attempted to cover fairly when we are covering what is essentially a political debate." (Getler, 2009)

Yes, this is a "political debate." This is the key point. The *PBS NewsHour* and essentially all the media, have refused to cover the unresolved scientific debate. They confuse the political opinion that man-made climate change is dangerous, with science. The "science," if we can use the term, is the challenge to the consensus, not the consensus.

The climate alarmists have won with the new media. They want the public ignorant, uneducated, and fearful. They framed the discussion such that the "science is settled." That way they win the debate before it starts. The public, fortunately, is much smarter than the news media and isn't buying it.

Factcheck.org

The *PBS NewsHour* ombudsman refers Russell Cook to an article on the Factcheck.org website, which the ombudsman calls a "respected" site. The fact check (Henig, 2009) warrants some discussion because it illustrates the general ignorance in the media about science and the scientific process. FactCheck.org tries to cover scientific issues, but they do a poor job of it. They aren't blatantly and openly biased, like Politifact.com (May, 2016m) discussed in the next section. But their ignorance of climate science, causes them to make a mess of it.

They begin their article by stating:

> "Climate skeptics are claiming that [the climategate emails] show scientific misconduct that amounts to the complete fabrication of man-made global warming. We find that to be unfounded." (Henig, 2009)

Henig refers later in the article to a similar statement by Saudi Arabian climate negotiator, Mohammad Al-Sabban, who said, "It appears from the details of the scandal that there is no relationship whatsoever between human activities and climate change." Probably Al-Sabban meant to say "the *climategate* emails reveal there is no proof of human-caused climate change," which is true and almost the same thing, just worded more clearly. The comment from Al Sabban is poorly worded, but a literal interpretation of what he said holds water. He didn't say anyone fabricated evidence, he only said that the *climategate* emails make it appear there is no evidence humans are causing climate change (Costella, 2010, pp. 3-10). This is true, most agree we probably influence climate change to some extent, there just isn't any evidence we do, other than unvalidated computer models.

Later in the same BBC interview Al-Sabban says, more reasonably, "Climate [has been] changing for thousands of years, but for natural and not human-induced reasons." (Black, 2009). Henig selected a slightly hyperbolic sentence by a non-scientist so he could set up a strawman to falsify. This is a common deception and logical fallacy in media fact checks. On scientific issues, the media fact-checking organizations usually miss the scientific point completely and tend to focus on some trivial political issue or misstatement.

Jess Henig's headline includes: "Hacked e-mails show climate scientists in a bad light but don't change scientific consensus on global warming." As if the "scientific consensus" mattered, it doesn't.

Humans probably cause some changes to climate, just like many other species, for example ocean-dwelling phytoplankton. Phytoplankton consume CO_2 and produce oxygen. But, enough about Mohammad Al-Sabban, he is a politician and economist. What does a real climate scientist say about the *climategate* emails?

"there are two broader issues raised by [the *climategate*] emails that are impeding the public credibility of climate research: lack of transparency in climate data, and 'tribalism' in some segments of the climate research community that [are] impeding peer review and the assessment process." (Curry J. , 2009)

This is from a blog post, written by then Professor Judith Curry, a famous climate scientist. She is retired now but was the Chairman of the School of Earth and Atmospheric Sciences at the Georgia Institute of Technology. Both issues she raises are important, and completely missed by Henig.

89

Regarding Henig's cherished consensus, science is all about challenging the consensus view. Scientists check the numbers and data behind consensus conclusions. Are the conclusions reproducible? Is the data complete and correct? Are the results statistically significant? Every truly scientific study must stand on its own and anyone with the necessary skills and tools should be able to reproduce the study's results. Transparency is required. For this reason, the *climategate* emails are bad for science. If you read them with an informed and critical eye, it is reasonable to conclude from them that "there is no [evidence of a] relationship whatsoever between human activities and climate change."

Indeed, Keith Briffa, in a September 22, 1999 *climategate* email to Michael Mann, Phil Jones, Tom Karl and Chris Folland admits as much:

> "I believe that the recent warmth was probably matched about 1000 years ago. I do not believe that global mean annual temperatures have simply cooled progressively over thousands of years as Mike appears to and I contend that that there is strong evidence for major changes in climate over the Holocene." (Costella, 2010, pp. 14-15) and (Briffa K. , 1999)

Keith Briffa, who sadly passed away in 2017, was a friend of Michael Mann, a member of the "Hockey Team" and an expert on using tree rings as temperature proxies. Before he passed, he was a deputy director of the Climatic Research Unit (CRU) at the University of East Anglia. Thus, Mohammad Al-Sabban's comment was poorly worded, but his point was clear and truthful.

No real scientist would hide his data from other interested scientists. This author has published the results of many studies in peer-reviewed scientific journals. Sometimes others have requested the underlying data, we happily sent it to them without question, at our own expense. We have also published our computer code. This is routine and expected in the scientific community. The emails, which discuss hiding data or deleting it are anti-science, not science. In Curry's words:

> "I have some sympathy for Phil Jones' concern of not wanting to lose control of his personal research agenda by having to take the time to respond to all the queries and requests regarding his dataset, but the receipt of large amounts of public funding pretty much obligates CRU [the U.K. Climatic Research Unit] to respond to these requests." (Curry J. , 2009)

The key point is that "the receipt of large amounts of public funding …" puts an obligation on climate scientists to share their data with the public. If they funded their own work and did it without salary and on their own time, it is their data, but if the data were gathered or analyzed using government funds, it belongs to the public.

Besides the lack of transparency, the *climategate* emails also show unwarranted tribalism. Many of the prominent skeptics, such as Dr. Richard Lindzen, Dr. Tim Ball, Stephen McIntyre, Willis Eschenbach, and Anthony Watts are either retired or working outside the climate science community and receive no funding from anyone for their work. So, for the lavishly government funded "consensus" climate scientists to take an "us versus them" attitude is very inappropriate. The core of science is to challenge and attempt to disprove popular ideas. If you are a defensive scientist and afraid of others digging into your work, you might want to consider changing careers. Attempting to reproduce, or not, the work of others is an important part of science.

Henig writes that "some critics" claim the IPCC 2007 (AR4) report is invalidated by the emails but offers no quote to substantiate this claim. This is apparently another strawman. His excuse is that the University of East Anglia Climatic Research Unit (CRU) is not the only source of data and research used by the IPCC. However, he conveniently forgets that the emails were sent and received from all over the place, not just CRU. Further, the IPCC climate science community is small and insular, they have systematically excluded or marginalized very experienced and talented scientists that disagree with them, including Richard Tol, discussed in the next section. Others excluded or marginalized, to one degree or another for their beliefs, are long-time and famous climate scientists, such as Fred Singer, William Happer, Richard Lindzen, Tim Ball, Judith Curry, John Christy, Roy Spencer, Willie Soon, David Legates, Freeman Dyson, and many others. This only makes the self-appointed "IPCC climate scientists" more insular.

Curry sees the main problem with the emails, a problem that Jess Henig's article completely misses. But, while the Factcheck.org article is largely irrelevant to the discussion and not worth spending much time on, we will address a few more misstatements and errors, because they are so common in the non-scientific news media. His next statement contains the following:

> "plenty of evidence that the earth is getting warmer and that humans are largely responsible."

The first part of this statement is OK, there is direct evidence Earth is getting warmer. The second part is an unsupported assertion. The only evidence presented, that survived scrutiny, is based on computer climate models that have not been validated. An unvalidated computer model can be made to do anything the programmer wants it to. More on this in Chapters 6 and 7.

There is one more erroneous statement that requires comment, Henig writes:

> "[Phil] Jones, who wrote: 'I've just completed Mike's Nature trick of adding in the real temps to each series for the last 20 years (i.e., from 1981 onwards) and from 1961 for Keith's to hide the decline.' Skeptics claim the words "trick" and "decline" show Jones is using sneaky manipulations to mask a decline in global temperatures." (Henig, 2009)

Henig gets part of this right, but still misses the scientific point. "Hide the decline" does not refer to actual temperatures, as Henig makes clear. It refers to a prominent decline in tree ring proxy temperatures in the 20th century when measured temperatures are going up. Michael Mann used tree rings, in part, to estimate temperatures for the past 1,000 years. In Mann's reconstruction, North American tree rings were "found to be essential" to his millennial reconstruction (Mann & Bradley, 1999) or MB99, especially prior to 1600AD.

In fact, the top nine, of twelve total, series that he used to build his 1,000-year reconstruction were all tree ring series. The top three were from North America. By his own admission, if he withheld the North American tree ring data, the hockey stick changed dramatically. Yet, the "essential" tree ring series shows declining temperatures in the 20th century. Figure 1 in MB99 shows the most important series and its 20th century decline. How do we know they are accurate prior to the 20th century?

Is the 20th century divergence of the tree ring proxy temperatures from actual temperatures due to CO_2 as Mann speculates? Or could it be due to warmer temperatures? If it is due to warmer temperatures, did the divergence also occur in the MWP?

Henig admits that no one knows why the tree rings don't work now. Modeling tree ring proxy derived temperatures consistently, shows temperatures declining in the 20th century, this is illustrated by the dark heavy line in Figure 7, which is Keith Briffa's all tree ring temperature reconstruction from his 1998 paper in *Nature* (Briffa, Jones, Schweingruber, & Osborn, 1998). The heavy gray line in Figure 7 is Mann's smoothed hockey stick to 1973, it probably incorporates instrumental temperatures in the last part of the 20th century, since it appears that Mann used them to extend his smoothed curve (McIntyre, 2010).

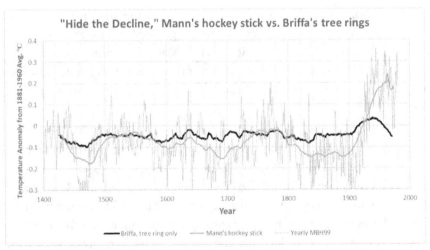

Figure 7. Hiding the decline means that the late 20th century decline in the tree ring proxy temperatures (heavy black line) is simply deleted. The heavy gray line is Mann's 50-year smoothed hockey stick through 1973. The faint gray line is Mann's yearly reconstruction. Briffa's 1998 tree ring reconstruction is from the NOAA NCDC database. Mann's data is from his ftp site at Penn State, the MBH99 directory.

The hockey stick relies mostly on tree rings prior to 1600. This unholy mixture of data invalidates the hockey stick, especially since no one knows why the tree rings are not working in the 20th century. This is an obvious point that whizzes right past Henig's head.

Both reconstructions in Figure 7 are smoothed with a 50-year moving average and reflect anomalies from 1881-1960. The version of Mann's hockey stick shown, is from his 1999 paper, MB99 (Mann & Bradley, 1999), but it is roughly comparable to the 50-year smoothed one shown in TAR on page 3 (IPCC, 2001). In the IPCC version, instrumental temperatures are overlain on the hockey stick to make the 20th century look anomalous. The faint gray line in Figure 7 is the MB99 yearly data.

Tree rings make poor temperature proxies, especially the bristlecone pine tree rings critical to the hockey stick reconstruction. As Keith Briffa writes in his 1998 paper, tree ring series are often "detrended" to "remove possible bias associated with changes in the age of the sample trees." Detrending preserves and enhances annual and decadal variability, but reduces long-term trends, that is century scale changes. It can eliminate or reduce climatic anomalies like the Little Ice Age and Medieval Warm Period.

The resulting detrended tree ring series are flatter than reality and the problem gets worse the farther back in time we go (National Research Council, 2006, p. 90) and (McIntyre & McKitrick, 2005c). According to Pages 2K Consortium (Pages2K, 2019, p. 2) this problem is especially serious before 1000 AD. Some of the flatness in Mann's hockey stick is due to this detrending process.

The decline of the tree ring proxy temperatures in the 20th century is a serious problem. The decline is clear in Figure 2 of Keith Briffa's first 1998 *Nature* article, "Reduced sensitivity of recent tree-growth to temperature at high northern latitudes" (Briffa, Schweingruber, Jones, Osborn, & Vaganov, 1998b). He discusses the "divergence" of temperature and tree growth curves since 1930 in the text but has no clear explanation for it. It is his line that declines in Figure 7. Briffa does mention that higher temperatures, themselves, might be a cause for the divergence between tree rings and temperature.

Michael Mann does not explain the divergence either, he does speculate that higher CO_2 might be a cause. Mann, or someone else in the IPCC TAR Chapter 2 team, simply deleted the adverse tree ring proxy records after 1960. Then, they overlaid the instrumental temperatures to form the final hockey stick shape. This causes the 20th century uptick in temperatures and the blade of the hockey stick. The "spaghetti graph" in TAR that compares the hockey stick to Briffa's tree ring only reconstruction has the end of Briffa's curve chopped off, as can be seen in Figure 8, when compared to Figure 7.

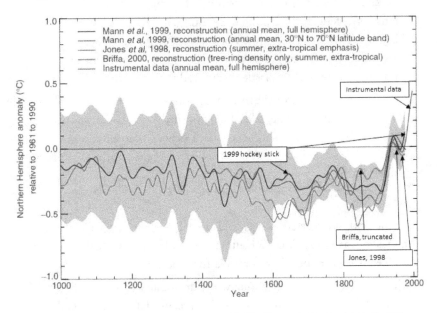

Figure 8. The "spaghetti graph" from TAR, Figure 2.21 (p. 134). Briffa's curve is truncated to "hide the decline." Used with permission.

The first version of the TAR graph shown in Figure 8 had all of Keith Briffa's reconstruction shown, but the Chapter 2 lead authors, Thomas Karl and Christopher K. Folland did not like it. In a 1999 email, Folland writes:

"A proxy diagram of temperature change is a clear favourite for the Policy Makers summary. But the current diagram with the tree ring only data [i.e. the Briffa reconstruction] somewhat contradicts the multiproxy curve and dilutes the message rather significantly. ... This is probably the most important issue to resolve in Chapter 2 at present." Christopher Folland as quoted in (McIntyre, 2010)

Michael Mann replies: "This is the problem we all picked up on ([sic] everyone in the room at IPCC was in agreement that this was a problem and a potential distraction/detraction from the reasonably concensus [sic] viewpoint we'd like to show w/ the Jones et al and Mann et al series." Michael Mann as quoted in (McIntyre, 2010)

95

Keith Briffa then writes:

> "I know there is pressure to present a nice tidy story as regards 'apparent unprecedented warming in a thousand years or more in the proxy data' but in reality the situation is not quite so simple... [There are] some unexpected changes in response that do not match the recent warming. I do not think it wise that this issue be ignored in the chapter.
>
> For the record, I do believe that the proxy data do show unusually warm conditions in recent decades. I am not sure that this unusual warming is so clear in the summer responsive data. I believe that the recent warmth was probably matched about 1000 years ago." Keith Briffa as quoted in (McIntyre, 2010)

In the end, the tidy story was told by deleting the end of Briffa's series and the issue was ignored, over Keith Briffa's objections. Briffa was a good Hockey Team soldier and did not raise a fuss about it.

Phil Jones was much less subtle when he applied what he called "Mike's Nature Trick." Jones simply deleted the recent data and spliced on the smoothed temperature record to "hide the decline" then smoothed it all together.

So, the long hockey stick handle is due to over-processed, poor, and inappropriate proxies. The blade is due to either splicing incompatible (to the proxies) measured temperatures or simply overlaying the instrumental temperatures and deleting contradictory data. These actions are inappropriate anyway, but they are especially inappropriate in this case because the measured temperatures do not correlate with critical proxies in the 20th century. The remainder of the blade is due to a mistake in centering the proxy series in Mann's statistical procedure. This "decentering problem" is complex and we will leave the details for Chapter 5.

Thus, the hockey stick, the only direct evidence of human influence on climate, is a complicated fiction. Henig has all the components of the fiction in his article, but clearly does not understand the implications. He supports the idea that humans control the climate, while listing the reasons it is not so.

Suffice it to say that the hockey stick was as close as the IPCC ever came to direct evidence that human's influence climate to some degree. Given our influence cannot be detected, there is certainly no evidence that we dominate or control climate change.

Mann's manipulation of his dataset was subtle and may have been done out of ignorance. But his attempts to withhold data and code, possibly to cover it all up, were still wrong. Enlisting and/or coercing others to hide contradictory data and keeping the paleoclimate tribe in line was also wrong.

McIntyre explains the various deceptions well in a climateaudit.com post, entitled "Keith's Science Trick, Mike's Nature Trick and Phil's Combo" (McIntyre, 2011). Well worth reading. This latter post also explains other tricks used by this group of climate scientists.

Jess Henig's "fact check" is anything but. He tries to whitewash all this. It is a climate alarmist advocacy opinion piece riddled with errors and unsubstantiated opinion, disguised as a fact check.

He tries to claim that the IPCC does not exclude the views of skeptical scientists. This is nonsense, they certainly ignored hundreds of papers, dating all the way back to 1965, on the Medieval Warm Period and the Little Ice Age, as pointed out by Willie Soon and Sallie Baliunas (Soon & Baliunas, 2003). They ignored dozens of papers, some by Soon and Baliunas (Baliunas, et al., 1995), that show the Sun is probably more involved in recent climate changes than they assume. Further, the IPCC has politically edited their reports and changed scientific conclusions approved by the scientist authors (Seitz, 1996).

We have debunked the major errors in the article but warn the reader that there are others. We rate this fact check as false. The implications and significance of the *climategate* scandal, as explained by Judith Curry, went completely over Jess Henig's head. He took the *climategate* affair as an attempt to discredit his unwarranted assumption that humans control Earth's climate, rather than evidence of dishonesty, lack of transparency, and juvenile tribalism by mainstream climate scientists. He missed the point. A sad piece of journalism.

Politifact.com

Politifact is one of the most biased of the fact check websites and unfailingly slants their "fact checks" to the far left. Unfortunately, Politifact is often characterized as an unbiased and credible source by the rest of the media (Kenny, 2019). We will discuss two well documented cases of the organization deliberately mischaracterizing the facts and misquoting sources on the climate change debate.

In their fact check of Senator Rick Santorum (Qiu, 2015) they misquoted Professor Richard Tol, of the University of Sussex, an expert on climate change economics, on several key points. Tol pointed out the errors and incorrect quotes, but Politifact did not publish corrections. This is all fully documented, including the full email exchange between Professor Tol and the Politifact reporter, Linda Qiu, in a Climate Depot article by Marc Morano (Morano, 2015). They also erroneously labeled Santorum's statement false. Santorum did confuse his numbers a bit but got the basics right. As Professor Tol described it in an email to Politifact:

> "I think you were unfair on Santorum. He mixes up his numbers here: 'The most recent survey of climate scientists said about 57 percent don't agree with the idea that 95 percent of the change in the climate is caused by CO2.'
>
> In fact, the statement is that 57% disagree that there is 95% confidence that 50% was caused by greenhouse gases. In other words, Santorum had the spirit right but the letter wrong." Richard Tol, source (Morano, 2015)

Linda Qiu of Politifact, like many in the news media, conflate "anthropogenic global warming" (man has some unknown amount of influence on climate) with "catastrophic anthropogenic global warming" (man is driving climate change with his greenhouse gas emissions and causing a climate catastrophe). In Professor Tol's words:

> "There is vigorous debate about how much humans have contributed to climate change, but no one argues the effect is zero. By emitting greenhouse gases, changing the landscape, rerouting rivers, and huddling together in cities, we change the climate – perhaps by a little, perhaps by a lot – but not one expert doubts we do." Richard Tol, source (Morano, 2015)

Politifact and Linda Qui, ignore the science completely, just as Jess Henig of Factcheck,org did in the last section. They also ignore the substance of what Senator Santorum was stating and set up Santorum's trivial misstatements as a strawman. Qui does not address the science behind what Santorum is saying, so why is she pretending to check the facts?

Next, Qiu jumps all over Santorum for calling Richard Tol the head of the IPCC, when he is actually the lead author of a chapter in AR5, the most recent IPCC report. That way they can rate Santorum's statements as false.

This is the problem with popular "fact checks" of complex scientific topics, they can easily set up a strawman, refute that, and leave the reader with the impression the larger issue is refuted. Articles of this type are merely elaborate lies, dressed up in fact check clothing.

As Richard Tol, Bjorn Lomborg (Lomborg B. , 2016), Randall Donohue (Oskin, 2013), Craig Idso (Idso C. , 2011), William Happer (Happer, 2011) and others have pointed out there are many benefits to global warming and increased levels of carbon dioxide. Computing whether global warming is net positive or net negative is complex and Professor Tol is an expert in the subject. In fact, Tol concluded in his working paper 75-2015 that:

"The impact of climate change on the economy and human welfare is likely to be limited at least in the 21st century." (Tol R. , 2015c, p. 9)

Figure 1
Fourteen Estimates of the Global Economic Impact of Climate Change

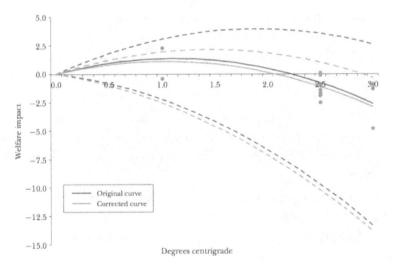

Figure 9. The horizontal axis is warming in degrees C and the vertical is the economic benefit. The heavy solid lines are the most likely relationship. The economic benefit stays positive until 2.1. to 2.2 degrees C of warming. Source: (Tol R. , 2014b)

Where Politifact has gone off the rails, is their implicit, but unstated, assumption (from ignorance, presumably) that warming is all bad and without any benefits. This is clearly wrong as can be seen in Figure 9. The figure is from a 2014 update to Tol's 2009 paper, "The Economic Effects of Climate Change," (Tol R. , 2009). The 2014 changes are minor (Tol R. , 2014b). The consensus of climate economists, according to an article in the *Spectator*, by Matt Ridley (Ridley, 2013), is that global warming impacts are positive for mankind's welfare until 2080, when they might turn negative.

Linda Qiu and Politifact claim Professor Tol parted ways with the IPCC, which is not true. He did refuse to allow his name to be associated with the *Summary for Policymakers* of the IPCC AR5 Working Group 2 chapters due to a disagreement on the negative tone of the summary (Tol R. , 2014c). He believes the summary was one-sided and ignored the benefits of warming and CO_2. But he has not left the IPCC, which he has been involved with since 1994. The IPCC still list him as a lead author of Chapter 10 of AR5 (IPCC, 2014c).

Tol describes why he refused to allow his name to be used in the Working Group 2 *Summary for Policymakers* as follows:

The scientific literature now acknowledges that many of the more worrying impacts of climate change are in fact symptoms of social mismanagement and underdevelopment.

The first rule of climate policy should be: do no harm to economic growth. But the IPCC was asked to focus on the risks of climate change alone, and those who volunteered to be its authors eagerly obliged.

The first paper on an issue is always dramatic. That is the only way to get something onto the scientific agenda. Follow-up papers then pooh-pooh the initial drama. But the IPCC chose not to wait for those follow-up papers.

IPCC reports are often two to three thousand pages long, but there are two or three main findings only.

Authors who want to see their long hours of IPCC work recognized should thus present their impact as worse than the next one.

It was this inbuilt alarmism that made me step down from the team that drafted the Summary for Policy Makers of Working Group 2. And indeed, the report was greeted by the four horsemen of the apocalypse: famine, pestilence, war, death all made headlines. (Tol R. , 2014c)

Tol recognized that the IPCC process focusses only on research that predicts doom and gloom and will lead to curtailing any human activity that might increase greenhouse gas emissions. They ignore and bury any benefits of warming or greenhouse gases. In other words, the IPCC *Summary for Policymakers* misrepresented the scientific work. Tol wanted nothing to do with this. They did not listen to him, not because his science was in any way inferior, but because he wanted an unbiased and accurate summary of the scientific work.

Politifact claim he is affiliated with the Global Warming Policy Foundation and this is true. The Global Warming Policy Foundation is a group of scientists and politicians who are skeptical of the projected negative economic impacts of global warming and concerned about the negative impacts of curtailing CO_2 and other greenhouse gases (GWPF, 2019). He is associated with them, but only in the way he is affiliated with the EPA or many other organizations he has advised. Are they saying he is a bad person because he is advising a respectable organization that happens to disagree with Politifact.com and their cherry-picked "consensus?"

They try and show he supports the 97% (or at least 91%) consensus when he clearly does not. Linda Qiu writes:

> "Tol takes issue with Cook's methodology. By his analysis of Cook's data, the real figure is around 91 percent. (Cook replied critiquing Tol's methodology and standing by his survey's original finding of 97 percent.)" (Qiu, 2015)

This is Ms. Qiu misreading or deliberately lying about what Professor Tol wrote to her. Below is a quote from an email Professor Tol sent her (2 September 2015):

> "Cook's analysis is a load of old bollocks. … Cook did not study 1,300 papers, but close to 12,000; not that Cook has been [able] to give the exact number."
>
> "Cook's 97% is the consensus rate, rather than the percentage. The percentage is 0.6%. I never claimed that the consensus rate is 91%.
>
> I see that you have yet to correct yesterday's post on the same topic. Please correct these errors post haste." Richard Tol, source (Morano, 2015)

. Qiu and Politifact also twisted other comments. The emails that Professor Tol wrote were clear. Seeing the email exchange on Climate Depot we can only surmise that Linda Qiu deliberately misquoted Professor Tol due to her bias. Politifact and Qiu presented only one side of the debate, thus acting as a political advocate, not independent fact checkers.

This debate is serious because in 2017 81% of the energy we used came from fossil fuels according to ExxonMobil. In 2040, they expect 75% of the world's energy to come from fossil fuels, fossil fuels are not going away (ExxonMobil, 2019). To reduce our carbon dioxide emissions, we need to curtail fossil fuel use, raise the cost of energy, and slow the development of poorer countries. This will increase poverty in the western world and prevent many of the existing poor in the rest of the world from rising out of poverty.

As Tol and Lomborg have said, we need to make sure that the net effect of any actions we take is positive for mankind. Many people claim that all fossil fuel use is bad and will harm mankind, but Richard Tol has demonstrated that even if carbon dioxide emissions cause a two-degree increase in average temperature the net effect on humans may be positive. Even if the Paris climate change agreement is followed by every country, which is very unlikely, the unvalidated IPCC climate models say it will only reduce temperature increases by 0.2°C (0.36°F) by 2100 (Lomborg B. , 2016b). How is this worth the cost, even if the models are correct?

Marco Rubio

Another Politifact article (Kliegman, 2014) claims that Marco Rubio's statement that human activity is not "causing these dramatic changes to our climate" is false. This is incorrect and not very honest. Rubio's full statement from the article is carefully worded and very reasonable:

"I do not believe that human activity is causing these dramatic changes to our climate the way these scientists are portraying it, and I do not believe that the laws that they propose we pass will do anything about it. Except it will destroy our economy." (Kliegman, 2014)

Rubio is correct. The article by Julie Kliegman chooses not to address what Rubio said, but illogically changes his statement into a strawman:

"Rubio said human activity isn't causing changes to the environment, he's got it all wrong." (Kliegman, 2014)

This statement is probably false, which may be why Kliegman manufactured it. She goes on to say, "the causes of global warming are backed up by thorough research, so we didn't see room for debate in Rubio's claim." There we have it, in the great Kliegman has spoken, the science is settled, no room for debate. She initiates her critique of Senator Rubio by assuming he is wrong and then attacking him on that basis. Obviously, this is not a "fact check," but an opinion piece and not a good one.

Rubio is criticized a lot for saying climate change legislation will destroy our economy, but he is in line with climate change economists Richard Tol and Bjorn Lomborg on this point. Both are concerned about the negative impact reducing fossil fuel use will have on the world economy. Bjorn Lomborg has written:

> "The World Health Organization estimates that the effects of climate change are currently responsible for 141,000 deaths annually. If we look far ahead, to 2050, the death toll is expected to climb to 250,000. By contrast, some 4.3 million people will die this year from indoor air pollution. That is the direct result of poverty, of almost three billion people using dung and wood to heat and cook." (Lomborg B. , 2015)

He also writes in the same article:

> "… trying to drastically increase the production of renewable energy would return less than a dollar for every dollar spent, despite the carbon dioxide reduction, because renewable forms of energy remain expensive and are available only intermittently." (Lomborg B. , 2015)

These are not simple issues and the first rule in fighting climate change, like in medicine, should be to do no harm. Rubio's assertion that fighting climate change "will destroy our economy" may well be true. It may very well lose more lives than it saves.

The notorious and widely discredited Cook, et al. 2013 "97% consensus" paper is also cited in Kliegman's Politifact article. As Richard Tol notes in an email to Linda Qiu:

> "Cook found 64 papers (out of some 12,000) that support the consensus. It is a long story why Cook thinks that 64 is 97% of 12,000."
> Richard Tol, email to Linda Qiu, source (Morano, 2015)

A similar flawed study by Peter Doran also claims a 97% consensus that "human activity is a significant contributing factor in changing mean global temperatures" is based on 75 papers out of 77 (Doran, 2009). That statement is so uncontroversial, that we are surprised that 77 of 77 didn't agree with it. Probably, some objected to the word "significant." While it is reasonable to assume that humans have contributed to recent global warming, the contribution may not be "significant" or even measurable.

Cook's study was flawed. Even the authors of many of the papers "classified" by Cook, et al. (Cook and his co-authors are not climate scientists) say their papers were misclassified. Tol's criticism of the "97% consensus" is instructive and we will cover it in more detail in Chapter 6.

There is no proof that man-made climate change, if it exists, is dangerous. Can climate change in a catastrophic way? Certainly, it has happened many times in the past, but the catastrophes were not caused by humans, they were natural. And, of course man being man, he always blames other men or women for these natural disasters as shown by Professor Wolfgang Behringer in his excellent book *A Cultural History of Climate* (Behringer, 2010). In this book we find a wonderful 1486AD woodcut of a sorceress conjuring up a hailstorm

Figure 10. A 1486 woodcut of a sorceress conjuring a hailstorm with the jawbone of an ass, Source: (Behringer, 2010, p. 129). Public domain illustration.

with the jawbone of an ass. Behringer labeled Figure 10 "Anthropogenic Climate Change." With all the scientific and technical advances of the past 2,000 years, we still seem to blame catastrophes on the "sins" of men and women. The climate change alarmism of today has as much evidence behind it as this woodcut did in 1486.

Further on this topic, the Archbishop Agobard of Lyons (769-840AD) said the following in his sermon "On Hail and Thunder:"

"In these parts nearly everyone – nobles and common folk, town and country, young and old – believe that human beings can bring about hail and thunder…We have seen and heard how most people are gripped by such nonsense, indeed possessed by such stupidity…" (Behringer, 2010, p. 69)

Today we are in the same place. Hopefully, the silly idea that man can control the weather and climate with carbon dioxide emissions will not lead to the execution of over 50,000 so-called witches as it did in 1600. The arrogance of non-scientists, like the journalists at Politifact.com, Senator Whitehouse, Al Gore, John Cook (cartoonist, blogger and sometime psychology graduate student), Naomi Oreskes (historian) have in claiming actual climate scientists such as Judith Curry, Willie Soon, Tim Ball, Richard Tol, William Happer, Richard Lindzen, Patrick Michaels, Nobel Prize winner Ivar Giaever, and over a thousand other qualified scientists are wrong is spectacular. And, just because of a group of unsubstantiated surveys by other non-scientists? This doesn't count the 31,487 American scientists who signed the Global Warming Petition Project (Global Warming Petition Project, 2007).

Given the obvious mischaracterization of the statements made by Professor Tol, Senator Marco Rubio and Senator Rick Santorum discussed above, one wonders why a journalist would do this? You change what someone says so the statement goes from true to false and then attack the changed statement? Is this journalism today? Is it no wonder that a majority of Americans do not trust newspapers, television and radio to report the news fully, accurately and fairly (Brenan, 2019)? Rasmussen found in July of 2020 that 63% of the U.S. public believes that most news organizations are politically biased (Rasmussen, 2020).

Chuck Todd

Chuck Todd is a very partisan journalist for NBC and host of *Meet the Press*. He dropped out of college without earning a degree and has no training in science. The degrees he was working for, were political science and music.

Todd shows us that climate science is no longer science and is fully political when he said:

> "[Meet the Press is] not going to debate climate change, the existence of it. The earth is getting hotter and human activity is a major cause, period.
>
> We're not going to give time to climate deniers. The science is settled even if political opinion is not." Chuck Todd, *Meet the Press*, December 30, 2018

Wow, the perfect example of scientific ignorance on air for all to see. He says the science is settled when it never is. Science questions every assumption, every "settled" idea. When someone refuses to hear the opposing side of a debate, we can be sure that they have no scientific training, interest in science, or the truth.

Next, he claims the "political opinion" is not settled, yet while science is never settled, political opinions can, and often are, settled by voting. To date, the vote has gone against the alarmists, the public does not want to either tax "carbon" (meaning CO_2 emissions) or shut down the fossil fuel industry. The public does not think the science is settled. The issue is now fully political, with 90% of Democrats concerned about it and only 39% of Republicans (Funk & Hefferon, 2019).

Politics is about persuading or intimidating the voters to settle on one idea, one solution. Politics bends the will of the minority to the majority view. Science never works that way; every individual has a veto. All they need are observations, data, and analysis that show everyone else is wrong. Scientists pick at the data, the analysis, and try and find anything that will invalidate the consensus view. After some length of time, once every interested scientist has tried to invalidate the idea and failed, the idea becomes an accepted theory. There is no declaration, the idea, such as man-made climate change, only becomes an accepted theory when everyone is satisfied.

The opposition, the so-called "deniers," have a lot of data showing the Sun and nature are responsible for most of the recent warming. Soon and his colleagues provide considerable historical evidence that natural forces can cause warming very similar to what we are observing now (Soon, Baliunas, Idso, Idso, & Legates, 2003b). In science you cannot outvote the "deniers." You must convince them with observations and analysis.

Chuck Todd and others like to claim that extreme weather events are much worse today than in the past because they affect more people and cost more in nominal dollars (dollars uncorrected for inflation). They combine this with the simultaneous rise in global temperatures and claim a cause and effect. However, careful work by Roger Pielke Jr. Has shown that when the costs are corrected for inflation, the increasing number of people living in dangerous areas, and the higher value of newer buildings and homes, the impact of extreme weather events either shows no increase or is falling (Pielke Jr., 2017). Pielke's conclusions are particularly clear when natural disaster losses are presented as a percentage of GDP. There will be much more on these topics in Chapters 6 and 7.

Journalists can write about science, but they should only write about it if they understand it and have studied the issue themselves from a scientific perspective. They should read the scientific journal articles first. Simply interviewing scientists, and then writing about what they say on an issue is not enough. Interviewing environmental activists, like Greenpeace, who have a reputation for lying, and then bragging about it, as discussed above, is even worse. This is normally where the news media go off the rails. Somehow journalists never hear the words describing the uncertainty of the conclusions. They only report "what the scientist thinks might happen."

Next, we will discuss how non-profit environmental organizations influence the politics of climate change. We find that their campaigns try and pull on the public's emotional heartstrings to get people to contribute money before they understand the issue they are donating to. Once they are educated and understand the issue better, they are less likely to donate. In the case of climate change, the history provided above shows that education caused the public to move from a binary choice between human-caused climate change and natural climate change, to the more nuanced and scientific question of how much of the current changes are caused by humans. Just a little education can make a big difference.

Chapter 3: Non-profits and Climate Change

> "When left-of-center and progressive foundations are covered in the U.S. press, coverage tends to be predominantly positive and uncritical, deepening a lack of public scrutiny relative to their philanthropic activities, successes, and failures." (Nisbet, 2018, p. 2)

There are thousands of non-profit organizations trying to influence public policy and politicians, especially regarding the environment and climate change. Some claim to do scientific research, but they all have a political agenda of some kind and lobby both the news media and governments. Few can be trusted to offer an unbiased report on any issue. In this chapter we will discuss a few international nongovernmental organizations or INGOs.

Greenpeace

An intriguing report on the Greenpeace business model and philosophy was published by the Heartland Institute in 2018 (Connolly, Connolly, Soon, Moore, & Connolly, 2018). Four of the five authors are shown in the photograph in Figure 11. Dr. Patrick Moore, who is not in the photograph, is one of the founders of Greenpeace. He was president of Greenpeace Canada from 1977 to 1986 and a director of Greenpeace International from its founding in 1979 to 1986. Moore has a PhD in ecology from the University of British Columbia and is the only founder of Greenpeace with significant scientific training. He left Greenpeace in 1986, claiming that the organization and the environmental movement, in general, "had abandoned science and logic in favor of emotion and sensationalism" (Kasprak, 2019).

Greenpeace now claims that Moore was not a founder of Greenpeace, but this is nonsense. When Patrick Moore joined the small group that eventually created Greenpeace, it was called the "Don't Make a Wave Committee." They chartered a ship in 1971 to sail to the Aleutian Island of Amchitka to try and stop nuclear testing in the area. The ship was nicknamed "Greenpeace" and the organization with that name was created after the voyage on September 13, 1971 (Kasprak, 2019). Greenpeace has always considered that date to be its birthday.

Figure 11. Four of the five authors of the Heartland Greenpeace report in 2015 on San Gregorio beach near San Francisco. From left to right, Michael Connolly, Willie Soon, Imelda Connolly, Carolyn Gannon (wife of the photographer, Terry Gannon), Ronan Connolly. Photo used with Terry Gannon's kind permission.

Moore has always believed that humans and the rest of nature can live in harmony and that protecting nature does not preclude human prosperity. He is an environmentalist. But he objects to any environmental organization that is anti-human, anti-progress, and does not base its decisions on sound science, logic, and reason. When Greenpeace evolved into such an organization, Moore left.

Greenpeace's annual income has more than doubled over the past 20 years from less than US$150 million to over US$350 million. Greenpeace is a Dutch company with assets of more than US$277 million, of which 64% is in cash and cash equivalents. Greenpeace is a nonprofit company and presents itself as a selfless soldier protecting the environment, but their prime motivation is to collect as much money as possible. Greenpeace shut down their Irish branch because they were not generating enough income (Haughey, 1997). According to Emily Luxon (Assistant Professor of political science at

109

the University of Michigan) and Wendy Wong (Associate Professor of political science at the University of Toronto) the Greenpeace structure is highly centralized. It commands local (that is, national) organizations to prioritize the Greenpeace global agenda (Luxon & Wong, 2017).

Luxon and Wong compared the organization of Amnesty International to that of Greenpeace. These two organizations are about the same size, with roughly three million members each. Amnesty International has 56 national affiliate organizations around the world and Greenpeace has 28. The differences between the two are in their organization. Amnesty International is more decentralized and in 2012 moved 500 of its research, campaign, and communications jobs away from its London headquarters to the national affiliates, especially those in the Southern Hemisphere, where most of the human rights abuses were taking place.

Greenpeace, on the other hand, has centralized the choice and control of their campaigns at their world headquarters in Amsterdam. The local or national affiliates are not allowed to start campaigns or initiatives or make independent decisions, they must "integrate with and complement global campaigns" (Luxon & Wong, 2017).

When the Greenpeace home office senses a problem in a national affiliate it responds quickly and harshly. Greenpeace USA had had some successes protesting overfishing near Seattle and water pollution in Louisiana, but they were not bringing in enough money in 1997 to satisfy the home office. As a result, the Amsterdam headquarters ordered Greenpeace USA to lay off hundreds of employees and fired the Greenpeace USA executive director (Goldberg C. , 1997). The ex-President of Greenpeace USA, Barbara Dudley, characterized the firing as a resignation and said she was exhausted from years of crisis management. The layoffs occurred in Seattle, Boston, Minneapolis, Santa Cruz, California and many other cities. Barbara Dudley characterized her time at Greenpeace as follows:

"A week didn't go by without personnel problems, international political problems, fundraising problems. I'm just worn out and want to be an activist again instead of an administrator of a huge organization." (Hazen, 1997)

A former Greenpeace USA insider, told Don Hazen, the former publisher of *Mother Jones*, that "There's been a fight for Greenpeace USA's soul – and the soul lost" (Hazen, 1997).

This was when Greenpeace narrowed its focus and became centrally controlled. They began to focus on "hot" issues that raised more money and dropped environmental issues that raised less. They ramped up their global warming and forest destruction issues and dropped toxic waste and overfishing. This was another sign that money rules at Greenpeace.

Greenpeace overdid the flashy actions of threatening whaling ships at sea and hanging from bridges, and the public paid less attention to them. Further, it became clear that Greenpeace was not a grassroots organization, but a highly centralized mega-corporation.

Dr. Chris Rose was a strategic advisor to Greenpeace International and is an expert on environmental campaigning. He wrote a book on the subject called *How to Win Campaigns* (Rose, 2010). Dr. Rose's recommendations can be summarized as follows. This is similar to a list from page 7 of the Heartland report (Connolly, Connolly, Soon, Moore, & Connolly, 2018):

1. Choose a campaign issue that you label as catastrophic and urgent.
2. Choose a villain (enemy agent) who can't put up much of a defense and a sympathetic victim.
3. You (the good guy) propose a plausible solution to the campaign issue and accuse the villain (for selfish reasons) of preventing the solution from being implemented.
4. Issue a call to action and provide a way for people to become engaged (protest marches, face painting, financial contributions, etc.), so they become committed to the campaign.
5. Choose media outlets where you control the narrative. Don't debate with the bad guys.
   Modified from (Connolly, Connolly, Soon, Moore, & Connolly, 2018, p. 7)

Rose argues that education increases knowledge and understanding, leading to a nuanced discussion of the topic, which undermines the campaign's call to action. As a result, Rose believes successful campaigners should fight against education by deliberately oversimplifying the problem and providing a plausible, simple solution. All other potential solutions are rejected as inadequate. Thus, the "problem" is shown to be avoidable. A specific and identified "enemy" (for example ExxonMobil or Proctor and Gamble) is needed to complete the story, enhance the drama, focus the public and, especially, the media. In Rose's words:

> "Campaign communications need to roll out before an audience like a story." (Rose, 2010, p. 43)

A sympathetic "victim" or victims are needed to focus the news media and provide great news photographs and film. Rose emphasizes this in his book:

> "... the most empathetic figure in the story is you, or on your side. Don't let the media fall out of love with your campaign through the natural tendency for it to dry out and become an elite dialogue." (Rose, 2010, p. 205)

By "elite dialogue" Rose means a nuanced and intelligent discussion of the issues surrounding the problem. In other words, do not allow the public or the news media to become educated on the issue. The modern news media is very poorly educated and uninterested in science and mathematics, so this is not difficult. From Rose's book:

> "CAMPAIGNING IS NOT EDUCATION
>
> Campaigning involves stimulating action, best achieved by narrowing the focus and eliminating distractions and reducing options, as in advertising ... Typically, it starts ... with a problem and moves a target audience through the stages of awareness ... concern and so on, to action.
>
> In contrast, education expands awareness of options and complexity ... It typically takes a problem and shows that it is not so simple as you may have first thought.
>
> The educational model is great for education but not for campaigning. It reaches understanding but not action. Using it to try and decide or stimulate action is likely to lead to confusion and frustration. ... Questioning fundamentals and reflecting on things is not how business, politics or war advances." (Rose, 2010, pp. 23-25)

So, we see the plan. Label an issue as catastrophic and urgent, find an enemy who will not defend itself (normally a publicly held company), propose a plausible solution, find an empathetic victim, issue a call to action, saturate the media (they won't look at it closely), avoid debating the science and technology, and claim the "science is settled." These are the critical aspects of a Greenpeace environmental campaign. They, and other environmental non-profit organizations, have used this formula over and over. They consider it imperative that the argument be kept on an emotional level, once a nuanced scientific analysis of the issue is out, the campaign dies. Since the details and the implications of the "solution" can't be kept secret for very long, each campaign has a lifetime. Greenpeace will milk each campaign until the money flow begins to decline rapidly. Then they move on to a new money-maker. We will now discuss the steps in the process in more detail.

Find a scary issue

In Figure 12, we see a plot of expenditures of two of Greenpeace's discontinued campaigns. Their biodiversity campaign died as people became aware that biodiversity was not declining (Dornelas, et al., 2014) and (Cardinale, Gonzalez, Allington, & Loreau, 2018). Instead species populations were just moving about. Then they switched to GM (genetically modified) food, which died in 2010 as GM food was shown to be safe and was saving lives and eyesight in developing countries (Freedman D. , 2013).

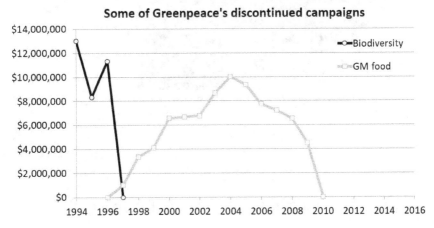

Figure 12. Expenditures for two discontinued Greenpeace campaigns. Source: (Connolly, Connolly, Soon, Moore, & Connolly, 2018). Used with Michael Connolly's kind permission.

Cornell University has studied GMO foods and concluded they are critical to alleviating malnutrition in the world (Norero, 2018). It is interesting that research and public education are the reasons these donation campaigns died. They were created with appeals to emotion, made Greenpeace a lot of money, and then they died due to education and scientific research.

In Figure 13 a breakdown of Greenpeace's campaign expenditures are shown. It shows a multiyear waxing and waning of campaigns over time. As the public learns about the issues, the donations decline, and Greenpeace reduces campaign expenditures. It is interesting that campaign expenditures on man-made climate change have started to decline.

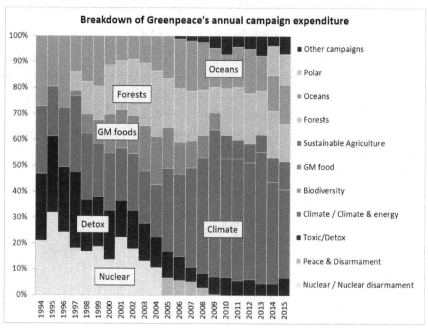

Figure 13. Greenpeace campaign expenditures 1994 to 2015. Source: modified after (Connolly, Connolly, Soon, Moore, & Connolly, Analysis of Greenpeace's business model and philosophy, 2018). Used with Michael Connolly's kind permission.

Find a scary villain, like ExxonMobil

For Greenpeace, the ideal villain is a public company, because they are normally afraid to fight back. They just want the issue out of the newspapers and off TV. Chris Rose wrote that an enemy is essential to the campaign because it focuses the public mind. In their "ExxonSecrets" campaign, Greenpeace chose ExxonMobil to be their enemy and claimed the company "knew" man-made climate change was dangerous and were hiding secret information that proved it. Worse, ExxonMobil was secretly funding "climate deniers." None of this was true as we will see later in this chapter.

Greenpeace claims that ExxonMobil spent $1.8 million per year funding "climate denial." They achieve this figure by counting any donation to any organization, regardless of the purpose of the donation, as funding "denial" if anyone in the organization had ever expressed any climate skepticism. Even this inflated amount is tiny compared to the more than $30 million per year, on average, spent by Greenpeace promoting an impending climate change catastrophe due to "carbon pollution." We compare ExxonMobil's spending on organizations that Greenpeace claims are "climate deniers" to Greenpeace's spending promoting climate alarmism in Figure 14.

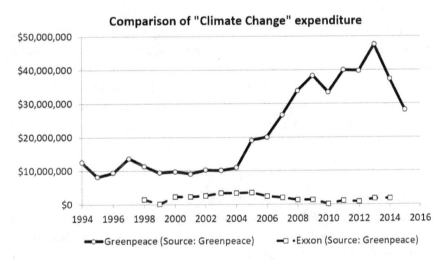

Figure 14. Greenpeace expenditures on climate alarmism versus ExxonMobil's spending supporting organizations that Greenpeace claims are climate "deniers." All Greenpeace spending data from Greenpeace annual reports (Greenpeace, 2016). The ExxonMobil donation data is also from Greenpeace (Greenpeace, 2020). The graph is modified from one in (Connolly, Connolly, Soon, Moore, & Connolly, 2018). Used with Michael Connolly's kind permission.

As we can see in Figure 14, "funding climate denial" does not seem to be a priority for ExxonMobil. Even if the list of climate-denying organizations

Greenpeace presents were real, and if ExxonMobil really thought man-made climate change was real, why would they spend only 0.0005% of their annual revenue fighting it? After all, Greenpeace is spending 32% of their annual campaign money trying to convince people that man-made climate change is a threat.

The list of "climate denying organizations" that ExxonMobil contributed to, according to Greenpeace, includes the U.S. Chamber of Commerce, George Mason University Law and Economics Center, the Smithsonian Astrophysical Observatory, and the National Black Chamber of Commerce (Greenpeace, 2020). These are not scary or radical organizations. This was a blatant attempt by Greenpeace and their allies in government to deny ExxonMobil their first amendment rights of free speech and to advocate for issues important to them and their business. Under the law, these rights apply to everyone and every company, not just to climate alarmist organizations, like Greenpeace. This attack was designed and implemented by Kert Davies and Cindy Baxter.

Davies and Baxter managed to plant the myth with a compliant news media that ExxonMobil and other fossil fuel companies are funding climate denial around the world, even though they presented little evidence of this. The news media didn't check their claims and accepted the lie uncritically and regularly repeated it as though it were fact. Being skeptical that humans control climate is not a crime. Doubting such an extreme statement is at the root of how science works.

Find a sympathetic Victim

Greenpeace victims are carefully chosen. They must be very empathetic, photogenic, and appealing to journalists. They can be animals (penguins and polar bears are excellent) or people, especially children. Chris Rose (Rose, 2010) emphasizes that the victim must be the most empathetic figure in the story. The story must have a clear narrative and appeal to the heart. Avoid any experts or business analysis. Make the victims (coral reefs, endangered species, etc.) the focus of the story, keep experts on tap, but in the background (Rose, 2010, pp. 205-206).

Rose specifically says the campaign must not educate the public, instead it should invoke emotions, especially concern, urgency, and anger.

Lots of heart-wrenching photographs are needed along with back-stories. Greenpeace have made themselves the victims on occasion with carefully choreographed demonstrations, such as their Proctor and Gamble protest. In this protest, March 4, 2014 in Cincinnati, they ziplined between two skyscrapers to hang banners. The banners protested supposed deforestation in the tropics to make palm oil. They wanted great visuals to get on television and increase donations. Appeal to emotions, not the intellect.

Greenpeace activists broke into Procter & Gamble's headquarters to let in another activist wearing a tiger costume. Then they installed huge banners denouncing their antidandruff shampoo, Head & Shoulders. Supposedly, Head & Shoulders put "tiger survival on the line." They hired a helicopter, videographer, and photographer to record the whole thing.

However, while they implied that Head & Shoulders was somehow causing problems for tigers, Greenpeace members admitted to Aaron Gell, of *Business Insider*, that Head & Shoulders' activities had nothing to do with tigers and the tiger was really "a kind of decoy" (Gell, 2014). They had just picked the "threatened tigers" as an issue because they find the public are more concerned when they think a photogenic animal is involved.

According to Phil Radford, an ex-executive director of Greenpeace, USA, "It's easy to say, 'If you're destroying forests, you're destroying tiger habitats." He continues, "It's harder to say, 'Do you know that forests store carbon and if we save the peat bogs, we will trap all this carbon and methane in the soil?' They say both, but they put the photogenic animals up front. Another Greenpeace executive, Nicky Davies, says:

> "We're not going to win by telling people what they should care about. And winning is the objective." (Gell, 2014)

Greenpeace has not strayed far from their original motto: "It does not matter what is true, it only matters what people believe is true." Winning is their only objective.

The strategy, which Greenpeace calls "market-based campaigning," is effective. They pick an area of concern. Identify producers whose actions are contributing to the perceived problem. Look at the producer's customers and find a connection to a multinational corporation that peddles a widely known consumer product. Send them emails, pointing out the company's "exposure" and suggesting an alternative. Issue a public report. If the desired response is not forthcoming. roll out a media campaign, ideally starring a beloved animal species and featuring a hashtag.

Then do embarrassing and flashy demonstrations, with lots of pictures, video and news coverage. This will involve dangerous stunts, perhaps breaking into buildings and getting arrested. What seems to happen, inevitably, is the multinational company, eager to remove the stigma from its signature brand, promises to ensure that its products are sustainable and begins cancelling contracts with any third-party suppliers who fail to guarantee compliance.

Eventually, broad new industry protocols are adopted. Rinse and repeat (Gell, 2014).

According to Aaron Gell, Greenpeace's mafia-style shakedown approach has been very successful. It might be excusable if the "perceived problems" were real problems, but they rarely are. These shakedowns are only to gain media hype and increase donations. The flashy shows they put on are entertaining and people will pay for entertainment. Unfortunately, they often close mines and factories and cost jobs, especially hard-to-get third world jobs. But Greenpeace doesn't care, the shows help them raise more than $350 million in annual contributions (Gell, 2014).

Gell observes that Greenpeace will often choose an "enemy" that is only indirectly related to the problems they base their campaigns on. They want the campaign itself, punishing the right company or organization is not a priority. Greenpeace will offer to publicly praise a targeted company if they do what Greenpeace wants, they have named this tactic "spank and thank" (Gell, 2014).

Greenpeace has been wrong in many of their campaigns and done much harm. The most obvious example is their campaign against DDT, which is highly effective in preventing malaria, a very deadly disease (May, Greenpeace Crimes and Lies, 2016j). Another good example is their campaign against fossil fuels.

Greenpeace provided an Indian village, Dharnai, with solar power in 2014. The village had been without electricity for 33 years. The village rejected it as inadequate and demanded "real electricity." They meant 24 hour on-demand electricity, not electricity only when the Sun was shining (Jha, 2014)

Propose a plausible solution

Greenpeace must propose a solution to the problem and furiously reject all other proposed solutions as inadequate. For example, suppose we temporarily accept their untrue assumption that CO_2 is dangerous. Replacing

118

coal with natural gas reduces CO_2 emissions by 60%, as proven in the United States (Connolly, Connolly, Soon, Moore, & Connolly, 2018). But, to have enough natural gas, wells must be "fracked" which Greenpeace is opposed to. Likewise, switching from coal to nuclear power plants reduces CO_2 emissions, but Greenpeace is opposed to nuclear. Hydroelectric is out because it requires dams on rivers. They work through the list of possible solutions and reject all of them except for solar, wind and tidal power sources. Solar and wind power are intermittent and currently require backup by fossil fuels or hydroelectric since battery technology is insufficient and too expensive (Clack, et al., 2017). Regardless of efforts by Greenpeace and other environmental organizations, the public has become aware of how inadequate these sources are and how impractical and expensive eliminating fossil fuels is, witness the November 2018 demonstrations against a carbon tax in France.

While Greenpeace will offer a plausible solution, they prefer one that cannot be implemented. If they propose a real, practical solution, it will be implemented, and their donations dry up.

Regarding energy solutions, they recommend the world switch to 100% renewable energy (excluding nuclear and hydroelectric) within a few decades. Like everyone else they must realize this is impossible, which suits them and their objectives. Baseload electricity can be required for a long time in most areas during periods when the wind is not blowing and it is nighttime or very cloudy, batteries are not adequate for these periods and expensive. This is a complex topic and we will not cover it in this book, the interested reader is referred to this blog post for more details and references (May, Exergy and Power Plants, 2017k).

Issue a call to action

An essential part of Greenpeace's campaigns is a "call to action" by the public. If the public can do something, they "buy into" the campaign and are more likely donate money. Examples abound, but one example "solution" is to stop using "single use" plastics. The Heartland Greenpeace business model report (Connolly, Connolly, Soon, Moore, & Connolly, 2018, pp. 29-48) discusses in some detail how the Greenpeace visual of "giant ocean garbage patches, twice the size of Texas" are largely a fiction and photographic trick. The concentration of plastic material in some parts of the oceans (the "ocean gyres") is higher than in the rest of the ocean, but still extremely low. Dr. Andres Cózar of the University of Cádiz, in Spain, examined surveys of plastic concentrations in the oceans and created a map of them. The map is shown in

Figure 15 (Connolly, Connolly, Soon, Moore, & Connolly, 2018), originally from (Cózar, et al., 2014).

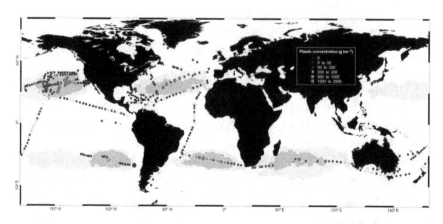

Figure 15. Ocean transits to trawl for plastic in ocean surface water. The dots are transits, the gray areas are the "gyres." Plastic and other trash collects in the gyres. Source: (Connolly, Connolly, Soon, Moore, & Connolly, 2018, p. 32). Original source: (Cózar, et al., 2014). Used with the kind permission of Andrés Cózar and Michael Connolly.

Figure 15 shows the location of the gyres, the light gray and dark gray areas, where plastic concentrations are highest. They are also identified by the larger dots. The largest dots have 1 kg to 2.5 kg of plastic per square kilometer (5.7 to 14.3 pounds per square mile) of ocean, a very small amount.

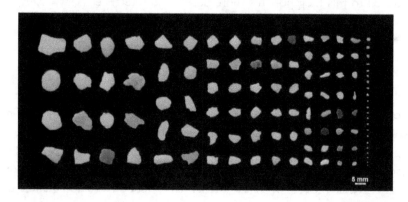

Figure 16. All the plastic fragments found in one sweep of the ocean in a dark gray area in the South Atlantic Gyre. Source: (Connolly, Connolly, Soon, Moore, & Connolly, 2018, p. 33). Original source: (Cózar, et al., 2014), figure S11 in the supplementary materials. Used with the kind permission of Andrés Cózar and Michael Connolly.

The plastic fragments captured in the nets are quite small. Figure 16, also from Cózar, et al., shows all the plastic fragments found in one entire transit with a fine mesh net in one of the denser dark gray areas.

The trawl pass that collected the plastic shown in Figure 16 was in the heart of the South Atlantic gyre "garbage patch." This trawl pass covered between 0.4 and 0.9 miles of the ocean. Yet, the 110 fragments shown (note the 5 mm or 0.2 inch, graphical scale) are all that were found. The largest fragment is around ½ inch across. One-hundred and ten fragments, all less than ½ inch across, is hardly a "garbage patch." The trawl net has a fine mesh, since the smallest plastic particles recovered are much less than a millimeter across. Most plastic degenerates in ocean water quickly due to sunlight, wave action and biogenic activity (Barry, 2009). A blog post by Kip Hansen (Hansen K., 2017) has some excellent microphotographs of degrading plastic. There are a few types of plastic that do not degrade rapidly, polyvinyl chloride or PVC, is one durable type, but most do.

Interestingly, the plastics concentration in most of the gyres is not increasing, thus the problem cannot be called "urgent." However, the concentration is increasing in the North Pacific gyre, which suggests that the additional plastic is coming from Asia, mainly China. The concentration of plastic fragments (most of them less than 1/16 inch or 1.6 mm across) is quite small, generally less than a few hundred fragments per square mile. Despite this, Greenpeace has convinced much of the public that there are massive floating islands of plastic twice the size of Texas in the oceans (Liu, 2018), which is simply not true. In the words of Professor Angelicque White, College of Earth, Ocean and Atmospheric Sciences at Oregon State University (White, 2011):

> "There is no doubt that the amount of plastic in the world's oceans is troubling, but this kind of exaggeration undermines the credibility of scientists."
>
> "The amount of plastic out there isn't trivial. But using the highest concentrations ever reported by scientists produces a patch that is a small fraction of the state of Texas, not twice the size." (White, 2011)

White offers another analogy. She asks us to compare the amount of plastic found to the amount of water in which it was found. If we were to filter a football field sized area in waters having the highest concentration of plastic ever recorded, the amount of plastic recovered would not even extend to the 1-inch line of a football field. The news media simply must stop repeating stories from Greenpeace without checking them. Publishing a false statement from Greenpeace and simply saying "Greenpeace reports …" is not a direct lie, but it is repeating a lie, which is just as bad.

Carefully choose the media outlets used, control the narrative

Greenpeace spends over $30 million per year on media and communications. They also carefully cultivate contacts in many media organizations and provide them with great film, stories, and photographs. Yet often these releases are misleading or complete fiction. In some cases, the fictitious press releases are deliberately malicious, as in the now infamous attack on Dr. Willie Soon discussed in Chapter 2.

The onus is on the news media to check the facts. Just because the source is Greenpeace, or the Sierra Club, does not mean the press release is correct.

In the words of the Wilderness Society vice president of public policy Rindy O'Brien:

"Greenpeace has tended to look for ways to publicize problems instead of ways to actually solve them." (Goldberg C. , 1997)

Carey Goldberg, a reporter for the *New York Times* adds:

"Her [O'Brien's] comments echoed longstanding criticism by others that Greenpeace is too much of a self-promotion machine.

I do think the public, … are looking for solutions rather than … extremists, … and I think that separates Greenpeace from the other environmental groups.'" (Goldberg C. , 1997)

Greenpeace actively tries to control the narrative, reduce the options to a binary choice, and push an emotion laden decision. They do not want to debate the issues; they do not want to educate the public on the details of the supposed problem. They want an us versus them, a cute animal versus the giant corporation type of choice. They do not want people to understand the implications of the decision; they want them to think they are protecting the cute victim.

When people are aware of these tactics, they find them easier to fight. A scientist always questions everything, "Is that true?" "How can I test that idea?" "What is the evidence?" Science is the opposite of the Greenpeace campaign goals; science is about understanding. Remember what Chris Rose said about education, quoted in the first section of this chapter, "The educational model is great for education but not for campaigning. It reaches understanding but not action" (Rose, 2010, p. 25). He could have simply said environmental campaigning is the opposite of science.

TomKat Foundation

Tom Steyer made his fortune at Farallon Capital Management, an investment "hedge fund" company he started in 1986, in San Francisco. Farallon invested heavily in energy companies, especially Kinder-Morgan, an oil and gas pipeline company. Other investments included BP and various coal mining companies.

Steyer left Farallon in 2012 to become an environmental activist and asked Farallon to divest his holdings in fossil fuels. He and his wife had started the TomKat Foundation in 2008. The name comes from a combination of their first names, Tom and Kat or Kathryn. By 2012, Steyer wrote that he, "no longer felt comfortable being at a firm that was invested in every single sector of the global economy, including tar sands and oil" (Valdmanis, Jensen, & Paul, 2014). The divestment process is still incomplete.

As of 2020 (Beitsch, 2020), financial disclosure statements in 2019 still showed he was invested in coal mining and oil and gas around the world. These fossil fuel assets are owned by private equity firms run by Mark Carnegie. Steyer has between one and six million dollars invested with him. Carnegie's funds are heavily invested in coal-bed methane projects in Australia. In addition, Steyer has between six and 31 million dollars invested with Tinicum Capital, a firm with large oil and gas holdings. He is also invested in Direct Petroleum Exploration Inc. (Allison & Maloney, 2019).

While Steyer ran Farallon, they invested in Kinder-Morgan, an oil, gas and CO_2 pipeline company. He also had a large investment in El Paso Oil and Gas, which Kinder-Morgan bought in 2012. The combined holdings made up a large portion of Farallon's fund in 2012.

Steyer was born in 1957 in Manhattan, New York, his father was a lawyer and his mother was a teacher. Steyer graduated from Yale and joined Morgan-Stanley in 1979. After two years, he left and earned an MBA at Stanford. He then joined Goldman Sachs and worked there from 1983 to 1985. In 1986 he founded Farallon Capital Management in San Francisco. By the time he left Farallon, it was managing over $20 billion.

Steyer was always politically active and very liberal. He worked on Walter Mondale's campaign in 1983 and was an early supporter of Hillary Clinton and Barak Obama. Steyer ran for president in 2019 and as part of his platform said he would declare a nationwide climate change emergency if he were elected. Climate change seems to be his main issue, besides impeaching Donald Trump, but it is hard to understand why.

Investing is like science in a way. To invest well you need to be clear-eyed, objective, and dig into and understand the details. You must leave all biases and emotion at the door and let the data guide you. Steyer was obviously good at investing and invested in fossil fuels as a part of a well-diversified portfolio. This was smart, objective, and data driven.

As we describe in this book, there are no data, outside of dubious climate model output, that support the idea of an impending man-made climate change disaster. Given this, and the slowdown in warming since the late 1990s, why does Steyer want to declare a climate change national emergency? It makes no sense. Ignorant politicians, like Al Gore, or emotion-driven news media types, like Chuck Todd are likely to fall for this fantasy, but a hard-nosed investor like Tom Steyer? It is hard to see him miss the obvious.

Despite the contradictions between his investing and his stated views on the supposed climate change problem, his views do seem to be genuine. He does seem to believe that man-made climate change is an urgent and high priority problem. This is at odds with much of the public. This is no longer a scientific debate, the alarmists, including Steyer, refuse to debate the science, to them it is settled by consensus. The debate is now political. Sixty-two percent of Democrats think a man-made climate catastrophe is very likely, but only 24% of Republicans and 42% of independents do (Rasmussen, 2019).

So, it seems, that Steyer's liberal political views have overwhelmed his rational self and made him a climate change partisan. The Rasmussen poll also found that 61% of voters think that politicians only raise the climate change issue to get elected. Polls also show the voting public does not believe that the scientific debate on climate change is over and do not think the science is "settled" (Rasmussen, 2016).

A review of what Tom Steyer has said about climate change does not show any understanding of climate science. He has repeatedly said that he thinks it is the number one problem in the United States (Daniels, 2019), but has never explained why.

The closest we could get to his personal understanding of climate science were the reports of the Risky Business Project, which he participated in with Michael Bloomberg and Henry Paulson (Risky Business Project, 2020). Their main concerns seem to be additional risk to coastal property and infrastructure over the next century or so, but these risks are not increasing as clearly shown by Roger Pielke Jr. and colleagues (Weinkle, Maue, & Pielke Jr., 2012), (Mohleji & Pielke Jr., 2014), and (Pielke Jr. R. , 2010). Further, as acknowledged in the report itself, these are local risks, not worldwide risks and should probably be dealt with locally. Rather than eliminating fossil fuels worldwide, areas in danger of rising sea level or extreme weather should build better infrastructure and place restrictions on building in dangerous areas. A national or worldwide solution to these small scale and minor risks is not warranted.

They also emphasize that temperatures are likely to rise in specific areas, causing greater use of air conditioning. They acknowledge that temperatures will also increase in colder areas, reducing the need for heating. Again, these are local problems and benefits of global warming. The arguments in the report are similar to those made by liberal politicians everywhere. They want to apply poorly thought out global solutions to local problems. The true risk here is that the proposed global solution, reducing or eliminating the use of fossil fuels, will not change the climate, and it will cripple the world's energy economy. It would happen, perhaps, just when we need energy the most, whether the climate changes are natural or man-made.

They seem to think that agriculture will suffer in some areas due to climate change, but it has been clearly shown by many researchers that agriculture is benefiting worldwide from recent warming and increasing CO_2 (May, 2018). The IPCC AR5 report acknowledges this on page 502 of their report:

> "Thus, with high confidence, the CO_2 fertilization effect will lead to enhanced NPP [net primary plant productivity], but significant uncertainties remain on the magnitude of this effect..." (IPCC, 2013, p. 502)

Thus, there seems to be no basis, in the scientific literature, for Tom Steyer and Michael Bloomberg's concerns regarding the possible dangers of climate change or global warming. They are both analytical people; they just have a blind spot regarding climate change.

Union of Concerned Scientists

The Union of Concerned Scientists (UCS) claims to be committed to "seek the truth, and let our findings guide our conclusions" (Union of Concerned Scientists, 2020). That may have been true when the group was founded in 1969, but currently they are an activist left-wing political organization with little scientific input. They advocate fighting man-made climate change by eliminating or reducing fossil fuel use and blame fossil fuel companies for "preventing climate action." (Union of Concerned Scientists, 2020d). They do not want to debate the cause of climate change; they only want to discuss their proposed solution. They have already decided that human greenhouse emissions are the cause, a very anti-scientific decision for a supposedly scientific organization.

The UCS sued the government to obtain documents to stop President Trump's plan to relocate two research agencies of the USDA (U.S. Department of Agriculture) to Kansas City. The move was a logical attempt to move the Agriculture Department closer to the farmers they serve. The UCS attempt to stop this move was a blatant attempt to curry favor with the federal bureaucracy. One wonders why they care. Governments and companies relocate people all the time (Union of Concerned Scientists, 2020b).

By January 29, 2020, before anyone was nominated by the Democratic Party to run for president, the UCS was already recommending a vote against President Trump (Union of Concerned Scientists, 2020c). One would think that a scientifically oriented group would want to know who the opponent is first. Quite obviously, science second, politics first. The report containing this recommendation is titled, "Presidential Recommendations for 2020." The authors are listed as Jacob Carter, Taryn MacKinney, Genna Reed, and

126

Gretchen Goldman (Carter, MacKinney, Reed, & Goldman, 2020). It is a highly partisan report, as it is not choosing between two nominated candidates, it is just against one, no matter who his opponent is. This sort of blind recommendation is offensive to any true scientist or logical person. The report concludes:

> "The Trump administration's unprecedented attacks on science highlight an urgent need for the next president to restore integrity in science-based decision making. This administration has sidelined scientific guidance from experts inside and outside of agencies, directly censored scientists, suppressed federal scientific reports, and created a chilling environment that has demoralized federal scientists and led to self-censorship of their work. The consequences of sidelining science for the past four years will only intensify if future leaders do not restore the role of independent science and expertise in decision making." (Carter, MacKinney, Reed, & Goldman, 2020)

Has Trump attacked science? Or has he simply supported and agreed with scientists with different opinions and ideas than those in government agencies and the Union of Concerned Scientists? Lay people, especially politicians and those in the UCS, tend to accept opinions that they share and consider every other opinion "wrong." If UCS agrees with a group of scientists, they call it "science," if they disagree it is an attack on "science." A true scientist will look at observations and analysis from both sides and acknowledge when the data and reasoning are inconclusive, which is most of the time. Then he may form an opinion about what is correct. Either way, opinions, no matter how well informed, are not science. Science is a systematic method of disproving opinions.

Opinions are not "science." The "science," if you want to use that word to describe a specific thing, is the attack on the opinion.

Trump has not "sidelined scientific guidance from experts inside and outside of agencies." Trump has challenged their ideas, and sometimes disagreed with their opinions, which is his job. If these experts are offended that someone would challenge their ideas, they might want to run for office. No scientist is offended when challenged, they expect it.

A RICO scheme and The ExxonKnew plot

Peter Frumhoff, the director of science and policy at The Union of Concerned Scientists (UCS), admitted, on July 31st of 2015, that the organization was actively working with state attorneys general to investigate opponents of the man-made climate change hypothesis. This admission was made in an email from Frumhoff to Professor Edward Maibach of George Mason University. Maibach is a close ally of Senator Sheldon Whitehouse, who was discussed in Chapter 1. Maibach and Whitehouse, together with Jagadish Shukla, concocted a scheme to use the RICO laws to prosecute conservatives. The exact wording, in an email from Alex Bozmoski, of George Mason University's Energy and Enterprise Initiative, to Maibach, was "You're talking about prosecuting conservatives." Maibach's response, "LOL. Good points." (Tuttle, 2016).

The RICO act or the Racketeer Influenced and Corrupt Organizations Act is designed to go after the heads of large criminal organizations. Whitehouse's idea, as discussed in Chapter 1, was to use the act to punish people who had opinions different from his, by claiming that the opposing opinions endanger society in some fashion. Whitehouse, Maibach, and Shukla wanted to impose "financial penalties against corporations [that] fund climate denial" (Tuttle, 2016). The emails discussing this are in a pdf on the eelegal.org web site (eelegal, 2016). This is an action that would be expected from a king or dictator. If a scientist disagrees with someone, the natural process would be to research the topic and publish why the other person's opinion is wrong.

The chain of emails was uncovered through a Competitive Enterprise Institute (CEI) Virginia FOIA (Freedom of Information Act) request. The emails were under seal until they were forced into the public domain by a judicial order on April 22, 2016 (Watts, 2016). The director of the FME Law Clinic, David Schnare, commented:

"We need to protect the work of academics as set forth in Freedom of Information Acts, which laws make exception for information that should be legitimately protected, for example relating to research. But when professors voluntarily enter the policy arena, particularly in this case when they use their positions specifically to advance a political agenda, they are no different than any other government employee and the law treats them accordingly." (Watts, 2016)

In plainer English, he is saying the UCS is acting like a politician, not an academic or a scientist, so they will be treated like a politician. Jagadish Shukla, professor of Climate Dynamics, George Mason University, was the author of a letter to President Obama in 2015 that sought to encourage him to pursue using the RICO statute against "corporations and other organizations that have knowingly deceived the American people about the risks of climate change" (Shukla, 2015). The letter was signed by 20 academics who later became known as the "RICO-20" (Watts, 2016). Among the RICO-20 were six George Mason University academics. It is interesting that Kert Davies and Greenpeace, on their ExxonSecrets.org web site, call George Mason University Law and Economics Center an "academic bastion of conservative policy ideals" and label them a "Climate Denial" organization (Greenpeace, 2020).

The scheme to use the threat of a RICO investigation to deprive corporations and individuals of their first amendment rights failed spectacularly later in the year. It turned out Professor Shukla and his organization, called IGES (Institute for Global Environment and Security, Inc.), were using federal grant money inappropriately. Shukla violated National Science Foundation (NSF) policies and the policies of George Mason University in spending far too much of his grant money on himself, his wife and his daughter according to Stephen McIntyre and Roger Pielke Jr. (McIntyre, Shukla's Gold, 2015). Shukla also managed to pass some of the grant money to his hometown in India.

After receiving over four million dollars from the government for climate research, Professor Shukla had only written one paper, but he enriched himself, his family, and friends. Most of this is documented in Shukla's 2014 IRS Form 990 filing for his company. It was uncovered by Roger Pielke Jr. (Institute of Global Environment and Society, 2014). A summary of sources on the Shukla RICO debacle can be seen at Climate Depot (Morano, 2015). CEI's Chris Horner pointed out:

> "This victory puts on notice those academics who have increasingly inserted themselves into politics, that they cannot use taxpayer-funded positions to go after those who disagree with them and expect to hide it," said Chris Horner, CEI fellow and co-plaintiff. "These records are highly relevant to the state attorneys general campaign that these academics hoped for and will be of great assistance to the public in trying to understand how their tax dollars are being used for political fights." (Watts, 2016)

After the emails and Shukla's IRS filings were revealed in the press and on the web, the federal RICO investigation died a well-deserved death.

This is an extremely important point. How can federally funded university professors use public funds to attempt to create a politically motivated federal investigation of a public corporation for a non-crime with no victims? George Mason University (GMU) tried to say that no records existed regarding Shukla's RICO letter, but other universities provided proof that claim was not true.

Peter Webster, Judith Curry's husband, was a friend of Shukla and wrote to him several times asking that he retract his RICO letter publicly. After the blistering attacks on him from Curry, Pat Michaels, Roger Pielke Jr. and many others, Shukla very much wanted to retract the letter (email from Edward Maibach to Jeff Nesbit, September 26, 2015). He actually drafted a retraction, but Edward Maibach dissuaded him from releasing it to the press.

Shukla came to realize what a terrible idea it was to use such a law to attack someone who simply had a different opinion about the merits of a scientific hypothesis like man-made climate change. He also came to understand that Judith Curry, Pat Michaels and Roger Pielke Jr. felt the letter personally attack them, with considerable justification. Shukla believed that the letter only attacked corporations, not realizing that it also applied to individuals. Perhaps because he was raised in India, he didn't realize there is only a tiny legal difference between corporations and individuals in the United States. Besides the danger of RICO being used against individuals, Peter Webster and Judith Curry jointly own a company called CFAN (CFAN, 2020) that could be attacked. Some of this is discussed in an email from Edward

Maibach to Jeff Nesbit, dated September 26, 2015 (eelegal, 2016). The eelegal pdf also contains Shukla's draft of a retraction. Suffice it to say, Shukla's letter and Whitehouse's op-ed about RICO were poorly thought out and thankfully went down in flames.

Even the enthusiastic Peter Frumhoff backed away and said that the UCS did not think the case was strong enough for a federal attorney general to get involved. However, he volunteered that he was pursuing a similar strategy with some state attorneys general. Oddly, this email from Frumhoff to Maibach is dated July 31, 2015 (Brown, 2016) which is just two months after Sheldon Whitehouse's *Washington Post* RICO op-ed, discussed above and in Chapter 1 (Whitehouse, 2015). The conspiracy to pursue a RICO investigation, at either the federal level or the state level, had to have been well under way when Whitehouse wrote his op-ed.

ExxonKnew

Greenpeace and Kert Davies' 2004 ExxonSecrets scheme to attack ExxonMobil, mentioned in Chapter 2, failed (Horner, 2018). While the ExxonSecrets campaign was on the decline, it helped spawn a 2012 conference in La Jolla, California, hosted by Peter Frumhoff of the Union of Concerned Scientists (UCS) and Richard Heede of the Climate Accountability Institute, both heavily funded by the Rockefeller Brothers Fund. Others who helped organize the conference were Naomi Oreskes, Angela Ledford Anderson, and Lewis Branscomb. A complete list of organizers and participants can be seen in Seth Shulman's report, "Establishing Accountability for Climate Change Damages: Lessons from Tobacco Control." (Shulman, 2012). The organizations funding the conference itself are also listed in Shulman's report, they include the V. Kann Rasmussen Foundation, Mertz Gilmore Foundation, and the Grantham Foundation for the Protection of the Environment. Besides Shulman's report on the conference we have relied heavily on Christopher Horner's blog posts for this section. The La Jolla conference would set in motion the activities that eventually resulted in the ExxonKnew campaign.

This was a meeting, led primarily by lawyers and mostly for lawyers. Scientists, public opinion, and communications experts were present, but they were to help the lawyers come up with winning arguments and to boost public support. Greenpeace International was represented by Jasper Teulings, their chief legal officer and the head of Greenpeace International's Legal Unit.

The goal of the meeting was to plan a strategy like that used in the "Big Tobacco" lawsuits, but targeted against energy companies, especially

ExxonMobil. They wanted to explore how recent climate change could be "most compellingly attributed to human activities, ... both scientifically and in the public mind." (Shulman, 2012).

As noted above, there is a well-established direct link between tobacco use and cancer and damages to the public and government can be computed. The RICO attacks on tobacco companies had some merit, especially since internal tobacco company documents showed that they knowingly lied about the dangers of smoking (Bates & Rowell, 2019).

There is no established connection between fossil fuel greenhouse gas emissions and any climate change dangers. This is acknowledged in Seth Shulman's summary of the meeting, where he writes, "we currently lack a compelling public narrative about climate change" (Shulman, 2012, p. 4). Seth Shulman is a senior staff writer for the UCS. Shulman reports that Claudia Tebaldi, a climate scientist at Climate Central, told the group:

> "If you want to have statistically significant results about what has already happened [on the health impacts of climate change]," she said, "we are far from being able to say anything definitive because the signal is so often overwhelmed by noise." Claudia Tebaldi (Shulman, 2012, p. 15)

Thus, there is no way to compute any damages that are due to fossil fuel use. What Tebaldi says about health impacts, also applies to all other supposed negative impacts of climate change. We only have climate change projections from unvalidated climate models. The shaky output from these models is then fed into shaky economic models to determine the potential economic dangers. The potential economic dangers are twice removed from any direct evidence or data. The possible incremental future dangers of climate change, due to human activities, are close to pure speculation.

At the La Jolla conference, Matt Pawa and Sharon Eubanks presented plans to sue ExxonMobil and other "major carbon producers" to the attendees. Strategies to lobby potentially sympathetic attorneys general and members of Congress to help were also discussed (Walrath, 2019). Many of the attendees became central figures in the ExxonKnew campaign, like Matt Pawa, a lawyer who was the head of the Rockefeller-funded Global Warming Legal Action Project (Mundahl, 2018) and Naomi Oreskes. The Global Warming Legal Action Project was also funded by the Wallace Global Fund, the Tides Foundation, the Sustainable Markets Foundation and the Civil Society Institute.

Matthew Pawa is currently the head of the environmental section of a large class-action law firm named Hagens Berman Sabol Shapiro LLP. Pawa has a close relationship with all the state attorneys general who filed lawsuits against ExxonMobil. The idea of using the vague RICO (Racketeer Influenced and Corrupt Organizations Act) statutes in the lawsuit was probably his (Mundahl, 2018).

Sharon Eubanks led the RICO investigation of major tobacco companies by the U. S. Department of Justice from 2000 to 2005. In La Jolla, she spoke about how the tobacco legislation was pursued. Eubanks told the group that the key breakthrough in the public and legal case against the tobacco companies was when they uncovered documents showing the tobacco industry had knowingly misled the public. Eubanks and the others at the conference thought that similar documents might exist within the fossil fuel companies (Shulman, 2012). This led to the ExxonKnew plan to force ExxonMobil to release all their documents on climate change research.

Eubanks probably helped Pawa develop the legal strategy. She dismissed worries that using RICO in this way may lose in court and set precedents that would weaken the RICO laws. She responded, "If you have a statute, you should use it." (Shulman, 2012).

Rick Heede and Naomi Oreskes helped prepare for the lawsuits by writing academic papers that were critical of ExxonMobil and "big oil" in general. The goal of these papers was to point the blame for global warming at the producers of fossil fuels, not the consumers. The papers came out over the following few years.

Rick Heede started the "Carbon Majors" project and wrote several papers attempting to trace carbon dioxide emissions from major oil and gas companies back to 1810. The Climate Accountability Institute web site has links to his papers and articles (Climate Accountability Institute, 2019). In particular his *Climatic Change* paper, "Tracing anthropogenic carbon dioxide and methane emissions to fossil fuel and cement producers 1854-2010" was designed to help the lawsuits (Heede, 2014). His idea is that fossil fuel production companies are to blame for any damage that might occur in the future from man-made climate change should there be any.

In a similar vein, Naomi Oreskes who wrote *Merchants of Doubt*, in 2010 (Oreskes & Conway, 2010), went on to write papers accusing the major oil companies of concealing "dangerous" information on man-made climate change (Supran & Oreskes, 2017). She also published a paper claiming that recent climate projections were underestimating the dangerous impacts of climate change (Brysse, Oreskes, O'Reilly, & Oppenheimer, 2012). All of this was to lay an academic foundation for the lawsuits to come. Their plans to use peer-reviewed papers as fuel for planned future lawsuits shows how corrupt the academic peer-review process has become.

On January 8, 2016, another meeting was held at the Rockefeller Family Fund office in Upper Manhattan to discuss the path forward and the draft agenda contained the following goals:

- To establish in public's mind that Exxon is a corrupt institution that has pushed humanity (and all creation) toward climate chaos and grave harm.
- To delegitimize them as a political actor
- To force officials to disassociate themselves from Exxon, their money, and their historic opposition to climate progress, for example by refusing campaign donations, refusing to take meetings, calling for a price on carbon, etc.
- To call into question climate advantages of fracking, compared to coal.
- To drive divestment from Exxon.
- To drive Exxon & climate into center of 2016 election cycle. (Bruno, 2016)

They did not think ExxonMobil had committed a crime or done anything wrong, this was simply an attempt to destroy the company because they perceived that ExxonMobil disagreed with them on climate change. They could not even be sure ExxonMobil did disagree with them. ExxonMobil's public statements on climate change covered a broad spectrum of opinion as we will see in the next section.

The January 8 meeting included Matt Pawa, Lee Wasserman of the Rockefeller Family Fund, and Bill McKibben of 350.org. John Passacantando and Kert Davies, authors of ExxonSecrets.org and discussed in Chapter 2, were there. Finally, Naomi Ages of Greenpeace International and Sharon Eubanks, the tobacco lawyer, were in attendance. This was a strategy meeting to plan their attack against ExxonMobil and the fossil fuel industry in general.

No state attorneys general (AGs) were at this meeting. The final meeting agenda is available (Pawa, 2016).

The strategy and preparation were nearly complete by March 7, 2016 and formalized with a letter to numerous state attorneys general. It was announced to the press by New York AG Eric Schneiderman on March 29 (Schwartz, 2016). Six AGs joined Schneiderman in his lawsuits and nine other AGs were present to support the meeting, but not participating. The six participating AGs were from Vermont, Virginia, Massachusetts, Maryland, Connecticut, and the Virgin Islands. Prior to the meeting the AGs were briefed on the legal plan by Matt Pawa and Peter Frumhoff, the Director of Science and Policy and Chief Climate Scientist at the left-wing Union of Concerned Scientists (Frumhoff, 2016). The 16 state AGs named themselves "Attorneys General for Clean Power."

The state attorneys general went to extraordinary lengths to hide Pawa's involvement in the scheme because he was a famous, or perhaps infamous, class-action lawyer (ExxonMobil, 2018b). Several of them, including Vermont Deputy Attorney General Scot Kline and New York Assistant Attorney General Lemuel Srolovic, specifically coached Pawa not to discuss any of their plans with reporters. This was documented in an email from Lemuel Srolovic to Matt Pawa on March 30, 2016 (Srolovic, 2016). But it was to no avail, most of Pawa's PowerPoint slides, his emails and letters were obtained through discovery and FOIA requests and the full extent of the scheme was revealed to the public (Horner, 2018).

The AGs were concerned that by coordinating with one another they might be violating the law. The most obvious law they could be accused of violating is 18 U.S. Code § 241, which makes it illegal to conspire to deprive someone of their constitutional rights (Columbia Law School, 2020). There is also the so-called "color of law" concept that makes it illegal for anyone to use a government office or position to deprive someone of their constitutional rights. The fact they were going after ExxonMobil and not an individual makes no real difference. ExxonMobil and all corporations enjoy many of the same constitution rights that people do.

The most important rights that corporations have, according to the Supreme Court, stem from the Contracts Clause, Due Process clause, first, fourteenth, fourth, sixth, seventh and fifth amendments. The rights include free speech, freedom of the press, protection of their property and contracts from government seizure, and religious freedom. The fourteenth amendment protects people and corporations from discrimination, in other words the government is not allowed to single out a person or corporation for prosecution, they have to treat all corporations and people the same when enforcing the law. Corporations also have the right to petition the government, that is, lobby the government (Garret, 2014).

The AGs were concerned enough to draw up a "Common Interest Agreement" in April 2016. The agreement was to protect, as privileged, their discussions with one another. These agreements are common in legal proceedings, but they require that there be some sort of pending litigation. In the case of the AGs agreement, there was no expected legal proceeding in April 2016, and there still isn't. Their agreement required consultation between the AGs before responding to public records requests. They fought to enforce this agreement in court and used it to delay turning over FOIA requested data and documents, but in the end the court denied the validity of the agreement (Horner, 2018, p. 17).

One of the federal judges involved in the proceedings ask the AGs why they were fighting the release of documents. He commented that they should want to release all documents to show that these court actions were not political. He noted that Al Gore, Peter Frumhoff, and Matt Pawa; all political climate activists, were at the meetings where the "Exxon campaign" was discussed. This raised suspicions that the actions were political and had nothing to do with justice. So, the judge asks, why are the AGs not eager to release the documents to remove this suspicion? (Horner, 2018, p. 19).

The judge threw the agreement out and forced the AGs to release everything about their scheme. This resulted in the publication of the details of the AGs meetings and the plans to "get" ExxonMobil and the fossil fuel industry. The release blew up their plans and the "informal group" of class-action lawyers and attorneys general were publicly humiliated and had to disband.

The Vermont AG, Scot Kline, fought a CEI (Competitive Enterprise Institute) records request for so long, he made the judge (Judge R. H. Wallace, 96th Judicial Circuit, Tarrant County, Texas) in the case angry. He ordered Vermont to pay full legal fees and full hours to CEI, which amounted to $66,000. Kline's policy was to "always litigate those issues." Kline also admitted in court that he investigated the people who requested public documents and if they were affiliated with "coal or Exxon or whatever," they give it some thought before they shared the records (Horner, 2018, p. 22). Vermont fought every FOIA request and court request, but eventually ExxonMobil and the CEI were given access to almost everything. Pity the poor Vermont citizens that had to pay for this nonsense. One wonders who was prosecuting criminals in Vermont.

While the original scheme fell apart with the disclosures, Michael Bloomberg resurrected it in a very sneaky way. He hired a network of private lawyers, through NYU, and placed them in attorneys general offices. These lawyers were superficially "pro bono" lawyers working for free, but in reality, they were paid by Bloomberg and sworn to "advance progressive clean energy, [the] climate change [agenda], and environmental legal positions." These lawyers were also to send regular reports about their work to NYU (Horner, 2018, p. 29). Bloomberg launched this scheme at the New York University (NYU) Law School on August 15, 2017. He called it the "State Energy and Environmental Impact Center."

Private lawyers, placed in government attorneys general offices, promoting Bloomberg's political agenda, called "Special Assistant Attorneys General" and given some prosecutorial powers. It doesn't get more corrupt than that. However, in most states, it was technically legal and just on the edge of illegality. One exception was New York, where the "Special Assistant Attorneys General" probably were illegal.

New York's Schneiderman admitted that one reason he needed the free lawyers from Bloomberg was that "non-litigation advocacy," which he defined as leading the resistance to President Trump, was depleting his manpower (Horner, 2018). In other words, the New York AG was using taxpayer resources for political purposes (going after Trump) to such an extent that he did not have anyone to do *additional* political work, such as going after ExxonMobil for challenging the "consensus" on man-made climate change. Was there any work being done on New York crime?

Schneiderman also had one advantage the other states did not, he could use New York's Martin Act against ExxonMobil. The Martin Act gives the New York Attorney General broad powers to investigate securities fraud. In this case the fraud would be ExxonMobil withholding information about the dangers of climate change and the subsequent risk to investors.

It goes without saying that placing privately funded lawyers in law enforcement, with prosecutorial powers is dangerous. Most troubling about the plan was that the private lawyers were brought in to target specific people and companies. This was not prosecution; it was persecution of people for their jobs and beliefs. In the end, six jurisdictions brought in the Bloomberg-funded special prosecutors, they were Maryland, Massachusetts, New York, Oregon, Washington, and the District of Columbia.

Various foundations, including the numerous Rockefeller foundations, the Tides Foundation, Greenpeace and others were (and are) spending over one billion dollars per year promoting climate change alarmism. While the climate alarmists do not have the facts on their side, they do have a lot of money and resources. The one billion dollars per year figure is from an October 3, 2017 email from Dan Carol, who worked for Governors Jerry Brown and Gavin Newsom of California (Horner, 2018, p. 5).

A second meeting was held at Harvard Law School April 25, 2016. This meeting was hosted by Peter Frumhoff of the Union of Concerned Scientists. It was characterized as a "climate science and legal theory meeting" by Shaun Goho, a Harvard Law School instructor. Goho organized the meeting. The meeting agenda was entitled "Potential State Causes of Action against Major Carbon Producers" (Horner, 2018, p. 26). It was supposed to be a secret meeting and the Vermont AG, Scot Kline, fought releasing the meeting agenda for over a year, but eventually it was released. The Union of Concerned Scientists paid for the airfare and expenses for some of the AGs attending the meeting (Horner C. , 2019).

Presenters included Naomi Oreskes, Sharon Eubanks, Peter Frumhoff and Carrol Muffett. The participants learned by May 6, 2016 that FOIA requests were in the system that would reveal that the meeting had occurred and possibly reveal who was in attendance. Frumhoff recommended that they all act as if this was no big deal and that the meeting was perfectly normal. We know this from an email that Peter Frumhoff sent to the attendees (Frumhoff, 2016b). In the end their effort to "get Exxon" failed miserably.

> "A U.S. District Court dismissed a previous suit against ExxonMobil brought by Pawa on the grounds that regulating greenhouse gas emissions is 'a political rather than a legal issue that needs to be resolved by Congress and the executive branch rather than in the courts." (Horner, 2018, p. 39) and in (ExxonMobil, 2018b, p. 16)

The idea of placing privately funded special prosecutors in AG offices raises 14th Amendment due process issues. This amendment, passed in 1868, prohibits states from making a law that abridges the rights, liberty, or property of any person without the due process of law. It applies to corporations as well as people. Private prosecutors hired to go after one company or a group of companies that have not violated any laws would seem to violate that concept. Particularly when the proposed action is a civil lawsuit.

Supplying free prosecutors provides an incentive to AGs to pursue the cases that can utilize the prosecutors. This unduly changes the AG priorities. The New York AG's application for a second Bloomberg lawyer specifically mentioned additional environmental litigation it could pursue, if they could get a second lawyer.

In 2018, U.S. District Judge William Alsup (San Francisco), received a five-hour briefing on climate change from both the oil companies being sued (Shell, BP, ConocoPhillips, Chevron, and ExxonMobil) and the New York and California cities suing them over global warming. Judge Alsup was appointed by President Clinton, and after hearing both sides, dismissed the idea that the oil companies were involved in a conspiracy to suppress climate science from the public. He said the cities had shown "nothing of the sort," when he dismissed the lawsuit.

Naomi Oreskes, a Harvard professor and one of the organizers of the La Jolla and Harvard Law School conferences, as mentioned above, published a "content analysis" with Geoffrey Supran in 2017 (Supran & Oreskes, 2017) that she claimed proved ExxonMobil knowingly misled the public about climate change. Supran and Oreskes is often abbreviated S&O. The authors claim that there was, "a discrepancy between what ExxonMobil's scientists and executives discussed about climate change privately and in academic circles and what it presented to the general public."

In a March 1, 2018 ExxonMobil filing in a Texas court, content analysis expert Kimberly Neuendorf picked apart S&O until there was nothing left (ExxonMobil, 2018a). Neuendorf's conclusions were:

> "I [Neuendorf] have concluded that S&O's content analysis does not support the study's conclusions because of a variety of fundamental errors in their analysis. S&O's content analysis lacks reliability, validity, objectivity, generalizability, and replicability. These basic standards of scientific inquiry are vital for a proper content analysis, but they are not satisfied by the S&O study." (ExxonMobil, 2018a, Attachment A)

Most of the errors identified by Neuendorf spring from poor sampling of ExxonMobil content. S&O improperly grouped together communications that vary across time and by author and audience. They also group statements by Exxon and Mobil, before they merged, as if they were one entity. Further, S&O coded the communications themselves rather than using objective and uninvolved coders, this renders their work non-replicable and unscientific.

S&O claim that they used a technique they label "consensus measurement." Naomi Oreskes is no stranger to the idea of using a political "consensus" to decide scientific issues. In a 2004 paper (Oreskes, 2004) she claims to have examined 928 papers on climate change and could not find any that did not agree with the consensus position that most of the observed warming over the last 50 years is due to human greenhouse emissions.

Her sample was cherry-picked. She missed hundreds of papers written by famous climate scientists like Professor Richard Lindzen, Professor Patrick Michaels, and Dr. John Christy. She also missed important papers by astrophysicists Dr. Willie Soon and Dr. Sallie Baliunas. A later study by Klaus-Martin Schulte used the same database search Oreskes used and found that only seven percent of the papers explicitly endorsed the "consensus view" (Schulte, 2008).

Naomi Oreskes is not a scientist; she is a historian of science. She clearly does not understand how science works, although in her position she should. Further, as we have seen in this chapter, Oreskes is not driven to find the truth, she is only driven by her radical left-wing agenda.

Oreskes seems to believe that we should vote for or against making a scientific hypothesis like man-made climate change a theory. Voting is not a valid scientific procedure. Anyone can challenge a scientific hypothesis.

The disgraceful legal attack on ExxonMobil by the Union of Concerned Scientists, Harvard Law School, the Climate Accountability Institute, and the various Rockefeller Foundations went down in flames. The New York Supreme Court dismissed the case "with prejudice" on December 10th, 2019 (Stevens, 2019). The Supreme Court ruled that the New York "Attorney General [Schneiderman] produced no testimony from any investor who claimed to have been misled by [an ExxonMobil] disclosure." By dismissing the case "with prejudice" the court essentially precluded trying the case again in New York. The loss was so devastating, it is unlikely a suit like ExxonKnew will ever be brought again anywhere in the U.S.

But what about the various peer-reviewed and internal documents that they based their legal attack on? We go over these in the next section. One does not need to be a lawyer to see the flaws in Matthew Pawa's case.

The ExxonMobil Climate Papers

As for the idea that ExxonMobil was hiding evidence that man-made climate change was leading to a global catastrophe, a review of the documents shows that they published all their findings on climate change in public scientific journals.

As discussed above, New York Attorney General Eric T. Schneiderman, other state AGs, the Union of Concerned Scientists, and others accused ExxonMobil of lying to the public and their investors about the risks of climate change. The "Attorneys General for Clean Power" launched an investigation and issued subpoenas demanding extensive financial records, emails and other documents (Gillis & Krauss, 2015). They had no evidence a crime had been committed; it was purely a fishing expedition to find documents they could use to concoct a crime.

All the AGs, but one, were Democrats. The remaining attorney general was Claude Walker of the US Virgin Islands, a Green Party leaning Independent.

The author reviewed the 22 internal documents from 1977 to 1989 made available by ExxonMobil, the documents, and much more, can be downloaded from the author's website (May, 2020b). The 104 publications (most are peer-reviewed) with ExxonMobil personnel as authors or co-authors were also reviewed. To see an annotated bibliography of all the documents go to the author's website (May, 2016p). We will just summarize the results here.

The documents are interesting reading, they fill in the history of modern climate science very well. Much of the current debate on climate change was being debated in the same way, and often with the same uncertainties, in 1977.

Between 1977 and the fifth IPCC report (IPCC, 2013), ExxonMobil Corporate Research in New Jersey investigated the effect of increasing CO_2 on climate. If they withheld or suppressed climate research from the public or shareholders, it is not apparent in these documents. Further, if they found any definitive evidence of an impending man-made climate catastrophe, the author didn't see it. The climate researchers at ExxonMobil participated in the second, third, fourth and fifth IPCC assessment reports making major contributions in mapping the carbon cycle and in climate modeling. They calculated the potential impact of man-made CO_2 in several publications. They investigated methods of sequestering CO_2 and adapting to climate change. They also investigated several potential biofuels.

The internal documents are generally summaries of published work by outside researchers. Some of the documents are notes from climate conferences or meetings with the DOE (Department of Energy). For many of the internal documents one must read carefully to separate what is being said by the writer and what he is reporting from outside research. Exxon (and later ExxonMobil) did some original research, particularly measuring ocean and atmospheric CO_2 concentrations, from their tankers. But, most of what they produced was by funding research at Columbia University or the Lamont-Doherty Earth Observatory. All their internal research and the work at Columbia was published as far as I can tell, so it is difficult to accuse them of hiding anything from the public or shareholders.

At the heart of Schneiderman's accusation, according to the *New York Times*, is a list of statements made by ExxonMobil executives that he believes contradict internal company memos (May, 2016p) and (New York Times, 2015).

In fact, the internal memos and documents do not contradict the ExxonMobil executives in any way. The internal documents and publications all clearly describe the considerable uncertainties in climate science and align with the executives' statements. Two of the most notable are quoted below:

Ken Cohen, ExxonMobil Vice President for Public and Government Affairs, 2015 (Blog Post):

"What we have understood from the outset – and something which over-the-top activists fail to acknowledge — is that climate change is an enormously complicated subject.

The climate and mankind's connection to it are among the most complex topics scientists have ever studied, with a seemingly endless number of variables to consider over an incredibly long timespan."

Duane Levine, Exxon's manager of Science and Strategy Development, 1989 (Internal Document #21)

"In spite of the rush by some participants in the greenhouse debate to declare that the science has demonstrated the existence of [man-made global warming] today, I do not believe such is the case. Enhanced greenhouse is still deeply imbedded in scientific uncertainty, and we will require substantial additional investigation to determine the degree to which its effects might be experienced in the future." (New York Times, 2015)

We like Mr. Cohen's phrase "over-the-top activists." This is an apt description of Naomi Oreskes and many others in the climate alarmist community. They all fail to appreciate the considerable uncertainty in the estimates of human influence on the climate. They accuse anyone who does appreciate it of "spreading doubt about man-made climate change" as if that were a crime.

Notice Duane Levine's use of the phrase "enhanced greenhouse." The greenhouse effect existed before humans evolved, the debate is over the incremental or "enhanced" greenhouse effect that is due to human greenhouse gas emissions. We notice Levine's opinion is the same as Roger Revelle's, as described in Chapter 1.

Even if there were a contradiction between the executives and the ExxonMobil climate researchers, who is to say which of them is wrong? Free speech is a fundamental first amendment individual right in the U.S. and executives can disagree with their employees. Oreskes may consider ExxonMobil to be monolithic, but it isn't. As University of Tennessee Law Professor Glenn Harlan Reynolds has written in USA Today:

> "Federal law makes it a felony 'for two or more persons to agree together to injure, threaten, or intimidate a person in any state, territory or district in the free exercise or enjoyment of any right or privilege secured to him/her by the Constitution or the laws of the United States, (or because of his/her having exercised the same).'
>
> I wonder if U.S. Virgin Islands Attorney General Claude Walker, or California Attorney General Kamala Harris, or New York Attorney General Eric Schneiderman have read this federal statute. Because what they are doing looks like a concerted scheme to restrict the First Amendment free speech rights of people they don't agree with. They should look up 18 U.S.C. § 241." (Reynolds, 2016)

ExxonMobil filed court papers in Texas, in April of 2016, to block a March 22nd subpoena issued by the attorney general of the U.S. Virgin Islands Claude Walker. They argued that the subpoena was an unwarranted fishing expedition into ExxonMobil's internal records. Later in the year Walker withdrew his subpoena.

As discussed in the last section, environmentalist groups, like the Rockefeller Family Fund and 350.org organized a legal attack against ExxonMobil based on the tobacco company lawsuits. They feel like their presumed imminent man-made climate disaster is being ignored and they want to make ExxonMobil a scapegoat. As Lee Wasserman (Rockefeller Family Fund) said "It's not really about Exxon" (Harder, Barrett, & Olson, 2016).

Mr. Scheiderman may have made the error of assuming facts that are not in evidence. He and the other parties in the lawsuit, assume that man-made greenhouse gases are a significant factor in climate change and that the resulting enhanced climate change is dangerous. There is no direct evidence of either assertion. He also assumes that Exxon's early research proved these assertions to be true, with little or no doubt. Therefore, Mr. Scheiderman believes the Exxon executives are lying.

One document, by Exxon scientist, Brian Flannery and colleagues (Flannery, Callegari, Hoffert, Hseih, & Wainger, 1985), suggests that the effect of CO_2 variations on climate, based on geological data from the Cretaceous Period, is 50% or less. Other documents express concern that there is a "potential problem amid all the scientific uncertainties."

Along this line of thought, the ExxonMobil court filing against Mr. Walker and the US Virgin Islands says in part:

> "… [ExxonMobil] has "widely and publicly confirmed" that it recognizes "that the risk of climate change and its potential impacts on society and ecosystems may prove to be significant." (Schwartz, 2016b)

Brian Flannery states in 2001:

> "Although we know the human emissions fairly well, we don't know the natural emissions well at all. Added to this uncertainty is the fact that natural emissions can change as a result of long-term climate changes." (Flannery, 2001)

The key problem is that ExxonMobil management and most, if not all, their researchers do not think there is any evidence that man-made climate change is dangerous. Further, Dr. M. B. Glaser agrees with Roger Revelle, when he writes:

> "we have time to evaluate the uncertainties even in a worse-case scenario." (1982 report by M. B. Glaser)

This was true in 1982 and in 1991, when Roger Revelle said the same thing. It is still true, even today.

In the same 1982 report by M. B. Glaser, he discusses the potential effect of doubling CO_2 in the atmosphere and the discussion is instructive. The CO_2 level prior to the industrial revolution (roughly 1840-1850) is unknown. They give two possibilities (260-270 ppm or 290-300 ppm). The temperature increase from 1880 to 2012, according to the 5th IPCC Assessment (IPCC, 2013) is 0.85°C from the HADCRUT 4 global temperature dataset (Met Office Hadley Centre, 2017). The Exxon researchers did not think a clear anthropogenic signal was detectable in 1979, because at that time the total temperature increase from 1850 had not exceeded 0.5°C (0.9°F), their assumed value for natural variability. They thought man-made warming might be clearly detected by the year 2000.

We are now well past the year 2000 and according to the data shown in Table 6 of Internal Document #3 (May, 2020b), we are on track with their most benign scenario of a temperature increase of 1.3° (2.3°F) to 1.7°C (3.0°F) per doubling of CO_2 (ECS). This assumes an initial concentration of CO_2 of 265 to 295 ppm and a natural variability of ±0.5°C. The initial CO_2 concentration assumption is reasonable, the assumption of 0.5°C for natural variability may be too low. However, if the assumptions are true, they probably eliminate the possibility of higher climate sensitivity to CO_2 (ECS>2°C). This is also supported by recent empirical estimates of ECS by Judith Curry and Nic Lewis (Lewis & Curry, 2018). There are considerable uncertainties in this approach. We don't know the CO_2 level when we started emitting a lot of fossil fuel CO_2, we don't know the net effect on our climate, and can't be certain we have seen any impact of man-made CO_2 on our climate to date.

Even Brian Flannery, one of the Exxon researchers who has been deeply involved in the IPCC process stated in internal document 22 (ExxonMobil, 2016): "While uncertainty exists, science supports the basic idea that man's actions pose a serious potential threat to climate." This is the most alarmist statement I could find anywhere, but it still says "potential" and notes that uncertainty exists. Dr. Haroon Kheshgi and Dr. Benjamin White state in 2001:

> "Many previous claims that anthropogenically caused climate change has been detected have utilized models in which uncertainties in the values of some parameters have been neglected (Santer, Wigley, Barnett, & Anyamba, 1996b). In section 5 we have incorporated known parameter uncertainties [in a model and] ... inclusion of uncertainty in aerosols forcing would likely lead to rejection of the hypothesis of anthropogenically caused climate change ..." (Kheshgi & White, 2001)

They are concerned here and in other papers, that the GCMs (global circulation climate models) have used fixed parameters for their calculations for variables that have a great deal of uncertainty. By fixing these variables across many models, the modelers produce a narrower range of outcomes. This gives a misleading appearance of consistency and accuracy that does not exist.

As Professor Judith Curry has often said there is an uncertainty monster at the science-policy interface. The ExxonMobil scientists are good, they write well and their superiors in ExxonMobil understand what they are saying. Man-made climate change is a potential problem, but it is shrouded in uncertainty. The internal and published documents show that Exxon has worked hard to define the uncertainty and they have even succeeded in reducing the uncertainty in some areas, especially in the carbon cycle. But still, the remaining uncertainty is large, and it covers the range from zero anthropogenic effect to perhaps 4° or 5°C to this day. The same as in 1977 when they got started.

The following quote from internal document #11 (ExxonMobil, 2016), the 1982 Exxon Consensus statement. I think it speaks well for ExxonMobil and puts Schneiderman (and many in the media) to shame:

"As we discussed in the August 24 meeting, there is the potential for our research to attract the attention of the popular news media because of the connection between Exxon's major business and the role of fossil fuel combustion in contributing to the increase of atmospheric CO_2. Despite the fact that our results are in accord with most major researchers in the field and are subject to the same uncertainties, it was recognized that it is possible for these results to be distorted or blown out of proportion.

Nevertheless, the consensus position was that Exxon should continue to conduct scientific research in this area because of its potential importance in affecting future energy scenarios and to provide Exxon with the credentials required to speak with authority in this area. Furthermore, our ethical responsibility is to permit the publication of our research in the scientific literature; indeed to do otherwise would be a breach of Exxon's public position and ethical credo on honesty and integrity." (ExxonMobil, 2016)

This is the only thing I found in the internal memos that was not published. In 1982 they thought the media might distort their research results or blow them out of proportion. Well, that certainly happened. For science to work properly, research outcomes cannot be dictated. All interested parties must be allowed to investigate the problem and publish their results. They must have access to data, computer programs and models that are publicly funded. But, above all, they should not be punished, jailed, intimidated, or sued because they are skeptical of a popular scientific thesis. They should be judged only on the quality of their scientific work and not who they work for or who funds them.

Chapter 4: Bureaucrats and Climate Change

> "environmental policy has been hijacked by radicals intent on imposing their ideology by government fiat on the rest of us whether we like it or not. …
>
> contrary views are not tolerated by the Federal Government and those who hold them are not welcome to be employed by the Government." 38-year senior EPA employee Alan Carlin, now retired (Carlin, 2015).

Trofim Lysenko

Lysenko was a Russian bureaucrat who effectively destroyed the science of biology in Russia. His story does not involve climate change but is included here to illustrate the most extreme effects of bureaucratic and political interference in science. Dr. William Happer describes "Lysenko's Destruction of Biology in the Soviet Union" in Chapter 1 of *Politicizing Science, The Alchemy of Policymaking*, edited by Michael Gough (Gough, 2003). The following story is condensed from Happer's narrative.

Agriculture was collectivized in the Soviet Union in 1928 by force. All land, livestock and farm machinery were seized by the state. After the harvest, all grain was taken, even the seed grain needed for the next year. There were massive famines in 1929 and for several years afterward. Millions died in the Ukraine and the army had to collect the harvest because entire villages had starved to death.

Of course, to the Communist Party, the cause of the famine could not be seizing the farms and communist mismanagement. It had to be the grain, so they ordered the rapid development of a better variety of wheat. The agricultural research institutions in the Soviet Union were ordered to improve crop yields, disease and pest resistance, ease of harvest and food value within one year.

Russian wheat was the best in the world at the time and the Russian scientists were world class. Some varieties of Russian wheat were introduced to the United States as early as the 1850s by German immigrants and were successful. The introduction of Turkey Red wheat, from the Ukraine, in the 1870s is when wheat really took off in Kansas and other central states, supplanting other crops. It was so popular that it dominated the middle part of the country by the turn of the century. Turkey Red was a heritage wheat, which meant it was not hybridized. It is very nutritious, grows in poor soils, does not need fertilizer and is naturally pest resistant. In the 1940s it was replaced by hybrids that produced higher yields per acre but required fertilizer and pesticides.

Russia was well ahead of the rest of the world in the quality of her grain, but one year isn't nearly long enough to develop a new variety. The Russian scientists told the party leaders this and were labeled "enemies of the Soviet People." Along came Trofim Lysenko who claimed that Mendel's peas and Thomas Hunt Morgan's fruit flies were lies and a capitalist plot. Lysenko claimed that environment determined the performance of plants and that acquired characteristics could be inherited. He thought he could instantly improve agricultural production.

Lysenko told all the farmers to soak their seeds in the fall, bury it in sacks in the snow and then plant it in the spring. It was nonsense, but Stalin liked Lysenko, so this new process, called "vernalization," was implemented. Lysenko had no education and when educated biologists tried to tell him he was wrong, they were imprisoned or shot.

After the war, Stalin gave Lysenko his full support and in 1948 he announced at a conference of the All-Union Academy of Agricultural Sciences that there was only one approved biology in the Soviet Union, the biology of Lysenko, and that discussions of genes and chromosomes was tantamount to treason. The science was settled.

EPA

Alan Carlin, a former employee of the EPA or the Environmental Protection Agency, wrote a book called *Environmentalism Gone Mad*. Much of this section is based on that book. Carlin joined the EPA in 1971 and worked there for 38 years. He has an unrivaled perspective on the agency, its successes, and its failures.

Carlin believes that most decisions should be made in the marketplace and government regulations should only be imposed when necessary and when fully justified. Problems arise when the government tries to dictate what people buy, such as Obama's 2011 decree that cars and trucks average 54.5 miles per gallon by 2025 (White House Press Secretary, 2011). This Lysenko-like order was made without thinking it through, if it were followed, more people would die when they crashed in much lighter and less crash-worthy vehicles. There are trade-offs in manufacturing, and it is best to leave such decisions to the marketplace, whenever possible, rather than dictating them from the top. As Lysenko proved, and Obama confirmed, technology cannot be dictated.

Obama's rules on appliance energy efficiency are another example. The Department of Energy (DOE) acknowledged that Obama's new air conditioner standards cost so much, both in purchase price and in additional repair costs, that consumers will never recover enough in energy savings to recoup their investment (Lieberman, 2019). The new Obama energy efficient dishwashers are widely criticized because they don't clean dishes well and take far too long, according to Ben Lieberman (Lieberman, 2020). After the CEI (Competitive Enterprise Institute) filed a petition about the new dishwashers, the DOE complied and changed the regulations to allow dishwashers to be made that can finish a load in an hour or less.

Federal regulations eliminated convenient and inexpensive top loading washing machines (Kazman, 2011). Front loading machines use less water and energy, but they were unpopular with customers and take longer to clean a load. Plus, you can't open the lid and add a wayward sock like you can with a top loader. Further, front loaders cost several hundred dollars more than top loaders, but the government won and top loaders disappeared (Lieberman, 2000).

President Richard Nixon formed the EPA (Environmental Protection Agency) in December 1970. Alan Carlin was approached by a former co-worker at the RAND corporation, where he was working, and asked to take the job of director of their new Implementation Research Division. This group was later to become "ORD" or the Office of Research and Development.

This was a new position and meant to deal with pollution issues that crossed old organizational boundaries, such as from ocean pollution to land pollution. It was also supposed to deal with economic issues related to pollution and pollution controls. Carlin was particularly interested in economic analysis that would show both the positive and negative benefits of regulations, and the costs related to each. Cost-benefit analysis was not part of the original EPA mandate, but Carlin thought it was important.

True cost-benefit analysis became required in 1981 under President Ronald Reagan. This was what Carlin had been pushing for and he was pleased to implement the new rule. But other management at ORD did not cooperate, so Carlin managed to move his group into the EPA's Policy Office. Once in his new location, he continued his economic research.

During President Reagan's time in office, the Policy Office had considerable influence. They often shot down regulations requested by outside organizations, like Greenpeace and the Sierra Club, usually for good reasons. This created a lot of animosity and when Clinton took office, these organizations insisted that one of their own be made Assistant Administrator of the Policy Office. The new administrator was hired from the Sierra Club and began to methodically remove the office's power over regulations. These powers were not returned when George W. Bush became President, and all new hires were much more liberal and anti-business than those retiring and leaving.

Carlin also managed a large contract with the National Academy of Sciences (NAS) that prepared background reports for the EPA. The background information was used to determine whether regulatory action should be considered. At this time, the NAS documents were not used to create regulations, that work was done internally by the EPA.

In the Obama administration, outside work by NAS, the IPCC and other organizations began to be used directly to create regulations, without reproducing the work inside the EPA (Carlin, 2015). It was this sort of uncritical use of outside work that led to the notorious 2009 CO_2 "endangerment finding" (Sobczyk & Koss, 2018) and the 2015 rewrite of the Waters of the U.S. rule (WOTUS) (Sonderegger & Owens, 2019). Both rules have been significantly modified by the Trump administration to place fewer onerous restrictions on power plants, farms, agricultural businesses, and consumers. The overwhelming costs that these rules placed on the economy, businesses, and consumers were not properly considered by the Obama administration.

The Obama administration created new classes of costs that allowed them to implement these rules. They added "social" costs of carbon dioxide and other creative costs so that the expensive rules could be implemented and still shown to "save money."

On October 22, 2019, the EPA and the Department of the Army repealed the 2015 Clean Water Rule definition of the Waters of the United States. It restored the definition of the WOTUS that had been used prior to 2015. Part of the reasoning was that the Obama rule encroached unlawfully onto private and state property. The Trump administration did not believe that the Obama rule properly observed the legal limits set by the Congress and the Supreme Court. The new Trump EPA rule went into effect on December 23, 2019 (EPA, 2020b) and (U.S. Federal Register, 2019).

CO$_2$ endangerment finding

In April 2007 the Supreme Court made a monumental 5-4 decision to rule that the EPA, on its own, could use the 1970 Clean Air Act (EPA, 2020) to regulate greenhouse gas emissions, if it determined that they caused or contributed to air pollution which may reasonably be anticipated to endanger the public health or welfare. The EPA were not required to do this but could do so.

The 2007 Supreme Court ruling was *Massachusetts v. EPA*. It made the EPA's so-called 2009 "CO$_2$ endangerment finding" possible (Kovacs, 2020). Once the EPA ruled CO$_2$ a dangerous pollutant in 2009, Obama applied nationwide rules to limit CO$_2$ emissions. The rules essentially killed the use of coal to produce electricity in the U.S. Trump replaced these rules with ACE (the Affordable Clean Energy rule) August 27, 2018. It requests that the states manage their own CO$_2$ emissions. No minimum CO$_2$ reduction targets were set by Trump's EPA (EPA, 2020c).

Prior to the Supreme Court ruling, the EPA did not believe it had the authority to declare CO$_2$ a pollutant. In many ways, this ruling is a key example of the Supreme Court creating law and circumventing Congress. EPA Administrator Lisa Jackson called the ruling "the most important decision ever handed down in the annals of environmental law." Rupert Darwall, in his book, *The Age of Global Warming: A History*, called it the "most stupid" (Darwall, 2013, Kindle 8633). We agree with Rupert, who was well trained in history and economics at Cambridge University.

Once the EPA could legally declare CO$_2$ a pollutant, they used public reports and peer-reviewed academic papers from the IPCC, NOAA and other organizations to provide the scientific basis. Obviously, they were careful to choose reports and papers that said CO$_2$ was dangerous and they ignored the large number of papers that said the opposite. They did not conduct their own investigation or replicate any of the outside work. CO$_2$, or carbon dioxide, is clearly not a pollutant, life on Earth requires it to survive. Plants use it as a major part of their food supply and plants are the primary source of food for all animals, including humans.

The Clean Air Act (CAA) was not written with the idea of regulating climate and the "endangerment finding," which claims that CO$_2$ controls climate, supplies no proof that is the case. But, the Supreme Court gave them the power to issue the regulation anyway, which was clearly a mistake (Carlin, 2015, Kindle 2994). Since no further action by Congress is required, this was a ruling that all but forced the EPA to manufacture laws.

Alan Carlin offered one of the few EPA critical comments on the draft endangerment finding in 2007 when it was circulated to management. The EPA senior staff and managers were only given one week to comment. This strongly suggested the decision to move ahead was already made and the request for comments was a mere formality. Carlin summarizes his comments as follows:

> "[The] CAGW [Catastrophic Anthropogenic Global Warming] hypothesis is invalid from a scientific viewpoint because it fails a number of critical comparisons with available observable data, ... the TSD [Technical Support Document] draft was seriously dated and the updates made to the 2007 version of the draft were inadequate[. Carlin felt] that EPA should conduct an independent analysis of the science of global warming rather than adopting the conclusions of the IPCC and outside U.S. Government reports." (Carlin, 2015, Kindle 1967)

In other words, the EPA accepted the word of the United Nations IPCC agency and other U.S. government agencies that CO_2 was a dangerous pollutant. This was because it supposedly causes dangerous atmospheric warming. The EPA did not check any of the scientific evidence behind these presumptions themselves. They did this even though the IPCC and U.S. government agencies had failed to predict global temperatures accurately. This is as anti-science as it gets. One of the oldest scientific bodies in the world is the Royal Society in the U.K., founded in 1660 (Royal Society, 2020). Their motto is *nullius in verba*, translated from the Latin, this loosely means take no one's word for it. The EPA is guilty of appealing to authority and accepting an assumption without checking it.

The logic of Carlin's arguments did not prevail. The fix was in. Even the EPA IG objected to the rapid pace of the endangerment finding approval process and the lack of adequate peer-review. Not long after Carlin's critical comments were suppressed, he was ordered not to spend any more time on climate change, the decision was made and the science was settled (Carlin, 2015, Kindle 2027).

EPA Transparency

When President Obama took office, he sent a memo to the heads of the executive departments and agencies that transparency and public participation were priorities in his administration. His appointee to the head of the EPA, Lisa Jackson, agreed and emphasized that following the science and being transparent were her priorities as well.

It was all talk, both Obama and Jackson fought all requests for documents tooth and nail. Even when they released documents, they were so heavily redacted as to be useless. Yet, on March 9, 2009, President Obama sent a memo that states:

> "The public must be able to trust the science and scientific process informing public policy decisions. Political officials should not suppress or alter scientific or technological findings and conclusions. If scientific and technological information is developed and used by the Federal Government, it should ordinarily be made available to the public. To the extent permitted by law, there should be transparency in the preparation, identification, and use of scientific and technological information in policymaking." (Carlin, 2015, Loc. 1829)

Yet, even after this memo and repeated declarations by the EPA administrator and inspector general, the stonewalling continued, even became more intense. It was at this time the EPA, at the direction of the White House, made the creation of the CO_2 endangerment finding a crash priority.

In the next section, we see that when Scott Pruitt and Andrew Wheeler said the same thing, the permanent EPA bureaucracy howled. The EPA is a very secretive organization.

In response to the President's memo, the EPA was supposed to create a Scientific Integrity Committee. The committee was to implement and update a policy of scientific integrity. Yet, in August of 2013, one and a half years after it was created, the Scientific Integrity Committee had yet to create a policy or form an integrity training program. They had also not created the required annual reports on the status of scientific integrity within the EPA.

Scott Pruitt

The EPA secretary, Scott Pruitt, testified before the House of Representatives Energy and Commerce Committee on Thursday April 26, 2018. He was charged with spending too much money on travel, security, and a secure phone booth for his office. Certainly, these are reasons to reprimand him, but a full day of Congressional hearings for charges like these seems a bit over the top. Besides Scott Pruitt had spent far less on travel than either of his immediate predecessors at the EPA and the security issues were not his decisions. Scott Pruitt said the following at the hearing:

> "I promise you that I more than anyone want to establish the hard facts and provide answers to questions surrounding these reports. Let me be very clear, I have nothing to hide as it relates to how I have run the agency for the past 16 months. I'm not afraid to admit that there has been a learning process. When Congress or independent bodies find fault in our decision-making, I want to correct that and ensure that it does not happen again. Ultimately, as administrator of the EPA, the responsibility of identifying and making necessary changes rests with me and no one else.
>
> With that being said, facts are facts and fiction is fiction. And a lie doesn't become truth just because it appears on the front page of a newspaper. Much of what has been targeted toward me and my team has been half-truths or stories that have been so twisted they do not represent reality." (Daly M. , 2018) about 15:36 minutes in.

The hearings were more likely due to Pruitt's efforts to rein in the EPA's new limits on private property rights for the "greater good." When a government official begins talking about the "greater good" grab your wallet and hide your children because they are about to steal something or do something worse. Representative David B. McKinley, Republican of West Virginia, told Mr. Pruitt during the hearing that the attacks on him "have an echo of McCarthyism." He meant using trivial infractions as a club to extort a change in his policies. Rules, regulations, and laws can be used for nefarious ends.

We see in the March 16, 2018 *Scientific American* that Scott "Pruitt Expected to Limit Science Used to Make EPA Pollution Rules" (Waldman & Bravender, 2018). The article is by Scott Waldman and Robin Bravender. It originally appeared in E&E News at eenews.net.

We will spend a lot of space picking this article in *Scientific American* apart, because we see a strong anti-science bias in it. As we will show, more serious scientific journals, like *Nature* and *Science*, believe that transparency and reproducibility are essential elements of a scientific study. This means the underlying raw data used in the study and the computer code to process it must be made available to the public. Otherwise how is the study reproduced? That a magazine with "Scientific" in its title would recommend otherwise is very odd. The article states:

> "[Pruitt's] initiative is expected to require EPA—when issuing rules—to rely only on scientific studies where the underlying data are made public. It's an idea that House Science, Space and Technology Chairman Lamar Smith (R-Texas) has been championing for years. He and others argue that EPA has been crafting regulations based on "secret science" to advance its regulatory agenda." (Waldman & Bravender, 2018)

Pruitt's plan was modeled on Lamar Smith's HONEST act, bill H.R. 1430. It requires that Environmental Protection Agency (EPA) regulations be based upon science that is:

> "publicly available online in a manner that is sufficient for independent analysis and substantial reproduction of research results, except that any personally identifiable information, trade secrets, or commercial or financial information obtained from a person and privileged or confidential, shall be redacted prior to public availability." (Smith, 2017)

Yogin Kothari, of the Union of Concerned Scientists, is quoted in the *Scientific American* article as claiming that the act is a bad thing because some data cannot be released for reasons like patient privacy concerns or industry confidentiality (Waldman & Bravender, 2018). It would help if he read the bill before commenting. Smith's HONEST act specifically excludes the data he is concerned about.

In other words, Pruitt and Smith want EPA science that is true science. A scientific publication, whether internal to the EPA or in a scientific journal, should always stand alone, with results that can be replicated using the paper itself and the supporting data. The EPA can do their work in secret, or they can do it scientifically, they cannot do both.

One expects that scientific research for the military or the intelligence agencies will be done in secret. We also expect that medical patient privacy is guaranteed. But the EPA has the power to render private property worthless or even take private property through environmental regulations. A secret study should not be used for these purposes, it must be out in the open.

The acronym HONEST stands for "Honest and Open New EPA Science Treatment." The act passed the House, but not the Senate, so it died at the end of the 115th Congress. Hopefully, it will be passed again in the next Republican Congress. In court when someone is accused of a crime, they can examine all evidence against them. The rules for the EPA should be the same. Lamar Smith and Scott Pruitt are not "limiting the science used," they are just insisting on transparency and reproducibility.

In the *Scientific American* article, Waldman and Bravender say:

> "Pruitt is expected to roll out plans soon to restrict the agency's use of science in rulemakings, pitting him against critics who say it would threaten public health and environmental protections." (Waldman & Bravender, 2018)

How is transparency "restricting science?" It is an essential element of good science. These rules have been fought furiously by Democrats, who seem to have become the party of Lysenko, they want to dictate scientific outcomes and outlaw opposing views. Transparency improves science, but it limits the power of EPA bureaucrats to dictate rules and cherry-pick scientific studies, which is their real concern. They want to allow the EPA to use studies from outside organizations, without reproducing them in-house. Are we really to turn regulatory decisions over to Greenpeace and the Sierra Club?

Betsy Southerland, a former EPA official quoted in the *Scientific American* article by Waldman and Bravender, claims that "publishing raw data" opens scientists (presumably EPA scientists) "up to attack from industry, which can twist and distort data to shape a deregulatory agenda" (Waldman & Bravender, 2018). Well, how do we know the EPA did not twist and distort data? In science you examine the data, the analysis and the conclusions and attempt to reproduce them. If you are to regulate an industry or farmer and cost them money and property, shouldn't they be allowed to analyze the data and contest the EPA analysis and conclusions? Both sides should be heard, no one elected EPA scientists to be judge and jury, science is a debate, not a diktat.

Southerland goes on to say,

> "This is just done to paralyze rulemaking. It's another obstacle that would make it so hard and difficult to go forward with rulemaking that in the end, the only thing that would happen – in the best case you would greatly delay rulemaking; in the worst case you would just prevent it. It would be such an obstacle you couldn't overcome it." (Waldman & Bravender, 2018)

All government rules add costs to individuals, businesses, and farms, they should be extremely difficult to create. A rule should be overwhelmingly needed before it is implemented. According to Rasmussen, in 2017, 50% of the country thinks there are too many government regulations on business (Rasmussen, 2017). This number decreased after President Trump started removing regulations according to Gallup (Swift, 2017).

The *Scientific American* article goes on to say that requiring data transparency would cost hundreds of millions of dollars because it would require EPA staff to track down data from study authors and create an online management system to store and present the data. Are they seriously saying that they are not doing this now? If a published study is used to create a burdensome rule that costs U.S. businesses millions of dollars to comply with, one would certainly hope the data are downloaded and the results replicated using the author's data. That is basic due diligence. If the EPA is not doing that, transparency is even more important. This reveals an inexcusable sloppiness in their work, somebody needs to be checking it.

These EPA employees seem to be saying their time is more important than the time and money required by the businesses and farms they regulate. The annual regulatory cost of one employee in the United States in 2012 was about $10,000 on average (Crain & Crain, 2014). It was worse for manufacturing companies, $19,564 per employee. The National Association of Manufacturers estimates that complying with U.S. federal government regulations cost over two trillion dollars (12% of GDP) in 2012 (Crain & Crain, 2014, p. 1). The GAO estimated that the cost was $607 billion in 1993, but now seems to believe they cannot estimate a cost (GAO, 1996). To have the EPA worried about slowing down new regulations and adding a few hundred million dollars to their budget to be transparent seems a bit ridiculous.

The U.S. Constitution contains many protections for private property. Article I, section 8 secures intellectual property. Sections 9 and 10 prohibit states and the federal government from passing ex post facto laws that change existing contracts. The fifth amendment prohibits the taking of property by the government without just compensation. The second amendment prohibits confiscation of arms, the third prohibits forced quartering of troops in private homes, and the fourth and fourteenth forbid unreasonable searches and seizures of private property. These protections of private property rights were all in response to common actions by the British prior to U.S. independence.

The EPA has skirted the edge of these constitutional prohibitions many times. Have they gone over the edge? The EPA writes regulations on its own, under the President's authority and without effective public or Congressional oversight (Yeatman, 2016). The Supreme Court, in 2007, granted them the power to write a law calling an essential gas, CO_2, a pollutant, without an act of Congress.

Their regulations normally must be rooted in a Congressional statute, but the statutes are only interpreted by the EPA. This and the Supreme Court have allowed regulatory excesses like the CO_2 endangerment finding (EPA, 2009). This gives the agency great power. There are many modern ways to restrict private property rights. These include building codes, rent controls, zoning, usury laws, price controls, blue laws, gun control, etc. Environmental regulations can be the most egregious. The restrictions and regulations can be so burdensome that the land is rendered useless and effectively taken away. This was at the root of complaints against the Waters of the U.S. rule ("WOTUS") and other environmental and land-use regulations. As mentioned above the original 2015 WOTUS rule has now been repealed by the EPA under Andrew Wheeler (EPA, 2019).

Scott Pruitt intended to fix this, and President Trump charged him with the task. But the EPA bureaucracy succeeded in removing Pruitt. Will the agency bureaucrats prevail over an elected President and his chosen managers? Only time will tell. It took a while, but currently Andrew Wheeler is the permanent Administrator of the EPA, he was approved by the Senate on February 28, 2019. Wheeler strongly supports Pruitt's proposed rule to ban the EPA from using studies that do not make raw data publicly available. The "scientific" community and the EPA bureaucrats still oppose the rule.

The EPA is charged with protecting the environment in the United States. Their mandate is to use regulations and restrictions on the use of private property so that one property owner does not endanger the water, land or air

159

for all the people around them. This is reasonable if the actions of the property owner are truly causing dangerous pollution. But the EPA has abused this power.

Private property rights are as fundamental to our freedom as free speech and a free press. Thus, if the EPA takes away a person's rights, they have a duty to explain why and present all the evidence to the public for scrutiny. Regulatory costs diminish our standard of living and eliminate jobs. Every regulation needs a solid and public justification. The burden of proof remains with the EPA.

There are many measures of freedom, but one is certainly the strength of a country's private property rights. Or, put another way, how easy is it for the state to take away private property or render it unusable by the owner? This can be thought of as the inverse of how socialistic a country is, since the lack of private property defines socialism according to Merriam-Webster:

> "Socialism: Any of various economic and political theories advocating collective or governmental ownership and administration of the means of production and distribution of goods. A system of society or group living in which there is no private property." Merriam-Webster Dictionary.

Property rights are ranked for countries around the world by the Heritage Foundation (Heritage Foundation, 2020) and the Property Rights Alliance (Property Rights Alliance, 2019). In 2020, out of 181 countries, Venezuela and Haiti are ranked last by the Heritage Foundation, which isn't surprising. They put Singapore in first place with the strongest property rights, followed by Hong Kong, New Zealand, Finland, and the U.K. Finland is listed first by the Property Rights Alliance. The United States is ranked 25th by the Heritage Foundation and 12th by the International Property Rights Index. It is interesting that the "Democratic Socialist" countries of Sweden, Denmark, the Netherlands, and Norway all have stronger private property rights than the United States. That is, they are less socialistic.

The arguments against transparency all sound very weak and boil down to "trust the EPA, they would never do anything wrong." The EPA has 20 federal advisory committees and Andrew Wheeler has recently insisted that their meetings be more transparent and that they discuss the scientific studies used to make the new rules to ensure they are consistent with the underlying science (Wheeler, 2020). This is a significant change from the past. The EPA had stacked these advisory panels with academics that depend upon government money for their research, creating a conflict of interest. Pruitt ended this and banned advisory board members from receiving government money.

The bottom line is that industries affected by EPA regulations should be allowed to examine the data and draw their own conclusions as to the merits of the studies. Argument is a founding principle of the United States and scientific inquiry. Debating the merits of new rules will only improve them.

Polls show that most people agree that there should be some restrictions on private property rights to protect the environment. Probably most people also agree that private property rights should not be taken away unless the EPA makes a sound scientific case for doing so. Prior to the Trump administration, the law did not require transparency. The HONEST act is a good start, it should be passed by Congress and become law.

We live in an age when many scientific studies cannot be replicated and when scientific research contains considerable political bias. The only way to be sure that a study's results are valid is to independently duplicate the project. No less an authority than the journal *Nature*, probably the premier scientific journal in the world, has made this point:

> An inherent principle of publication is that others should be able to replicate and build upon the authors' published claims. A condition of publication in a Nature Research journal is that **authors are required to make materials, data, code, and associated protocols promptly available to readers without undue qualifications.** Any restrictions on the availability of materials or information must be disclosed to the editors at the time of submission. Any restrictions must also be disclosed in the submitted manuscript.
>
> After publication, readers who encounter refusal by the authors to comply with these policies should contact the chief editor of the journal. In cases where editors are unable to resolve a complaint, the journal may refer the matter to the authors' funding institution and/or publish a formal statement of correction, attached online to the publication, stating that readers have been unable to obtain necessary materials to replicate the findings. (Nature.com, 2018), bold in original.

No one should assume the EPA is always right and the businesses they regulate always wrong. Businesses (or "industry" if you prefer) make all the money we have, all the money the EPA has, and all the money the government has. Every regulation has a cost. That cost reduces everyone's income. Rules and regulations matter but should not be made willy-nilly or at an unelected bureaucrat's whim. They should only be implemented when fully and publicly justified.

McIntyre and McKitrick, blew up Michael Mann's "hockey stick," while attempting to replicate it, as discussed in the next chapter. Once they received Mann's raw data, they found numerous errors, which they corrected, and published the result in *Energy and Environment* (McIntyre & McKitrick, 2003). This was followed with two more papers in 2005, both critical of Mann's hockey stick reconstruction. Once these articles were published, the National Academy of Sciences (NAS) investigated the hockey stick and substantiated McIntyre and McKitrick's findings.

Replication is critical to verify scientific studies. The EPA should adopt a similar policy.

In a famous peer-reviewed study published in *Science* (Open Science Collaboration, 2015) it was found that only a third to a half of the papers published in 2008 in the top three psychology journals could be replicated. If this is true of the scientific work done at the EPA or used by them, then half or more of their regulations, that have real economic impact on landowners and businesses in the United States, may not be based on sound science. We cannot know if this is true if the data and the studies are secret. It is interesting that the *Science* paper's opening words are:

> "Reproducibility is a defining feature of science, but the extent to which it characterizes current research is unknown. Scientific claims should not gain credence because of the status or authority of their originator but by the replicability of their supporting evidence." (Open Science Collaboration, 2015)

This is a good way of putting it. Reproducibility is not part of the definition of science, but it certainly is a "defining feature" of science. No matter how brilliant the scientific work might be, if it cannot be replicated by someone else, it is useless. Thus, for the scientific work to matter and have value, the "materials, data, code, and associated protocols [must] promptly [be made] available to [the public] without undue qualifications" (Nature.com, 2018). Not providing the data and code causes enormous problems and delays the scientific process as we will see in the next chapter.

Chapter 5: Lawsuits and Climate Change

> [Dr. Tim Ball] watched [his] chosen discipline—climatology—get hijacked and exploited in service of a political agenda, watched people who knew little or nothing enter the fray and watched scientists become involved for political or funding reasons—willing to corrupt the science, or, at least, ignore what was really going on. The tale is more than a sad story because it set climatology back thirty years and damaged the credibility of science in general. (Ball, 2014, p. 4)

Lawsuits regarding climate change are all over the place, we have already discussed many of them in previous chapters. But this chapter is devoted to Michael Mann's personal lawsuits over differences of opinion and jokes about him that are in poor taste. These disputes should never have been allowed in the courtroom, but they got there.

Science is built upon a set of accepted facts. These are bits of knowledge that are accepted by everyone as true, at least for a long period of time, if not forever. At the front edge of the scientific process are scientific ideas and opinions. These are endlessly debated, the advocates present evidence and the skeptics present counterevidence. Time moves on and the stronger ideas become facts or established theories, the weaker ideas fade away. Man-made climate change is one idea currently being debated.

Lawsuits to squash an opposing scientific view are the ultimate political corruption of science. In science, opposing views should be fought with data and analysis. Roger Pielke Jr. has written about the problem in an article entitled: "A Litigious Climate Threatens Scientific Norms," in the *Wall Street Journal* (Pielke Jr. R. , 2017b).

The seven lawsuits in this chapter were all filed by Michael Mann, he has sued a wide variety of organizations and individuals for various insults about his hockey stick temperature reconstruction, primarily the 1999 version that covers the past 1,000 years and appears in TAR, the third IPCC climate assessment report (Mann & Bradley, 1999). Some of the public remarks made by those he sued were inappropriate and personal, but Michael Mann's lawsuits were an over-reaction. Courts are not the appropriate place to resolve disagreements over scientific issues or minor tasteless jokes and comments. This is particularly true for a public figure like Michael Mann.

Mann believes he can sue his detractors because he is "right." Yet, he weakens his case by refusing to produce his data and computer code to make his case. When ordered to produce the data and code by the British Columbia Supreme Court in his lawsuit against Tim Ball he didn't do so, even after two years. He then lost the court case.

Michael Mann sues Tim Ball, FCPP, and a reporter

On March 25th, 2011 Michael Mann filed a lawsuit accusing Tim Ball of making "false, malicious and defamatory" remarks about him. The key statement made by Ball was in response to a reporter's question. The reporter was from the Frontier Centre for Public Policy (FCPP) of Winnipeg, Manitoba. He asked Ball if "governments and academic agencies have whitewashed the *climategate* scandal so far. Do you think anyone will be prosecuted for fraud?" Ball replied in part:

> "… Michael Mann at Penn State should be in the State Pen, not Penn State." (Mann M. , Notice of Civil Claim, 2011)

Mann claims that Ball made the remarks with the knowledge that the meanings conveyed by the words above were "false, or alternatively, with reckless indifference whether they were true or false." He then requested damages (Mann M. , 2011).

Dr. Ball is a very well-known climate scientist who is now retired, but he still writes about climate science and does interviews, such as the one quoted above. Ball was a professor in the Department of Geography at the University of Winnipeg until he retired in 1996. He received his PhD from the University of London. Ball's thesis was in historical climatology, he used records from Hudson Bay Company's forts in Canada to reconstruct a climatic history from 1714 to 1850 of eastern Canada. Ball has studied and written about climate and climatic history his entire career.

Obviously, for a statement to be defamation, it must be untrue. If it is true, it is not defamation. In context, what Ball was saying, partially in jest, was that the 2009 *climategate* emails (Costella, 2010) showed that Mann had deliberately changed and misrepresented data to create his famous hockey stick (Mann & Bradley, 1999). Mann's Northern Hemisphere average temperature reconstruction of the last 1,000 years, aka the "hockey stick," as presented in the third IPCC assessment report (IPCC, 2001) is shown in Figure 28, in Chapter 7.

In 2011, besides the *climategate* emails, there was a considerable amount of peer-reviewed and published evidence that Michael Mann had changed data and manipulated his statistical analysis, perhaps intentionally, perhaps not, to generate the hockey stick. The evidence is presented in peer-reviewed papers by Stephen McIntyre and Ross McKitrick in *Energy and Environment* (McIntyre & McKitrick, 2003) and in two later papers published in 2005 (McIntyre & McKitrick, 2005) and (McIntyre & McKitrick, 2005c). Still more details are given in an excellent book by Andrew Montford, called the *Hockey Stick Illusion* (Montford, 2010).

Beyond the documented data manipulation and improper statistical analysis, the hockey stick is easily shown to be wrong because it does not show the well documented Medieval Warm Period (MWP) or the Little Ice Age (LIA). As discussed in Chapter 2, these climatic anomalies are documented in two key 2003 papers by Willie Soon, Sallie Baliunas. Craig Idso, Sherwood Idso and David Legates.

We will dig a bit deeper into the criticism of the hockey stick here to put Mann's lawsuits into proper scientific context. We also hope to show that the courts are no place to resolve scientific disputes. Criticism of scientific ideas, like the hockey stick, is part and parcel of science. If you want to be a scientist, you need to get used to it.

Absent thermometer data prior to the 19th century, Mann used tree rings, ice core oxygen isotope ratios, marine and lake sediment cores, and other temperature proxy data from around the Northern Hemisphere to reconstruct temperatures prior to the early 20th century. Then he overlaid the instrumental (thermometer) hemispheric temperatures onto the end of the proxy-based temperatures in a very controversial way.

As already discussed, proxy temperature reconstructions are noisy and imprecise and processing them into a reconstruction causes them to have a much lower variability than instrumental observations. The instrumental record of global average temperature is only 170 years long and the proxy temperature reconstructions probably show essentially no variability over periods that short. Mixing the proxies with measured temperatures is an apple and oranges comparison. Mann's claim that 1990s are the hottest decade and 1998 the hottest year in 1,000 years have no basis. This irritated Tim Ball, and

166

many others, not just because he was improperly mixing two different measurements, but also because he mostly relied on tree ring data. The tree ring data doesn't correlate with 20th century instrumental data, as previously discussed. The bad correlation goes back to 1930, so how do we know it correlates with ancient temperatures (Briffa, Schweingruber, Jones, Osborn, & Vaganov, 1998b)?

The various proxies for the millennium have different start and end dates and each proxy is called a "series." Mann's various series were manipulated with a regression-based statistical technique called principal components and then combined to make a single temperature reconstruction.

Mann's temperature reconstruction showed that recent warming (from measurements) was unusual and that temperatures (from proxies) were very flat for the 900 years before the beginning of the 20th century. This was considered strange by Tim Ball, and many other Earth scientists. Abundant historical, archeological, and geological evidence shows that the Medieval Warm Period was probably warmer than today and the Little Ice Age was much cooler, at least in the Northern Hemisphere and possibly globally. Ball's own work and Soon and Baliunas' papers clearly established these climatic events.

Soon and Baliunas, 2003

We covered Soon and Baliunas's 2003 papers in Chapter 2, but we will reiterate their conclusion here:

> "proxies duly represent local climate. Because each is of a different nature, the results from the proxy indicators cannot be combined into a hemispheric or global quantitative composite. ... [The proxies establish] both the Little Ice Age and Medieval Warm Period as climatic anomalies with worldwide imprints. ... the individual proxies can be used to address the question of whether the 20th century is the warmest of the 2nd millennium locally. Across the world, many records reveal that the 20th century is probably not the warmest nor a uniquely extreme climatic period of the last millennium." (Soon & Baliunas, 2003)

They are making two key points. First, since the proxies are all different, they cannot be legitimately combined into one record like the hockey stick. Tree rings can be precisely dated, but they reflect seasonal, not annual temperatures, and are not accurate thermometers. Dates from other proxies are often imprecise and often do not have annual resolution. Mixing proxies of differing resolutions and with mismatched dates and seasonal sensitivities creates a lot of problems. Second, when each of the proxies are examined separately, the 20th century is not unique. So, how can Mann have created a hockey stick from these proxies that shows the 20th century to be such a huge anomaly. Many were asking this question.

The hundreds of papers examine by Soon and Baliunas do not conclude that 20th century warming is unusual. In David Legates words, Mann's hockey stick was the scientific outlier.

Below in Figure 17, we have overlain Mann's hockey stick reconstruction with the HadCRUT4 surface temperature dataset. We did it very much like Mann did it. We just highlight the visual splice. Mann's data is from his website and the HadCRUT4 data is from the University of East Anglia Climatic Research Unit and the Hadley Centre (Met Office Hadley Centre, 2017).

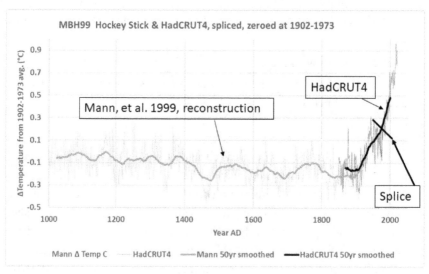

Figure 17. The "Hockey Stick." The Mann reconstruction is plotted using data from Michael Mann's ftp site. The HadCRUT4 data is from the Hadley-Climate Research Unit web site (Met Office Hadley Centre, 2017). They are smoothed with 50-year running averages and both normalized to 1902-1973 averages then plotted together. The apparent splice point is noted on the plot, it is between 1930 and 1960. The yearly HadCRUT4 data extends beyond the 50-year smoothed HadCRUT4 data, which is the heavy black line.

McIntyre and McKitrick, 2003

Like Soon and Baliunas, Stephen McIntyre was quite confused while reading Mann's paper and the supplementary material. He lived in Canada and he knew that it had been much warmer in Greenland and in Newfoundland during the time of the Vikings, from 900 to 1100AD. Viking artifacts in Greenland (Brooke, 2001) and in Norway are buried in ice today, after all (Cascone, 2020).

McIntyre downloaded the data that Mann claimed to have used from the original sources and, like Soon and Baliunas, did not see how the hockey stick could have come from it. Then, on April 8th, 2003 he wrote to Michael Mann and requested that he send him the specific data he used to make the hockey stick. Mann's colleague, Scott Rutherford, sent some of the data to McIntyre. McIntyre discovered that Mann, or perhaps Rutherford, had changed the data he claimed to have used in his reconstruction as follows:

---

1) Truncated 3 series with no justification.
2) Copied 1980 values from one series onto other series, resulting in incorrect values in at least 13 series.
3) Moved of 18 series one year earlier than the source data.
4) Unjustified extrapolations or interpolations to cover missing entries in 19 series.
5) Moved some series to the wrong geographic location.
6) Used seasonal (summer) temperature data as annual temperatures.
7) Used obsolete data in at least 24 series, when newer data was available at the time of the MBH98 calculations.
8) Mann listed proxies he did not use.
9) His calculation of all 28 tree-ring principal components was incorrect.
   (McIntyre & McKitrick, 2003)

The data manipulations listed are explained in detail in Andrew Montford's book (Montford, 2010) and in McIntyre and McKitrick, 2003. McIntyre painstakingly compared all the raw data that Michael Mann and Scott Rutherford sent him to the original data sources to discover the errors listed above. Afterward he corrected the errors and generated a new temperature reconstruction using the techniques described in Mann's paper. It looked nothing like Mann's, a comparison of the two can be seen in Figure 18 below.

McIntyre and McKitrick only generated this reconstruction to show how different it was from Mann's original, after the data errors were fixed. It was not presented as a new reconstruction of Northern Hemispheric temperatures. They were clear about this in their paper, but Mann and his colleagues tried to criticize the corrected curve as if it were intended to be a serious reconstruction.

When the errors were corrected, the 20th century was no longer the warmest period in the last 600 years. This 1998 version of Mann's hockey stick only goes back to 1400AD, the 1999 version, used in the IPCC third assessment report, goes back to 1000AD. In Figure 18, only proxy-derived temperatures are plotted, no instrumental data is overlain, as it is in Mann's figures and in TAR. For this reason, everything in Figure 18 is directly comparable. Notice that the hockey stick proxy temperatures decline after 1930, diverging from measured temperatures, as described by Briffa, et al. (Briffa, Schweingruber, Jones, Osborn, & Vaganov, 1998b).

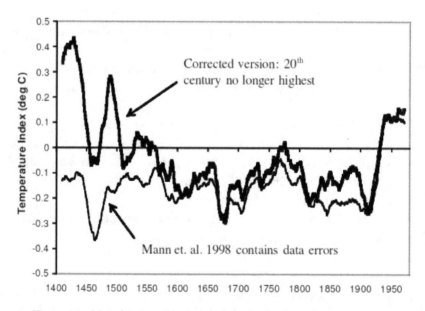

Figure 18. Mann's original hockey stick is the thin line, the heavier line was made using the same data with Mann's edits removed. The corrected line also includes the full series of proxy data that had been truncated by Mann, that is the "decline." A more complete description of the errors corrected can be seen in (McIntyre & McKitrick, 2003), which is also the source of the graph. Used with Stephen McIntyre's kind permission.

It turned out that McIntyre could not replicate Mann's hockey stick, even when he put the errors back in the data. He could not even replicate Mann's principal component series, an intermediate calculation. So, Mann had to have done some additional processing that was not explained in his paper or McIntyre and McKitrick did not have the datasets that Mann used.

McIntyre and McKitrick sent Mann the data they had received from Scott Rutherford and asked him if this was really the data he used. They also asked Mann about some of the errors they had uncovered. This was prior to publishing their landmark *Energy and Environment* paper in November 2003. But Mann cut off all communication at that point and claimed he was too busy. Then they asked several people, including a professional statistician, to review their work. The comments from the statistician and the others were positive and helped improve the paper.

They submitted the paper, which was sent out for peer review. The reviewer's comments were helpful and further improved the paper. When the paper was published, McIntyre and McKitrick made all their data and computer code available to readers. This was quite different from Michael Mann, who was still withholding some of his data and all his computer code.

The paper immediately caused a stir after hitting the internet, with *USA Today* reporting the following on October 28, 2003, just one day after the paper hit the internet:

"An important new paper in the journal *Energy and Environment* upsets a key scientific claim about climate change. If it withstands scrutiny, the collective scientific understanding of recent global warming might need an overhaul." (Shultz, 2003)

McIntyre and McKitrick's paper did stand up to scrutiny, as did the earlier Soon and Baliunas papers. They were followed by many others and the books by Andrew Montford and Mark Steyn already mentioned. However, as of this writing, Michael Mann has not admitted any wrongdoing and has not been formally accused of academic fraud. As a result, many ascribe the errors in his papers to his lack of understanding of principal components and basic statistical methods and analysis.

The critical books, subsequent investigations, and papers caused Mann to substantially change his hockey stick in a 2008 paper (Mann M. , et al., 2008).

The 2008 revised hockey stick is discussed below, but in addition to revising his graph, he also published his own book, *The Hockey Stick and the Climate Wars, Dispatches from the Front Lines* (Mann M. E., 2012). Mann's book is full of misleading, distorted, incomplete and exaggerated quotes from various sources. Brandon Shollenberger details these problems thoroughly in a blog post (Shollenberger, 2012).

Shollenberger's list of Mann's distortions is long, but worthwhile reading. Here we will only mention a few that are particularly important to this narrative. In the *climategate* emails, we will remember that Phil Jones, who was the Director of the Climatic Research Unit (CRU) at the University of East Anglia, wrote on November 16, 1999: "I've just completed Mike's Nature trick of adding in the real temps to each series for the last 20 years … and from 1961 for Keith's to hide the decline." (Costella, 2010, p. 17)

In his book, Mann tries to claim that the phrases "Mike's Nature trick" and "hide the decline" are not related. Although the text makes it clear they are. The decline in proxy temperatures can be seen in Figure 18 after 1930, when both reconstructions flatten out or decline. The decline is also apparent in Figures 7 and 8. In the published hockey stick this decline is "hidden" by truncating the reconstruction and overlaying the instrumental temperatures.

It is quite possible that Mann also added the instrumental temperatures to his reconstruction so he could smooth them together and extend the smoothed curve farther than he would be able to do otherwise. Certainly, the spaghetti graph in TAR had the end of Briffa's reconstruction clipped off to "hide the decline," as shown in Figure 8.

Next, Mann claims, on page 138 (Mann M. E., 2012, p. 138), that McIntyre and McKitrick published an alternative temperature reconstruction. He means the reconstruction compared to the hockey stick in Figure 18. This is not an "alternative reconstruction," as already mentioned, it is merely an illustration of Mann's reconstruction with his data errors fixed.

Later in in Chapter 8 of Mann's book, he tries to claim that there were no errors in his data and that Scott Rutherford had created the errors when he prepared the data for McIntyre and McKitrick. Mann also claims that McIntyre requested the data as an Excel spreadsheet, but the email chain presented by McIntyre shows that he did not. They also show that the data was delivered as a text file called pcproxy.txt, not as a spreadsheet. Rutherford had to gather and organize the data to send it to McIntyre, which surprised McIntyre (Montford, 2010, pp. 71-73). Why was the data not already prepared?

Later, the original data became available on Mann's ftp site, but the data problems remained, and more problems cropped up. Mann did himself and everyone else a great disservice by hiding his data and methods, eventually all the problems with his hockey stick came to light and even Mann had to fix them. He published a new graph that clearly shows the 20th century was not unusually warm, although he still stubbornly tried to claim it was, by inappropriately comparing the proxy reconstruction to twentieth century measured temperatures (Mann M. , et al., 2008).

Six years into the lawsuit, in 2017, the British Columbia (BC) judge in the case ordered Michael Mann to give Tim Ball and the court all his data and all his computer code related to the hockey stick. Since Tim Ball had accused Mann of fraudulently creating the hockey stick, the judge decided that he needed the chance to show that was the case. To do that he needed the data and computer code. A court order should not be needed for this.

The data were to be presented to the court by February 20th, 2017. Rather than surrender the data and code, Mann moved for an adjournment of the trial. Canadian courts always grant adjournments before a trial in the hope that an out-of-court settlement will be reached.

Eight long years after the lawsuit was filed, on June 7, 2019, the FCPP and the reporter settled with Mann out of court. They admitted to publishing "certain untrue and disparaging accusations which impugned the character of Dr. Michael Mann" (McIntosh, 2019).

Then a few months later the BC court dismissed the lawsuit against Tim Ball. The published statement by Judge Giaschi of the Supreme Court of British Columbia explains his decision (Giaschi, 2019).

The judge states that the lawsuit was filed March 25, 2011. There were a couple of amendments to the claim in 2011 and 2012, then nothing was done from 2012 until November of 2014 when Mann declared his intention to proceed. Mann did not deliver his data and code to the court by February 20, 2017. But, after requesting an adjournment, Mann filed a second notice to proceed in April of 2019 and a new trial date was set for January of 2021. The Judge declared that the delays were excessive and inexcusable. Mann provided no reasons for the excessive delays.

The judge found that "there has been actual prejudice to the defendant as a consequence of [Mann's] delay[s]" The judge found that:

> "because of the delay, it will be difficult, if not impossible, for there to be a fair trial for the defendant. This is a relatively straightforward defamation action and should have been resolved long before now." (Giaschi, 2019)

The judge granted Ball all costs associated with his defense. These are to be paid by Michael Mann. So, the Judge accurately called this a "straightforward defamation action," but Mann and his lawyers dragged it out for eight years. The judge pointed out that several of Tim Ball's witnesses died during the delay. He added that Dr. Ball is in his eighties, in poor health, and "has had this action hanging over his head like the sword of Damocles for eight years."

We have no idea where the money for Mann's lawsuits comes from, but obviously he has access to a lot of it. We are describing seven of his lawsuits in this book. Dragging out lawsuits and criminal actions to impoverish your opponents is an old game and very ugly and cruel. There are better ways to settle scientific disagreements. We will come back to the notorious hockey stick saga in future chapters.

Michael Mann sues Mark Steyn, *National Review*, CEI, Rand Simberg

In 2012 Penn State professor Michael Mann sued writer and singer Mark Steyn, *National Review* magazine, the Competitive Enterprise Institute (CEI) and reporter Rand Simberg for making "false and defamatory statements" (Mann M. , 2012). Mann's complaint states that the lawsuits were brought against the organizations and the two writers because of their accusations. Mann believes that they accused him, unjustly, of academic fraud and compared him to former Penn State assistant football coach Jerry Sandusky, a convicted child molester.

According to William Patrick in the *Epoch Times*, twenty-four media organizations, including the *Washington Post*, NBC, the ACLU, and Fox News have sided with *National Review* and CEI in the lawsuit (Patrick, 2019). Mann is a public figure and should not try and stifle criticism in the media through the courts.

In July 2012, a reporter, Rand Simberg, from CEI, criticized Michael Mann, a Penn State University investigation of him, and his hockey stick (Simberg, 2012). Simberg pointed out that the Penn State investigation of Michael Mann (Pennsylvania State University, 2010) was not a serious investigation.

Simberg and the other defendants have the peer-reviewed journal articles and Congressional reports, already mentioned, that criticize Mann's statistical techniques, show that Mann may have manipulated the input data, and the devastating *climategate* emails. However, Mann may have just made mistakes and perhaps none of these apparent screw ups were intentional. He did ground-breaking research; he did something for the first time. Problems with ground-breaking research are expected.

The most serious problem was that his unproven research was plucked from obscurity and prominently displayed, way too early, by the IPCC and Al Gore. Was that his fault? Perhaps, in part, he was a lead author of the third IPCC assessment (TAR) chapter that displayed and explained his hockey stick (IPCC, 2001, p. 166).

The IPCC leadership should have been much more skeptical of the graph. The graph attempted to invalidate hundreds of peer-reviewed papers that described the Medieval Warm Period (MWP) and the Little Ice Age (LIA) (Soon & Baliunas, 2003). How they blindly trumpeted the graph in the face of decades of research pointing in the opposite direction shows how desperate they were to find anything that supported their opinion that humans control the climate.

They had models, but lacked direct evidence, and were desperate to find some. As Oxford Professor Jonathon Jones said, "The hockey stick is obviously wrong. Everybody knows it is obviously wrong." It is obvious because the MWP and LIA are missing from the graph. If scientific reasoning had prevailed over politics, that would have been the end of it.

Given the evidence, many prominent skeptics accused Mann of fraud. The evidence was inconclusive, as shown by the National Research Council and other organizations. Was this justification for Mann to sue people and try to ruin them financially? That is the real question.

If politics, the IPCC, and Al Gore had not entered into this scientific debate, with name calling, absurd claims that the science is settled, etc. none of this would have happened and everyone would have hashed these questions out in the normal way with competing scientific studies and papers. Many studies were published in the ten years after Mann's pioneering study and we now see that his reconstruction from 1600AD to the present is barely plausible, but highly unlikely. The earlier part of his reconstruction is clearly wrong as are his main conclusions. He made a legitimate contribution and his study was the first of its kind, but he wouldn't let sleeping dogs lie.

Michael Mann's lawsuit against *National Review* magazine was filed in October of 2012, it was filed at the same time as his suits against Mark Steyn and the Competitive Enterprise Institute. The defendants asked the court to dismiss the lawsuit under the local anti-SLAPP (strategic lawsuit against public participation) law. A SLAPP lawsuit is intended to burden the person or organization being sued with legal costs until they finally give up.

Numerous amicus briefs were filed in support of the defendants on behalf of the ACLU, *Time*, *The Washington Post,* and other first amendment organizations. The oral arguments were made in November 2014. The ruling on the dismissal was issued December 22, 2016. It was against the Competitive Enterprise Institute and the other defendants, but it did dismiss several of Mann's complaints. The defendants then petitioned for a rehearing and the court issued an amended opinion that the defendants found flawed, so they petitioned for a rehearing a second time, which was denied.

The defendants appealed to the Supreme Court, but it refused to hear the case. The defendants say this is a matter of freedom of the press and free speech, Mann says they made factually false assertions. The judges believe that the matter must go to court because it is up to juries "to distinguish fact from opinion" (McGurn, 2019). As of February 2020, the case was headed to trial and discovery was under way. In an email uncovered in discovery, Michael Mann described *National Review* as a "filthy organization," that was a "threat to our children." He stated that his intent was to bring the newspaper "down for good" (National Review, 2020).

Partly in response to Mann's lawsuit, Mark Steyn published the already mentioned book *A Disgrace to the Profession* (Steyn, 2015). The book is a compendium of critical comments about Mann and his hockey stick.

The ACLU is helping to defend the *National Review* and the other defendants. The ACLU D.C. legal director, Art Spitzer said the following about the lawsuit:

"The only way to protect free speech for our allies is to protect it for our adversaries. Today it's unacceptable to deny climate change, but yesterday it was unacceptable to deny that homosexuality was sinful, and tomorrow it may be unacceptable to deny that robots are better parents than humans. Society can't progress unless people are free to express and consider heretical ideas, because there's no way to predict which heretical ideas will be tomorrow's truths." (McGurn, 2019)

How true. The most interesting investigations of Michael Mann and his hockey stick are described next.

The Penn State Investigation

The Penn State committee that investigated Mann reviewed all the *climategate* emails and published attacks of Mann's activities. They also interviewed William Easterling (Dean of Earth Sciences at Penn State), Michael Mann, William Curry (Senior Scientist at the Woods Hole Oceanographic Institution), Jerry McManus (Department of Earth and Environmental Sciences, Columbia University), and Richard Lindzen (Department of Earth, Atmospheric and Planetary Sciences at MIT). The interviews occurred between April 12th and May 5th, 2010.

They solicited the opinions of Dr. Gerald North (Texas A&M), who led the National Academy of Sciences (NAS) investigation into Mann, as well as Dr. Donald Kennedy (Stanford University), the former editor of *Science* Magazine (Pennsylvania State University, 2010). Notably, they did not solicit the opinion of Dr. Edward Wegman, who also led a Congressional investigation of Dr. Mann (Wegman, Scott, & Said, 2010). We will discuss Dr. Wegman's results in detail in a later section. Wegman's report entitled, "Ad Hoc Committee Report on the 'Hockey Stick' Global Climate Reconstruction," was published in April of 2010, during the Penn State investigation.

The Penn State investigation dismissed three of the four allegations against Mann, without looking into them. The three dismissed allegations were that Mann falsified data, deleted emails that were requested through freedom of information (FOIA) requests, and the misuse of privileged information. These were dismissed without an inquiry because Mann was good at "obtaining funding," received a lot of "awards and recognitions," and published a lot of papers (Pennsylvania State University, 2010, pp. 17-18).

177

When Professor Richard Lindzen was informed of the dismissals he said to the committee:

> "It's thoroughly amazing. I mean these are issues that he [Mann] explicitly stated in the emails. I'm wondering what's going on?" (Pennsylvania State University, 2010, p. 13)

Indeed, what was going on? The committee did not respond to Professor Lindzen's question and instead directed him to the fourth allegation. This was that Mann had not followed accepted practices when he withheld data from other investigators and shared unpublished manuscripts. Professor Lindzen told the committee that the general practice is to share the data used for a study. Regarding computer code, he would share it if it was custom or nonstandard code. Generally, Lindzen thought that "if somebody asks you how did you get this, you really should let them know" (Pennsylvania State University, 2010, p. 14).

Clive Crook, in a biting *Atlantic* article on July 14, 2010, had hoped that the various *climategate* inquiries into Mann and his colleagues "would be severe" and help restore public confidence in the "scientific consensus" on climate change. But came to find that the "reports made things worse." He then opined:

> "At best they are mealy-mouthed apologies; at worst they are patently incompetent and even willfully wrong. The climate-science establishment, of which these inquiries have chosen to make themselves a part, seems entirely incapable of understanding, let alone repairing, the harm it has done to its own cause." (Crook, 2010)

There have been numerous investigations of Michael Mann, his colleagues, and his hockey stick, the vast majority of them are whitewashes intended to downplay the allegations and support Mann, et al. The Penn State investigation is one of the worst. The equally vacuous Muir Russell investigation in the U.K. is another bad one (Russell, 2010). None found any evidence that Mann intentionally deceived anyone. However, all investigations, that looked for it, found that the hockey stick graph was built incorrectly, inadequately documented, and misleading. The Muir Russell and Penn State investigations deliberately avoided these topics and only examined minor matters. This was apparently so they could appear to exonerate the accused of everything, but they only exonerate Mann and his colleagues for trivial infractions.

The Muir Russell investigation of Mann's colleagues at the University of East Anglia (UEA) Climate Research Unit (CRU), was clearly a whitewash. It carefully sidestepped investigating the serious problems identified in the *climategate* emails, but they did directly criticize the UEA and CRU staff for their unwarranted secrecy and for not sharing their data and methods openly. This was a useful result of their inquiry (Russell, 2010, pp. 14-15). At least these investigations have put all scientists on notice that they must be prepared to share all their data and code with anyone who asks for it. Are the EPA bureaucrats and *Scientific American* listening?

Comments on Mann's statistical methods

The better investigations found that the statistical process Mann used was inappropriate and the proxy datasets he used were corrupted. Many of the temperature proxies used did not reflect local or hemispheric temperatures.

Mann may not have understood the serious problems with his statistical methodology or proxy selection at the time he built the hockey stick. However, he made matters worse by keeping his data and code secret. He explained his methods and data so poorly in his papers and in the third IPCC assessment report (IPCC, 2001) that no one else could replicate his work and find the errors until years later (Wegman, Scott, & Said, 2010, pp. 4-5). Many scientists knew the hockey stick was wrong, the missing Medieval Warm Period and Little Ice Age made that obvious, but to explain how it came about required all the details about how it was made.

A review of these investigations reveals that Mann's chosen statistical method to combine the temperature proxies into a reconstruction, principal components, is not an appropriate technique and that simple averages are better. This was later shown to be the case by Bo Christiansen and Fredrik Ljungqvist (Christiansen & Ljungqvist, 2011). The National Academy of Sciences specifically does not recommend principal components be used to reconstruct temperatures (National Research Council, 2006, p. 113). But, even if principal components had been an appropriate technique, it was not implemented correctly by Mann (Wegman, Scott, & Said, 2010, pp. 28-29).

Mann centered his principal components in the period from 1902-1980, rather than the conventional principal components center of the entire series. By de-centering his series he, presumably inadvertently, forced a hockey stick shape as explained by McIntyre and McKitrick, the NAS report and Wegman's report. Proxies that rose rapidly in the 20th century were preferentially chosen as the first principal component because their variance was inflated, due to the de-centering. Their earlier values were forced down and the later values rose rapidly in the 20th century. In addition to the de-centering problem, proxies were moved to the first, second or third principal component that matched local temperatures best in the 20th century, which further forced a hockey stick pattern. These two serious problems are explained well in the National Academy of Sciences report (National Research Council, 2006, pp. 90-91, 113), the Wegman Report (Wegman, Scott, & Said, 2010, pp. 23-27), and in McIntyre and McKitrick's *Geophysical Research Letters* paper in 2005 (McIntyre & McKitrick, 2005).

Mann calibrated the proxies to the period from 1902 to 1995. This period is inappropriate because its upward trend is not representative of the millennium temperature profile. This third problem, alone, invalidates the principal components analysis technique (Wegman, Scott, & Said, 2010, p. 48).

Mann chose to use some bristlecone pine temperature proxies in his reconstruction and for several reasons these trees are not reliable indicators of ancient temperatures. The NAS investigation concluded that strip-bark bristlecone pine (*Pinus longaeva*) tree ring data should be avoided in temperature reconstructions (National Research Council, 2006, p. 52). Because of their characteristics they often dominate the principal components analysis and Mann's reconstruction. Wegman's report, Franco Biondi (Biondi, Perkins, Cayan, & Hughes, 1999), and Donald Graybill and Sherwood Idso (Graybill & Idso, 1993) note that bristlecones "are not a reliable temperature proxy for the last 150 years" (Wegman, Scott, & Said, 2010, p. 49). The primary investigators all recommend that bristlecone pine data not be used, but Mann admits in his book that these proxies were critical to the reconstruction (Mann M. E., 2012, p. 51)

So, while the investigations did not find that Mann did anything wrong, they all found serious problems with his hockey stick. They did *not* "affirm the hockey stick" as a very misleading headline in *Nature* screamed (Brumfiel, 2006). In fact the National Academy of Sciences investigation concluded that the hockey stick was far too uncertain to support any conclusions about 20th century warming versus the previous 1,000 years (National Research Council,

2006, p. 16&18). There are numerous temperature reconstructions that show the Medieval Warm Period is warmer than today. These include reconstructions by Moberg, et al. (Moberg, Sonechkin, Holmgren, Datsenko, & Karlen, 2005) and Bo Christiansen and Fredrik Ljungqvist (Christiansen & Ljungqvist, 2012). The Moberg, 2005 reconstruction is shown in Figure 19.

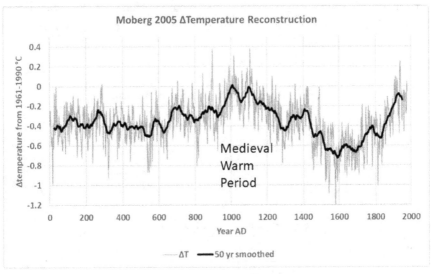

Figure 19. Moberg, et al., 2005 2,000-year Northern Hemisphere temperature reconstruction, it is referenced to 1961-1990 average instrumental temperatures. The reconstruction is shown to 1979 only. It shows the Medieval Warm Period was warmer than today. Data source: (Moberg, Paleoclimatology Data, 2020).

Anders Moberg's reconstruction shows a Medieval Warm Period that is warmer than today. If modern instrumental temperatures were spliced into Figure 19, they would be warmer than the Medieval Warm Period proxy temperatures shown, but they are from instruments and not proxies. As we have repeatedly noted, instrumental temperature measurements cannot be directly compared to proxy temperatures. Moberg used signal processing techniques (wavelet transforms), rather than principal components to build his reconstruction. His technique separated the proxies by their resolution and weighted the proxies differently at different time scales. This results in a different and better reconstruction than Mann's. At least it has more variability. His technique is still statistical, however, and applying this method to noisy proxies reduces variability (National Research Council, 2006, p. 86).

Christiansen and Ljungqvist created a temperature reconstruction without using regression. They used simple averages of locally calibrated proxy temperatures. This retained as much variability as possible. Their reconstruction is shown in Figure 20, where it is compared to Mann's hockey stick. The range of yearly, unsmoothed, estimated temperatures, from the Little Ice Age to the Medieval Warm Period in Christiansen's reconstruction in Figure 19 is almost 4.5°C, where the range in Mann' hockey stick is only 0.6°C. Many of the proxies are the same, the difference is mostly in the statistical methods used.

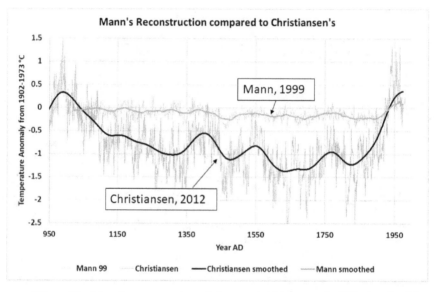

Figure 20. Mann's reconstruction of the past 1,000 years, the "Hockey Stick" is compared to Christiansen and Ljungqvist's 2012 reconstruction. The data used is from the respective authors. They are moved to the same zero point, 1902-1973. The light lines are the original yearly data, the smoothed lines are 50-year moving averages. The Christiansen reconstruction uses the data from Figure 5 of (Christiansen & Ljungqvist, 2012). Data sources: Mann's ftp site and the NOAA paleoclimatology data web site.

The peak of the Medieval Warm Period (MWP) was between 950 and 1050AD according to historical records, Greenland Ice Cores, the Bermuda Rise sea-surface temperatures (SST) and deMenocal's West African study. In Europe this was when the Vikings colonized Greenland and Newfoundland. This was also when grapes could be grown in England and at the highest altitude in Germany. In China and on the Tibetan Plateau records show that it was unusually warm from 800 to 1380AD, which corresponds with the warm period in Europe (Soon, Baliunas, Idso, Idso, & Legates, 2003b).

Historical records also support the Little Ice Age (LIA), as discussed in Chapter 2. This data is not quantitative, but it does tell us that Mann's flat hockey stick handle from 1,000AD to the mid-1800s is likely incorrect. Both Anders Moberg's reconstruction in Figure 19 and Christiansen's in Figure 20 are qualitatively consistent with historical records, Greenland ice cores, Bermuda Rise sea-surface temperatures (SST) and deMenocal's West African study, see Figure 21.

Christiansen's smoothed reconstruction shows a drop of about 1.7°C from the peak of the Medieval Warm Period to the depths of the Little Ice Age and Moberg's about 0.8°C. Which is closer to the truth is unknown, but Mann's hockey stick difference of 0.25°C is too small to explain the historical events we know took place during those times.

Besides numerous reconstructions that show a distinct MWP and LIA, there are many that have flat handles like Mann's. Those with flat handles use similar statistical methods to Mann's, suggesting that the methods (principal components and similar regression-based techniques) are part of the problem. That these warm and cool periods exist is accepted as fact in the National Academy of Sciences report as well as in the Wegman Report.

H. H. Lamb estimated that the temperature difference between the MWP and the LIA, in England, was likely between 1.2° and 1.4°C based largely on precipitation estimates. Wenfeng Deng and his co-authors (Deng, et al., 2016), show that the South China Sea and Western Pacific temperatures in the MWP were about the same as today, but the LIA temperatures were about 1.5°C cooler. They used oxygen isotope ratios from coral core samples to build a temperature reconstruction. These values tend to support the 1.7°C 50-year-smoothed difference observed on Christiansen and Ljungqvist's reconstruction in Figure 20.

Yair Rosenthal, Braddock Linsley, and Delia Oppo (Rosenthal, Linsley, & Oppo, 2013) show that Pacific water masses linked to both the North Pacific and the Southern Ocean were 0.9°C warmer in the MWP than during the LIA, These water masses were also 0.6°C warmer in the MWP than today, which tends to support Moberg's 0.8°C 50-year-smoothed estimate. Rosenthal et al. used well-dated seafloor sediment cores as a source for benthic (sea-floor dwelling) and planktonic (shallow-water dwelling) foraminifer shells. The magnesium/calcium and oxygen isotope ratios were used to construct a seawater salinity and water temperature reconstruction. When estimating changes in climate, 50-year smoothing is reasonable, since yearly changes are large and less meaningful from a climatic perspective. Some think 50 years is too short and recommend a longer period.

Moberg's yearly range (maximum minus minimum) of temperatures is 1.6°C and Christiansen's is 4.5°C. Thus, yearly variation is two to three times the 50-year climatic variation. Decadal changes, for example Mann's 1990s claim and yearly changes, like Mann's 1998 claim, are not meaningful.

Both Moberg and Christiansen's MWP peaks and LIA lows match historical records reasonably well. Moberg's yearly peak of 0.3°C occurs at 1105AD and his valley occurs at 1579AD, close to the historical records. Christiansen's yearly peak of 1.5°C, occurs at 990AD and his yearly low of (-3°C) at 1642AD. Christiansen's dates match historical records extremely well. Mann's peak is in 1942, ignoring the instrumental record he tacked on to the end of his reconstruction. Mann's MWP peak is in 1020AD, a reasonable match to history, but his low is in 1462AD, a full 200 years before the historical low in the mid-1600s.

We dig a bit deeper into the more serious investigations of the hockey stick in the following sections and in Chapter 7.

The National Academy of Science (NAS) Investigation

Mann's complaint against Mark Steyn, the National Review, Rand Simberg and the Competitive Enterprise Institute tells us that numerous organizations have investigated Mann's behavior and concluded he did not commit academic fraud. This is true. Mann's complaint continues with the following, which is misleading:

> "every such investigation - and every replication of Dr. Mann's work - has concluded that Dr. Mann's research and conclusions were properly conducted and fairly presented." (Mann M. , 2012)

This part of Mann's complaint stretches the truth a bit too much. All the investigations found serious problems with Mann's work. This section will only discuss the National Academy of Sciences investigation. The National Research Council is the working arm of the United States National Academies, which includes the National Academy of Sciences. The National Research Council conducted the investigation and wrote the report.

While Mann did not commit academic fraud, his hockey stick was incorrect, and his methods were explained poorly in his papers. His refusal to share his data and the details of his methods slowed the natural scientific process and allowed time for the IPCC and Al Gore to continue to promote his flawed temperature reconstruction.

The National Academy of Sciences concludes that little confidence (National Research Council, 2006, p. 4) can be placed in Mann's primary conclusion that "the 1990s are likely the warmest decade, and 1998 the warmest year, in at least a millennium" (Mann & Bradley, 1999).

Academic fraud includes intent, that is Mann would have to have been found to intentionally falsify his data or his statistical analysis to deceive. In the definition from the University of Virginia:

"False data is the fabrication or alteration of data to deliberately mislead. For example, changing data to get better experiment results is academic fraud." (University of Virginia, 2020)

Thus, absent proof that Mann did the data manipulation deliberately, he is not guilty of academic fraud. The National Science Foundation makes this clear in their final "closeout" assessment of Michael Mann's hockey stick work:

"Although [Dr. Mann's] data is still available and still the focus of significant critical examination, no direct evidence has been presented that indicates [Dr. Mann] fabricated the raw data he used for his research or falsified his results. Much of the current debate focuses on the viability of the statistical procedures he employed, the statistics used to confirm the accuracy of the results, and the degree to which one specific set of data [bristlecone pines] impacts the statistical results. ... Such scientific debate is ongoing but does not, in itself, constitute evidence of research misconduct." (National Science Foundation, 2011)

One of the original scientific papers that Mann published about the hockey stick was published in *Nature*. When the evidence of data tampering was published by McIntyre and McKitrick (McIntyre & McKitrick, 2003) they submitted an extended critique of the errors and misrepresentations in Mann's 1998 and 1999 papers to *Nature* magazine.

The papers by McIntyre and McKitrick, Soon and Baliunas and the *Nature* submission led to the National Academy of Sciences (NAS) investigation. Their results were announced on June 22, 2006 (North, et al., 2006). In this report they found that the final 400 years or so of Mann's temperature reconstruction were reproducible and they had confidence that the mid-to-late-twentieth century rise in temperatures was unprecedented since 1600AD. This is uncontroversial, since 1600AD was in the deepest part of the LIA, but this conclusion is quite different than the "warmest … in at least a millennium" claimed by Mann and Bradley.

The hockey stick from 1000AD to 1600AD was very much in doubt according to the Academy (National Research Council, 2006, pp. 18-20). Prior to 1600, there are too few temperature proxies, in too few locations, to tell whether the world was warmer or cooler than the late 20th century. The scarcity of precisely dated proxies before 1600, and the short length of the instrumental record, used to calibrate the proxies, made the hockey stick, and Mann's conclusions, questionable.

The National Academy of Sciences' review of Mann's work barely mentions data manipulation, but state that systemic uncertainties in climate records from before 1600 were not communicated in his papers as clearly as they should have been. We will often refer to the National Academy of Sciences report as the "NAS report." Some references will also refer to it as the National Research Council report or the NRC report. NAS did not feel the hockey stick should have been featured so prominently in the IPCC third assessment report (TAR). One of the NAS panel members, Kurt Cuffey said the following about the prominence of the hockey stick in TAR:

> "I think that sent a very misleading message about how resolved this part of the scientific research was." (Brumfiel, 2006)

Nature (Brumfiel, 2006) reported on the NAS study under the misleading title, "Academy affirms hockey-stick graph." The Academy did not affirm the graph, they simply said that they had confidence in the last 40% of the hockey stick. NAS points out that others had produced reconstructions like Mann's from 1600 to the present, this is true, but there are also many peer-reviewed reconstructions that are dramatically different. A good example is shown in Figure 20.

The NAS Press Release was entitled: "High Confidence That Planet Is Warmest in 400 Years; Less Confidence in Temperature Reconstructions Prior to 1600" (North, et al., 2006). This is true, but misleading because it is obvious, hockey stick or no hockey stick. Directionally, the hockey stick is correct since 1600, but the magnitude is off by a factor of three or more according to historical records. The hockey stick offers nothing we didn't already know and is quantitatively wrong.

The NAS press release is heavily spun to support the hockey stick as much as possible. It also contains a statement that is clearly false, "None of the reconstructions indicate that temperatures were warmer during medieval times than during the past few decades, the committee added." In 2006, many reconstructions showed the Medieval Warm Period was warmer than today, one was shown in the First IPCC Assessment Report in 1990 (IPCC, 1990, p. 202). Even more dramatic evidence that the Medieval Warm Period was warmer than today in the Northern Hemisphere is presented in deMenocal's paper in *Science* in 2000, six years before the NAS report was published. His reconstructions of temperatures in Greenland, Bermuda and West Africa are shown in Figure 21.

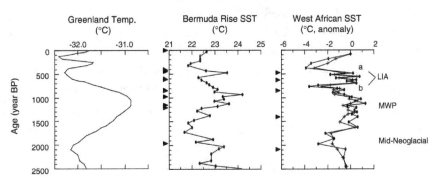

Figure 21. Temperature reconstructions of the North Atlantic surface. The Greenland reconstruction is from borehole temperature surveys. The Bermuda and West African SST (sea surface temperatures) anomalies are from oxygen isotopic analysis of planktonic (shallow water) foraminifera shells found in subsea sediment cores. Source: (deMenocal, Ortiz, Guilderson, & Sarnthein, 2000) used with Peter deMenocal's kind permission.

The full NAS report is entitled: "Surface Temperature Reconstructions for the Last 2,000 Years" (National Research Council, 2006). It is much more nuanced and critical of the hockey stick than either the press release, *Scientific American* or the *Nature* articles suggest. So much so, that Senator James Inhofe announced, after it came out, that the "NAS report reaffirms 'Hockey Stick' is broken" (Inhofe, 2006). After reading the report, we think this is more accurate than the *Nature* headline claiming the report "affirms" the hockey stick. The report is detailed, 161 pages long, and clearly says the hockey stick has many flaws.

The recommended citation says that the "National Research Council" is the author, but inside the report we can see the list of scientists involved. There were twelve authors working under the leadership of Gerald North, the chairman of the Committee. He is a professor of meteorology and oceanography at Texas A&M University.

Gerald North thinks that humans are causing global warming with their greenhouse gas emissions and that the warming might become dangerous at some point (Dressler & North, 2013). He is biased but has studied climate for decades and has a healthy respect for the uncertainties in the field. He has written that "there remains a large uncertainty in climate sensitivity to a doubling of CO_2." The range given by the IPCC today is 1.5°C to 4.5°C, which is the same range given in the Charney Report in 1979 (Charney, et al., 1979). He admits that the main sources of error in climate models are that we cannot model precipitation, feedbacks to additional CO_2, and temperature increases (North G. R., 2013). This is something any informed climate change skeptic might say. Basically, the uncertainty in the data is clear to Gerald North, but his opinion is that climate change is man-made and dangerous. Fair enough.

The others on the committee are Franco Biondi, an expert on using tree rings to infer ecological changes; Peter Bloomfield, a statistician from the University of North Carolina; John Christy, professor of atmospheric science at the University of Alabama; Kurt Cuffey, professor of geography, University of California; Robert E. Dickinson, professor of atmospheric sciences at the Georgia Institute of Technology; Ellen R. M. Druffel, professor at the University of California, Irvine in Earth sciences, an expert in radiocarbon dating; Douglas Nychka, professor of mathematics at the Colorado School of Mines, an expert in statistics; Bette Otto-Bliesner a scientist at NCAR (National Center for Atmospheric Research) in Colorado, an expert in paleoclimatology; Neil Roberts, professor at the University of Plymouth (U.K.), expert in using isotope data to infer paleo-temperatures; the late Karl

188

Turekian, professor of geochemistry at Yale, expert in using radiogenic isotopes to infer paleoclimate; and John (Mike) Wallace, professor of atmospheric sciences at the University of Washington.

This is an impressive list of scientists, John Christy was and is skeptical that human-caused global warming is dangerous or significant. Dr. Christy tells us that, in his opinion, Mike Wallace, Karl Turekian, and Franco Biondi were very reasonable and open minded on the issue. So, it cannot be said the composition of the committee was entirely biased.

However, besides these members, the rest are connected to Mann and his co-authors in one way or another and probably biased, at some level, in his favor. They believe that humans have a significant and potentially dangerous impact on climate. Regardless of the bias in their press release, the committee was honest in the report, and they showed how well they understand the scientific process. In the preface of the NAS report, we find this assessment of the controversy over Mann's hockey stick:

"hypotheses are proposed …. Other scientists work on the issue, producing supporting or negating evidence, and each hypothesis either survives for another round, evolves into other ideas, or is proven false and rejected. In the case of the hockey stick, the scientific process has proceeded for the last few years … Critics of the original papers have argued that the statistical methods were flawed, that the choice of data was biased, and that the data and procedures used were not shared so others could verify the work. … The reconstruction produced by Dr. Mann and his colleagues was just one step in a long process of research, and it is not (as sometimes presented) a clinching argument for anthropogenic global warming, but rather one of many independent lines of research on global climate change." (National Research Council, 2006, p. ix)

Mann's hockey stick was a proposal, an idea, or hypothesis. It was the first hemisphere-wide multiproxy temperature reconstruction. Very flawed, statistically inept, but the first, none-the-less. The National Research Council believed, with some justification, that the problem was less with Mann's work, and more with how prominently the hockey stick was displayed by the IPCC and Al Gore. Mann compounded the problem by withholding his data and code, the big problem is always the cover up.

Soon, et al., 2003 and McIntyre and McKitrick, 2003 showed the hockey stick was wrong and explained why. The NAS report found the same problems.

The NAS report confirms the hockey stick had its shape because the statistical methods Mann used forced it. Besides prominently displaying the graph, TAR repeats Mann and Bradley's unsupported conclusions on page 2 of the Technical Summary:

> "New analyses of proxy data for the Northern Hemisphere indicate that the increase in temperature in the 20th century is likely to have been the largest of any century during the past 1,000 years. It is also likely that, in the Northern Hemisphere, the 1990s was the warmest decade and 1998 the warmest year ([their] Figure 1b)" (IPCC, 2001, pp. 2-3)

To substantiate this statement, they point to the hockey stick reconstruction, which is their Figure 1b on page 3 of TAR. Once the graph was shown to be an artifact of flawed statistical procedures, the IPCC was humiliated. It was the last time they tried to show humans are the dominant cause of climate change with direct physical evidence. All subsequent reports try to make their case with climate models.

According to John Christy, Gerald North said during the press conference, after the report was completed, that the report confirmed the IPCC conclusions. This was clearly an error on North's part, his report explicitly says otherwise. Christy thought maybe North was using "confirm" in some vague, general sense. Probably he simply misspoke. But regardless the comment was taken to mean the NAS report confirmed the hockey stick which made Karl Turekian furious and he wanted to hold a second press conference to clarify that statement. But it didn't happen.

Turekian wanted the following points to be clearly made. First, Mann's methodology was flawed and second, strip bark bristlecone pine tree (*Pinus longaeva*) rings are not useful for climate reconstructions. The NAS report explicitly does not recommend the statistical methods used by Mann in his study and acknowledges the flaws in Mann's methods found by McIntyre and McKitrick (National Research Council, 2006, pp. 112-113 & 116).

The NAS report cites digital experiments that constructed "pseudoproxies" on a known set of temperatures at Mann's locations and then corrupted them with varying levels of statistical noise. They used Mann's methods to reconstruct the temperatures. In every experiment the temperature variability over time was attenuated. In other words, the upper temperatures were lessened, and the lower temperatures were increased, relative to the actual values. That means that comparing measured temperatures today to proxy derived temperatures in the distant past is invalid, the proxy derived temperatures will always have less variability than existed at the time (National Research Council, 2006, p. 86). This finding alone invalidates the hockey stick conclusions about 20th century warming.

This is a problem with all regression-based statistical techniques, like principal components. There are other methods that do not lose as much temperature variability, but they can lose accuracy (National Research Council, 2006, p. 86). Long after the NAS report was published, Bo Christiansen and Fredrik Ljungqvist, built a temperature reconstruction (Figure 20), using more recent proxies and a novel statistical technique that retained much more variability than any regression-based technique. They named their reconstruction technique "LOC," which stands for local (Christiansen & Ljungqvist, 2012).

The NAS report suggests that the true amplitude of temperature changes over the past 1,000 to 2,000 years is probably at least twice what is seen in a Mann-type reconstruction (National Research Council, 2006, p. 112). Christiansen's reconstruction suggests the true variability is almost eight times higher than shown in the hockey stick. Christiansen was careful about the proxies he used, and each proxy was tested for significance against local temperature records and rejected if not found to correlate.

Moberg's reconstruction, shown in Figure 19, also uses a statistical technique, but one that is designed to lose less variability than Mann's. Moberg separated his yearly data from the lower resolution proxies and used a novel wavelet analysis technique to retain as much variability as possible in his reconstruction.

Christiansen and Ljungqvist used 16 proxies in the end (Christiansen & Ljungqvist, 2012). All proxies reached back to 300AD or earlier and all correlated well to local, modern instrumental temperatures.

Besides the variability lost to proxy noise, the spatial gridding process used in some reconstructions dampens variability. Variability is lost in every step. Christiansen and Ljungqvist explain that this is a systemic bias and, as a result, not included in the confidence intervals provided with Mann's reconstruction (Christiansen & Ljungqvist, 2011).

Each of the proxies used in all reconstructions must be calibrated to the modern temperature record for the area where the proxy is located, whether it is an ice core, sediment core, a tree or a coral reef. This calibration typically is done with linear regression. This calibration process removes variability and it suffers from the short length of the measured temperature record, which is generally less than 150 years. Long term, century-scale variability is not present in the measured temperature record. Also, most of the measured temperature record is within the period of human fossil fuel emissions. CO_2 emissions affect corals, pollen, tree growth, tree rings and other temperature proxies. These problems affect nearly all proxy temperature reconstructions, but not measured temperatures.

Statistically, the MWP and the LIA anomalies shown in Figures 19 and 20 are significant at greater than the 95% level (Christiansen & Ljungqvist, 2012). Michael Mann's reconstructions (1998, 1999, 2008, and 2009) all fall outside the 95% confidence limits of Christiansen and Ljungqvist's reconstruction in the LIA. It is notable that Huang's global temperature estimates, based on worldwide borehole heat flux data and physical principals, for the past 500 years, are within Christiansen's 95% confidence limits in the LIA (Huang, Pollack, & and Shen, 2008). Mann's reconstructions are not supported by the Huang's borehole heat flux data.

Significantly, Christiansen and Ljungqvist's reconstruction shows a MWP that is, statistically speaking, at the same level as the modern warm period. This is also true of Moberg's reconstruction. This is in great contrast to Mann's earlier reconstruction (Mann & Bradley, 1999). Mann's revised reconstruction is shown below in Figure 22. It was created in 2008 (Mann M. , et al., 2008) to address the criticism of the 1999 hockey stick in the NAS report. It shows a distinct MWP that is statistically at the same level as the modern warm period, using only proxy temperatures and an apples-to-apples comparison. It is similar in variability to Moberg's reconstruction. Mann's 2008 reconstruction invalidates his own 1999 hockey stick.

Mann published another paper in 2009 that attempts to show that, "while the Medieval Warm Period is found to display warmth that matches or exceeds that of the past decade in some regions," it falls below recent levels globally (Mann M. E., et al., 2009). An interesting idea, but it still suffers from the serious flaw of comparing modern instrumental temperatures to regression-smoothed proxy data from one-thousand years ago. If Mann is going to convince anyone, he must ditch the short instrumental temperatures and rely only on proxies for his comparisons. Soon and Baliunas make this clear in their 2003 paper (Soon & Baliunas, 2003).

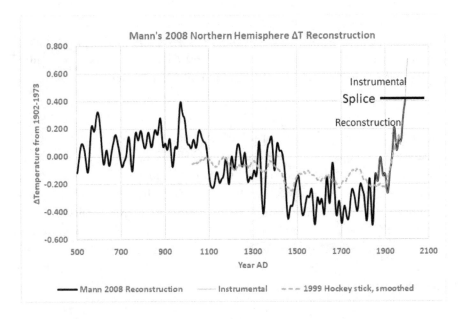

Figure 22. Mann's 2008 reconstruction was built to address the problems found in the hockey stick by the National Academy of Sciences (NAS). The original 1999 hockey stick, shown in the IPCC third assessment report, is shown as a heavy dashed gray line. Both reconstructions have been moved to a 1902-1973 zero line. The proxy temperature reconstruction ends in 1995, this is identified with the "splice" line, the instrumental extension that Mann shows in his paper is shown as a very faint line. The end of the reconstruction is at the same level as the Mann, 2008 Medieval Warm Period peak.

Mann used regression-based methods in 2008, including spatial regression, so some dampening of paleo-temperatures is expected. Whoever told Dr. David Deming that "We have to get rid of the Medieval Warm Period" (U. S. Senate Committee on Environment and Public Works, 2006) must have been very disappointed. Dr. Deming testified that a major climate change researcher told him that in an email but did not identify the individual. The Medieval Warm Period is a major thorn in the side of alarmists because it was likely as warm as today, yet humans could not have caused the warming.

The NAS report acknowledges the decline in tree ring proxy temperatures relative to measured temperatures in the 20th century as shown in Figures 7 and 18. The origin of the "hide the decline" scandal. They are of the opinion that this "observed discrepancy ... reduces confidence that the correlation between these proxies and temperature has been consistent over time" (National Research Council, 2006, p. 117).

The National Research Council committee found serious errors in nearly every part of Mann's first two papers. Mann's conclusions were incorrect, and his statistical techniques were inappropriate. They found that the principal components methods that Mann used, created hockey sticks from auto-correlated (meaning self-correlated) random numbers, exactly as described by McIntyre and McKitrick.

It was known by most climate scientists in 2006 that Mann's reconstruction from the present to 1600AD does not show enough cooling. But, since 2006 this has become even more likely. Temperatures, at least in the Northern Hemisphere, were 1.2 to 1.7°C cooler in the LIA than today as shown to be the case by S. P. Huang of Xi'an Jiaotong University and colleague's borehole temperature flux calculations (Huang, Pollack, & and Shen, 2008). Huang's borehole flux calculations also show the Medieval Warm Period to be comparable to today's temperatures. The relative Northern Hemisphere average temperatures between the MWP, the LIA and today are unclear, but larger than the hockey stick shows.

The National Research Council Meeting

Prior to writing their report, the National Research Council Committee invited many scientists to speak to the panel on topics relevant to the hockey stick. Stephen McIntyre and Ross McKitrick were speakers and attended the entire meeting. Another speaker was Hans Von Storch, an eminent climatologist who is one of the few truly politically neutral climatologists. He is respected by scientists on both sides of the climate debate (Montford, 2010, p. 186).

The NAS committee was doing its work for the Boehlert Congressional Committee and near the end of his presentation, Von Storch presented a slide entitled "Rep. Boehlert's Questions." In it he answered each of the original questions asked by Rep. Sherwood Boehlert. The slide caused a great deal of confusion among the panel members because Ralph Ciccerone, the head of the National Academy of Sciences, had not given the questions to the panel. Instead he rewrote the task statement, directing the panel to investigate less controversial issues.

John Christy was as surprised as the others when he saw the questions Von Storch put up. He believes that Ciccerone and the National Academy of Sciences decided to fund the study themselves, so they could replace

194

Boehlert's questions with their own and control the narrative. The changes Ciccerone made were significant and showed bias.

Boehlert wanted to know if Mann's hockey stick had been replicated and if sufficient information had been made available to replicate it. This question was not in the task statement, Mann's papers were not even mentioned. Representative Boehlert had clearly been outmaneuvered by the NAS bureaucracy. If the panel failed to answer the congressional committee questions, they would look foolish, but how could they if they were not given the questions? It is notable that even though Von Storch's presentation was before Mann's, none of the panelists ask Mann if the information needed to replicate his work was available (Montford, 2010, p. 234).

Perhaps the *Wall Street Journal* summarized the NAS report best when they printed the headline, "Panel Study Fails to Settle Debate on Past Climates" (Regalado, 2006). The NAS report confirmed the major criticisms of the hockey stick, then stepped on their own findings by spinning the report so it could be interpreted as "affirming" it.

The Wegman Investigation

According to Andrew Montford's definitive book, *The Hockey Stick Illusion*, the NAS panel of scientists was loaded with Mann supporters. With the exceptions noted above, this was generally true. One was Doug Nychka, who had co-authored a paper with Mann. Further Nychka was the only statistician on the panel until complaints forced Peter Bloomfield to be added. Others who were probably biased toward Mann and climate change alarmism were Bette Otto-Bliesner, Robert Dickinson, and the chairman Gerald North.

While Ralph Ciccerone, the head of NAS, had offered to do an investigation for Joe Barton, Chairman of the House Energy Committee. Barton turned them down because he suspected, correctly it turned out, that Ciccerone was biased. Then Ciccerone offered their services to Congressman Sherwood Boehlert, the chairman of the Science Committee who accepted the offer. Boehlert was a Republican congressman until he retired in 2007, but unlike Barton, he supported climate change alarmism and thought human-caused global warming was dangerous.

The NAS investigators bent over backwards to try and support Mann's hockey stick. They were not dishonest, they did report all the serious flaws known at the time, but they softened the language as much as possible.

Barton did not want the biased NAS committee to do another hockey stick whitewash unopposed, so he asked Edward Wegman to form a second expert panel to investigate Mann's statistical methods. Edward Wegman was a prominent professor of statistics at George Mason University until he retired in 2018. He had no connection to climate science and no stated position on global warming. Quite unlike the clearly biased Gerald North.

Shortly after the NAS report was published, Edward Wegman released his report on July 14, 2006. While the NAS report did not answer Boehlert's questions, the Wegman Report dealt with them in a forthright manner. Wegman had recruited David W. Scott, a professor of statistics at Rice University; and a former graduate student of Wegman's, Yasmin H. Said (The Johns Hopkins University), to help with the report.

The Wegman Report confirmed the criticisms published by McIntyre and McKitrick and reproduced them. They also produced a theoretical explanation and simulations to show why they were correct (Wegman, Scott, & Said, 2010, App. A).

The Wegman Report found that the writing of Mann's initial paper (Mann, Bradley, & Hughes, 1998) was "obscure and incomplete and the criticisms of [McIntyre and McKitrick, 2003, 2005a, 2005b] to be valid and compelling" (Wegman, Scott, & Said, 2010, p. 4). Wegman's report notes that Mann and his co-authors had little interaction with mainstream statisticians and their errors were likely due to ignorance rather than any intentional deceit.

The Wegman Report tells us that the paleoclimate community of scientists is small and that 43 of them have close ties to Mann. For this reason, "independent studies" that appear to confirm Mann's hockey stick may not be truly independent. They concluded that in such a small and isolated community, peer-review may not be an effective check on flawed studies, such as Mann's.

The Wegman Report recommends that when scientific studies are used to justify large public expenditures, such as the billions or trillions of dollars spent on climate change research and mitigation, peer-review should not be relied upon. In these cases, an "intense level of scrutiny and review" should be applied to the scientific work (Wegman, Scott, & Said, 2010, p. 5). They also believe that all federally funded research projects should make both their data and computer code available to other researchers upon reasonable request (Wegman, Scott, & Said, 2010, p. 6).

When a study relies as much on statistics as the Mann reconstructions and is used for public policy generation, the Wegman Report recommends that evaluation by statisticians should be required. It is required by the FDA for drug studies and they believe this requirement should be extended to high profile climate change studies due to the amount of money governments are spending on the topic.

The proper way to validate an important study, like a climate change study used to justify spending billions of dollars, is to independently replicate it. This requires access to the original data and computer code. Mann claimed the code was his property, even though it was developed using federal grant money. Mann did finally release nearly all his data and code, as demanded by Barton's Congressional committee, but did it in such a way as to make it nearly unusable (Wegman, Scott, & Said, 2010, p. 48). We agree with Wegman that all code and data developed with federal funds should be made available to any researcher making a reasonable request and it should be delivered clean and well-documented.

Like the NAS report, the Wegman Report finds Mann's conclusion that the 1990s and 1998 are the hottest decade and year in the past 1,000 years unbelievable. This conclusion is based on the well-known problems with tree ring proxies, especially in detecting century-level variations. It is impossible to claim that today is warmer than a time in the past by using a reconstruction like Mann's hockey stick.

Attacks on Wegman and Said

When anyone challenges Mann's hockey stick, he and his cohorts, the so-called "Hockey Team," typically attack the people rather than their scientific findings. Scientifically the hockey stick is very weak, as we have shown, so their only option is to attack the people. Wegman's report blew up the hockey stick in clear language, so Wegman was attacked viciously. Mann and the alarmists charged the authors of the Wegman Report with plagiarism (Vergano, 2011). The allegations were unfounded and mostly made to gain headlines.

Raymond Bradley's 1999 textbook, *Paleoclimatology, Reconstruction Climates of the Quaternary* (Bradley, 1999) was a source for the Wegman report and cited in the bibliography, in the table and figure captions, and in the text. Bradley is cited in the report 37 times and his 1999 book is cited five times. We will remember that Raymond Bradley was a co-author of both the 1998 and 1999 hockey stick papers that were heavily criticized in the Wegman Report. Some of the report's background sections, contained paraphrased material from Bradley's book and, perhaps from Wikipedia. However, the background material was not plagiarized.

George Mason University investigated and found, in February of 2012, that "no scientific misconduct was involved." The George Mason University investigating committee unanimously found "extensive paraphrasing of another work, in a background section, but the work was repeatedly referenced" (Stearns, 2012). Presumably, they are referring to Bradley's book. The accusations that Bradley made, could be made against nearly every academic work. The background material, to provide context, in a paper or report often comes from textbooks like Bradley's.

The Wegman Report was devastating to the cause of climate alarmism and the alarmists pulled out all the stops to try and discredit it, including clearly false allegations. If you can't win on facts, attack the person. Next we discuss what makes a fact.

Chapter 6: Facts and Theories

"Up to ten years ago, I [repeated] what the IPCC tells us, [without checking it]. Then at some point I started to check the allegations. The result: it started with doubts and then ended in horror, in the realization that a great deal of what the IPCC and the media are saying about climate change is incorrect and is not [supported] by scientific facts and measurements. I am ashamed of what I used to "recount" in my own lectures as a natural scientist. ...

From a scientific point of view, it is almost absurd to [think] some CO2-adjusting screws [produce] a nice, pleasant, stable climate." Physicist and meteorologist Dr. Klaus-Eckart Puls, translated from the original German (Hahne-Waldscheck, 2012).

People love end-of-the-world stories and always have. Environmentalists, puritans, and other cultists enjoy blaming humankind for the destruction they predict. The religious say humans sinned and are being punished by God. They point to the Genesis stories of Noah's flood and Lot's wife being turned into a pillar of salt.

Environmentalists say humans are being punished for industrializing and "harming" the "natural planet." Exactly why the planet is not natural is unclear. In the 1960s Paul Ehrlich predicted human overpopulation would supposedly cause hundreds of millions to starve in the 1970s (Ehrlich, 1968). In 2013, Sir David Attenborough said humans were a "plague on Earth" (Gray, 2013). It's all irrational self-loathing, just substitute God for Gaia or vice-versa. Gaia is the ancient Greek name for the mother goddess who protected Earth. According to some environmentalists, she is who humans are offending (Fund, 2014). Other environmentalists even crafted a "Gaia Theory" (Environment and Ecology, 2020).

Global Cooling

As Angus McFarlane shows in a 2018 well researched wattsupwiththat.com web post (McFarlane, 2018), some 65% of the peer-reviewed climate papers, that offered an opinion, published between 1965 and 1979 predicted that the global cooling seen at the time would continue. He references and is supported by a Notrickszone.com post by Kenneth Richard

(Richard, 2016). Wattsupwiththat.com is a popular climate science blog created by Anthony Watts and notrickszone.com was created by Pierre Gosselin.

Attempts to erase the "global cooling scare" from the internet by the notorious William Connolley, who has rewritten 5,428 Wikipedia articles in a vain attempt to change history failed. As James Delingpole explains in *The Telegraph*, Connolley systematically turned Wikipedia into a man-made global warming advocacy machine (Delingpole, 2009). He rewrote articles on global warming, the greenhouse effect, climate models and on global cooling. He tried to erase the Medieval Warm Period and the Little Ice Age. In the Wikipedia pages he trashed famous climate scientists who were skeptical of man-made global warming like Richard Lindzen, Fred Singer, Willie Soon and Sallie Baliunas. He also blocked people from correcting his lies.

William Connolley is friends with Michael Mann and his Hockey Team, which includes Phil Jones and Raymond Bradley, who we have already discussed. He is also a cofounder of the alarmist website Realclimate.org. Obviously, Connolley made sure that Mann and Bradley received glowing praise on Wikipedia until he was fired in 2009 and removed as a Wikipedia administrator (Delingpole, 2009).

We are not surprised that Connolley shows up as a co-author on the peer-reviewed paper, "The Myth of the 1970s Global Cooling Scientific Consensus" in BAMS, written by Thomas Peterson, William Connolley and John Fleck (Peterson, Connolley, & Fleck, 2008). The paper is nonsense and made no difference because facts are stubborn things. The fact that the paper passed peer-review illustrates how corrupt climate science has become. The paper begins with this:

> "There was no scientific consensus in the 1970s that the Earth was headed into an imminent ice age. Indeed, the possibility of anthropogenic warming dominated the peer-reviewed literature even then." (Peterson, Connolley, & Fleck, 2008)

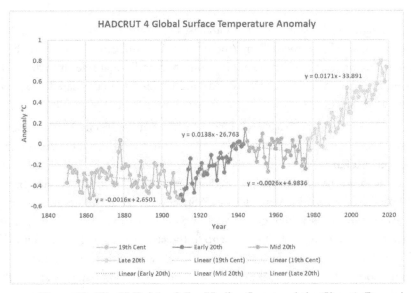

Figure 23. The U.K. Met Office Hadley Centre and the Climatic Research Unit (CRU) at the University of East Anglia global average temperature reconstruction since 1850. It shows, like other reconstructions, global cooling of about 0.09°C (0.16°F) from 1944 to 1977.

The global cooling scare of the 1960s and 1970s did exist, both climate scientists and the public were afraid that the global cooling trend, that began in the 1940s (see Figure 23), would continue and the world would turn very cold, maybe even return to a glacial period like the one that ended about 11,700 years ago at the beginning of the Holocene Epoch.

The Peterson, et al. paper carefully cherry picks 71 papers and claims that only seven papers between 1965 and 1979 disagreed with the "consensus" position that global *warming* would occur in the future. They found 20 that took a neutral position and 44 that agreed with the global warming consensus. But the world was cooling then and had been since 1944. Kenneth Richard researched this and expanded the time frame to 1960 to 1989. Richard found 285 papers that disagreed with the "consensus" position that global *warming* would occur in the future (Richard, 2016).

Of these 285 papers, 156 discussed the cooling since 1940 and predicted future cooling. Seven tried to show that CO_2 might be causing the cooling. A complete list of papers can be downloaded from Kenneth Richard's post. The alarmists fudged the numbers to show a 97% consensus that man caused global warming, then they fudged the global cooling consensus in the same way.

Angus McFarlane took the databases created by Kenneth Richard and Peterson, et al., merged them (there were 16 duplicates) and then did an independent search of his own. He found two additional relevant papers that were not already in one of the two databases. He then eliminated the papers that were outside the original Peterson et al. period of 1965-1979.

McFarlane's database is smaller than Richard's and only has 190 relevant papers, but this is 119 more than Peterson, et al. found and it covers the same period. McFarlane's review of the papers found that 86 predicted future cooling, 58 were neutral, and 46 predicted warming. Of the 86 cooling papers, 30 predicted a possible new "ice age." Strictly speaking, we are in an ice age, what they mean is a new glacial period where ice advances to a major new maximum extent like 19,000 years ago in the last major glacial maximum. The 86 cooling papers are 45% of the total. If we ignore the neutral papers, like John Cook, et al. did (Cook, et al., 2013) in his 97% consensus study, then cooling papers are 65% of the papers that offered an opinion. Using Cook's rules, we can comfortably claim there was a global cooling consensus in 1979.

However, once the mid-twentieth century cooling trend reversed and became a warming trend, it did not take long for the "consensus" to reverse as well. The global surface temperature trend changed to warming (about 0.017°C/year as shown in the graph) around 1977, and the peer-reviewed climate papers from 1977-1979 changed to a ratio of 52% warming to 48% cooling, a bare majority of warming papers, ignoring the neutral papers. During the 1980s the papers quickly changed to pro-warming.

The press in the mid-seventies reported that a consensus of climate scientists believed the world was cooling and the cooling would continue (Struck, 2014). Articles on the cooling consensus appeared in *Newsweek*, *Time*, the *New York Times*, and *National Geographic*. A landmark story by Peter Gwynne in *Newsweek* April 28, 1975 was typical (Gwynne, 1975). It was entitled "The Cooling World." In the overheated style of *Newsweek*, the article begins, "There are ominous signs that the earth's weather patterns have begun to change dramatically." Later in the article Gwynne breathlessly explains "… the earth's climate seems to be cooling down. … and the resulting famines could be catastrophic." Gwynne's cited sources include the National Academy of Sciences, Murray Mitchell (NOAA), George Kukla (Columbia University), James McQuigg (NOAA's Center for Climatic and Environmental Assessment) (Gwynne, 1975).

George Kukla of Columbia University and the Lamont-Doherty Earth Observatory did not change his view of a long-term global cooling trend, like many of his colleagues did. When he sadly passed away May 31, 2014, he still believed that a new massive glacial period would begin in the future, perhaps 5,000 years from now. Javier Vinós, in his blog post on "The next glaciation," (Vinós, 2018) predicts that the next major glaciation will begin in 1500 to 2500 years. It is fortunate that both predictions are far in the future.

When the next global cooling period begins, as it inevitably will, will climate scientists write more global cooling papers? Why should we believe climate scientists who say the world is warming dangerously now, when just 50 or 60 years ago they were saying it was dangerously cooling? A reasonable question. What direct evidence has arisen in the meantime that convinced them to reverse course? We had a consensus for cooling when the world was cooling, now we have a consensus for warming and the world is warming. Is that all there is to it? Both are hypotheses, what makes them become facts or theories?

Hypotheses are speculative ideas. A real scientist asks, "Is that so? Tell me why you think that." A rigorous scientific process must be used to demonstrate why observed events, such as global warming or global cooling, are occurring. To show they are potentially dangerous takes even more work. We will examine this process in the next section.

Consensus is a political thing. The public forms a consensus opinion, then vote and make laws or rules that reflect the opinion. In science, we first form a hypothesis or idea that explains an observed natural phenomenon, such as warming or cooling. The next step is to attempt to disprove it. If we fail the idea survives. We publish what we did, and others attempt to disprove the idea, if they fail to disprove it, it survives. Once this has gone on long enough, the idea becomes a theory. A scientific theory simply survives, it is never proven, it must always be subject to testing.

We mentioned above that seven of the papers examined by Angus McFarlane and Kenneth Richard suggested that CO_2 might be causing global cooling. A good example is Sherwood Idso's, 1984 paper in the *Journal of Climatology*. The paper is entitled "What if Increases in Atmospheric CO_2 Have an inverse Greenhouse Effect?" (Idso, 1984). Idso speculates that additional CO_2 will encourage plants to move into more arid areas, because additional CO_2 causes plants to use less water per pound of growth. Idso thinks that this might change Earth's albedo (reflectivity) in such a way as to lower temperatures. In a similar way, Richard Lindzen and Yong-Sang Choi

203

speculated that additional CO_2 would increase humidity in the tropics and thus cloud cover (Lindzen & Choi, 2011). Extremely small changes in average cloud cover can have a large cooling effect during the daytime.

Peter Webster presents an interesting discussion of Sherwood Idso's work in his *Climatic Change* paper, "The Carbon Dioxide/Climate Controversy: Some Personal Comments on Two Recent Publications" (Webster, 1984). Besides an interesting discussion of the emotions involved in the man-made climate change debate, we can see from Webster's discussion, and Idso's paper, how little we really know about the impact of additional CO_2 in the real world. Tiny changes in Earth's albedo, whether due to cloud cover or the distribution of plants can make a huge difference.

Empirical estimates of ECS (the change in air temperature due to doubling the CO_2 concentration) have never matched theoretical calculations from climate models. The empirical values (like Idso's or Lindzen and Choi's) are normally about half of model estimates, and can be negative, like Idso's. This is likely because the models are missing something and possible future changes in albedo due to changing cloud and plant cover are likely candidates.

Facts, Laws and Theories

Sometimes people ask climate skeptics if they believe in evolution or gravity. They want to ridicule our skepticism by equating man-made climate change to evolution or gravity. Evolution and gravity are facts and man-made climate change is a hypothesis. Equating "climate change" to gravity or evolution is valid, as all three are facts. Climate changes, gravity holds us to Earth's surface and species evolve.

Karl Popper, the famous philosopher, would say that these observed phenomena are not scientific hypotheses or theories because they are not falsifiable. How can you prove climate does not change?

There are other ideas that Popper calls pseudoscience. These are ideas that are framed in such a way that no matter what one observes, the observation can be seen to confirm the idea. Popper offers Marx's theory of history as an example. Popper observes "that a Marxist could not open a newspaper without finding, on every page, confirming evidence" for the theory. Freud's theories were the same, every clinical case was a confirmation of Freud's ideas. It was precisely this fact, that evidence always fit these ideas, that was their weakness. A theory that is not refutable by any conceivable event, is not scientific (Popper, 1962, pp. 35-36). Astrology is another example.

204

Popper ask himself in 1919 how Marxism, Freud and astrology differed from truly scientific ideas like Newton's law of gravity or Einstein's theory of relativity. He then realized that the latter could be tested and proven false. He was inspired by Frank Dyson, Andrew Crommelin and Arthur Eddington's confirmation of Einstein's theory during the solar eclipse of May 29th, 1919. Einstein's theory predicted that starlight would curve around the Sun, due to gravity. Newton's Law of Gravity also predicts a deflection, but Einstein's theory predicted a deflection twice as large. Their observations during the eclipse showed that it happened exactly as Einstein predicted (Coles, 2019).

This was the first real confirmation of Einstein's theory and it was based on a risky prediction. A confirmation of a theory must include a risky prediction of things that cannot or will happen if the theory is true. Theories should predict things successfully and they should forbid things and the more they forbid the better. Confirmations do not prove a theory, but they allow it to survive.

Popper draws a bright line between science and pseudoscience. Scientific hypotheses and theories predict what will happen and what will not happen if the idea is true. Pseudoscience draws no such line.

In other words, if a war happens and someone became rich from it, that does not verify Marx's view of history. Marx would have had to predict the man would become rich and would have to admit that if the man stayed poor, he was wrong. We must be able to imagine how the theory can be disproven.

Gravity and evolution have generally accepted theories of how they work. Einstein developed our current scientific theory of gravity. Newton provided us with his descriptive "Law of Gravitation." Newton's law tells us what gravity does and it is useful, but it tells us nothing about how it works. For that we need Einstein's theory of relativity.

In the scientific community, for both a law and a theory, a single conflicting experiment or observation invalidates them. Stories exist that either Einstein or Popper once said something like:

> "No amount of experimentation can ever prove me right; a single experiment can prove me wrong." (author unknown)

Both said similar things, both believed that no scientific theory is ever proven, they can only be disproven. So, let us examine our topics in that light.

Newton's descriptive law of gravity, based on mass and distance, are there any exceptions? Only on solar-system-sized scales, near black holes and on small atomic scales. In everyday life on Earth, Newton's law works fine. How about Einstein's theory of gravity (Relativity), any exceptions? None that we know of at any scale.

How about evolution? Species evolve, we can see that in the geological record (Jepson, Mayr, & Simpson, 1949). We can also watch it happen in some quickly reproducing species (Wilcox, 2011) and (Soltis & Soltis, 1989). Thus, we could describe evolution as a fact. It happens, but we cannot describe how without more work. Early theories of the evolutionary process include Charles Darwin's theory of natural selection (Darwin, 1859, p. Ch. 4) and Jean-Baptiste Lamarck's theory of heritable species adaptation due to external environmental stresses. Lamarck did not originate the idea of heritable adaptation; it was commonly believed long before he was born. But he did incorporate it into his ideas on new species evolution. Trofim Lysenko, described in Chapter 4, was a proponent of Lamarck's ideas.

Current epigenetic research (Nature, 2020) shows that Darwin and Lamarck were both right and that evolution involves both processes. For a summary of recent research into the epigenetic component of evolution see this *Oxford Journal* article (Mendizabal, Keller, Zeng, & Yi, 2014). Natural selection plays an important role in extinction, since species who cannot adapt to a new environment extirpate. Lamarckian-type heritable adaptation plays a critical role in how new, more robust varieties and species evolve.

Some dispute that Lamarck's theory of inheritance of acquired characteristics, first written in 1801 (Lamarck, 1801), could be called correct. After all, he didn't describe the details of how epigenetic factors changed with environmental stress and are passed on to offspring. But Lamarck never specified how it happened, only that it did happen. He adopted the "consensus" view that changes in animals due to environmental stress could be inherited. In this, he and the consensus, were correct.

Lamarck first presented his new idea that that the various species on Earth gradually evolved from the simplest to the most complex in two lectures on May 17th, 1802 at the Paris Museum of Natural History. The first lecture was to his students and the second to his fellow professors. The second was accompanied by a report (Lamarck, 1802). As Richard Burkhardt, a historian at the University of Illinois describes, Lamarck's ideas were ground-breaking and revolutionized biology, but this was not recognized at the time (Burkhardt, 2013).

Modern DNA research describes how adaptations can be inherited. John Smythies of the University of California and his colleagues explain that environmental stress normally leaves a creatures DNA unaltered, but sperm do not just carry DNA to the ovum, they also carry a wide variety of RNA molecules, which regulate the expression and the timing of various parts of the DNA. Stress affects these RNA molecules and they affect the development and characteristics of the offspring (Smythies, Edelstein, & Ramachandran, 2014).

As science progresses, well-established facts and scientific laws rarely change but theories do evolve. Facts and laws are easily dismissed when contradictory data are gathered and, sometimes, reinstated as we learn more. The modern theory of evolution is a good example of where competing theories can merge into one and a dismissed theory can be reinstated.

Most scientific theories begin as hypotheses. A hypothesis is best described as an idea of what might be causing a specific event to occur. As discussed above, both hypotheses and theories must be falsifiable. "Climate change" is not falsifiable, it is not a scientific hypothesis or a theory. Popper would describe "climate change" as pseudoscience since any weather event can be interpreted as supporting the idea.

"Man-made climate change" is a proper scientific hypothesis since it is falsifiable. Science is mostly skepticism. We look for what does not fit, we poke at established facts and laws, at theories and hypotheses. We try and find flaws; we check the numbers. Worse, science done properly means we spend more time proving ourselves and others wrong than we do proving we are right. Life is tough sometimes and as this book shows, scientists rarely win popularity contests.

Table 2, below, is a table of phrases. Each is identified as a fact, theory, law, hypothesis, or simply an idea. We can see that man-made climate change and the possibility of a man-made climate catastrophe are not comparable to the theories of relativity and evolution. Man-made climate change is more than an idea, it is based on some observations and reasonable models of the process. But none of the climate models have successfully predicted global warming with any accuracy. The theories of relativity and evolution have each made successful predictions with great accuracy and precision.

As Popper said, the proponents of man-made climate change must make risky predictions that become true to claim their hypothesis is a valid theory. Man-made climate change is still a work-in-progress and not a scientific theory. It is certainly not a fact.

Table 2. Classification of critical climate change phrases.

Common Phrases						
Phrase	Fact	Theory	Law	Hypothesis	Idea	Comment
Evolution	x					Species evolve
Natural Selection		x				Merged with epigenetics
Gravity	x					
Newton on gravity			x			How gravity works
Relativity		x				Gravity is curved space
Climate change	x					Climate changes
Global Warming	x					Warming is documented
CO_2 is a greenhouse gas	x					Verifiable in the laboratory
Man emits greenhouse gases	x					Observable and measurable
Man-made climate change				x		Humans affect climate
Man-made climate disaster					x	An idea unsupported by data.

Only validated and reproducible models and experiments, with no exceptions, can be used to support a scientific theory. The opinions of scientists and politicians are not relevant. This is not to say that man-made climate change or the possibility of a man-made climate change disaster are disproven, it is just to say that no valid evidence exists to support these hypotheses.

The idea of man-made climate change causing a catastrophe at the scale of Islamic terrorism or weapons of mass destruction, as John Kerry claimed in 2014 (Almasy, 2014), is pure speculation. The models used to compute human influence on global average surface temperature don't match observations, this is easily seen in Figure 24 which is John Christy's graph of IPCC climate model predictions versus satellite and weather balloon observations (Christy, 2016). Satellite and weather balloon measurements are independent of one another and they are independent of the various surface temperature datasets, like HadCRUT4 shown in Figure 23. All the curves on the plot have been smoothed with five-year moving averages. The five-year averages are to remove short-term weather events, like El Niños and La Niñas (NOAA, 2020). Climate is normally defined as changes over 30 years or longer.

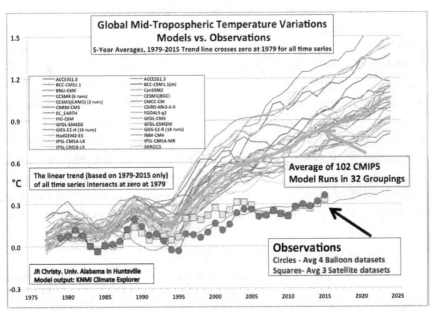

Figure 24. A comparison of IPCC/CMIP5 climate model predictions to 4 weather balloon and three satellite datasets. There is only one model that compares well to the observations, it is the Russian model INM-CM4, which does not predict any problems. This illustration is a B&W version of one Dr. John Christy presented to the House Committee on Science, Space and Technology February 2, 2016. (Christy, 2016). Used with Dr. Christy's kind permission. The figure is public domain from a U.S. Congressional report.

The line going through the observations is the Russian model "INM-CM4" (Volodin, Dianskii, & Gusev, 2010). It is the only model that comes close matching observations. INM-CM4, over longer periods, does very well at hindcasting observed temperatures. According to Ron Clutz, a blogger and Canadian management consultant with a degree in chemistry from Stanford. INM-CM4 uses a CO_2 forcing response that is 37% lower than the other models, roughly 2°C per doubling of CO_2. It uses a much higher deep ocean heat capacity (climate system inertia) and it exactly matches lower tropospheric water content and is biased low above that. The other models are biased high (Clutz, 2015). The Russian model predicts future temperature increases at a rate of about 1°C/century, not at all alarming and much lower than the predictions of the other models. The average of the other models predicts warming of 2.15°C/century. The observed linear warming trend for the globe, according the UAH (University of Alabama in Huntsville) satellite record, since 1979, is 1.3°C per century at the time of this writing (April 4, 2020) (Spencer, 2020).

One can consider each model to be a digital experiment. The range of predicted warming from these digital experiments is over 1.5 degrees from 1979 to 2025. This exceeds the average CMIP5 (Coupled Model Intercomparison Project 5) predicted warming of one degree since 1979. Compare the CMIP5 prediction to the actual warming trend of 0.5°C, as measured by UAH and reported by Roy Spencer (Spencer R. , 2020). The range of model results and the comparison to actual measurements does not give us confidence in the accuracy of the models. Yet, the IPCC uses the difference between the mean model temperature predictions with and without computed human impact since 1950 to compute the human influence on climate (Bindoff & Stott, 2013, p. 879). In Figure 25, after Bindoff and Stott, their Figure 10.1, page 879, we see the model runs as faint gray lines and the model averages as heavier gray lines. Overlain on the plot are surface temperature measurements as a heavy black line.

In Figure 25, graph (a), the models use a scenario that the IPCC believes represents both natural and human climate forcings. In graph (b) they use a model scenario that they believe represents only natural (that is, non-human) climate forcings.

210

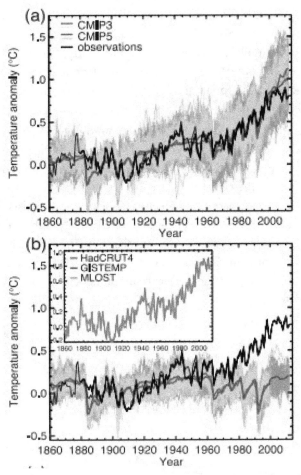

Figure 25. These graphs illustrate how the IPCC computes human influence on global warming, or climate change, if you prefer. The very dark lines are the observed global average surface temperatures. The gray heavy lines the average of the climate model predictions (AR4 & AR5). The faint gray lines are the model runs. Graph (a) includes model computed human and natural influences and graph (b) only the model computed natural influences. The graph is from Chapter 10, page 879, of the IPCC AR5 publication The Physical Science Basis (Bindoff & Stott, 2013). Used with permission.

The graphs are quite small and cover over 150 years, but even so, significant departures of the observed temperatures from the model mean are quite apparent from 1910 to 1940 and from 2000 to 2010. Further the range of model results is annoyingly large. The Figure 25(b) graph shows a flat natural climate trend and all the observed temperature increase from 1950 to today is attributed to human influence. This result has generated a lot of criticism from Willie Soon, Ronan Connolly and Michael Connolly (Soon, Connolly, & Connolly, 2015), as well as Judith Curry, Marcia Wyatt (Wyatt & Curry, 2014), and others. Soon, Connolly, and Connolly (SCC15) believe the IPCC chose an inappropriate model of the variation in the Sun's output (TSI or total solar irradiance).

There are many models of solar variation in the peer reviewed literature and which is correct is a topic of vigorous debate. Eight recent models are presented in Figure 8 of SCC15 (see our Figure 26). Only low solar variability models (those on the right of Figure 26) are used by the IPCC to compute man's influence on climate although just as much evidence exists for the higher variability models on the left. The scales used in the graphs are all the same, but the top and bottom values vary. At minimum, the IPCC should have run two cases, one for high variability and one for low. SCC15 clearly shows that the model used makes a large difference in the calculation of human influence on the climate.

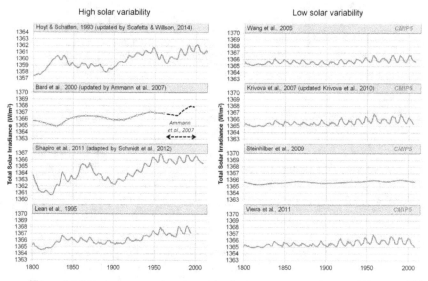

Figure 26. Various peer-reviewed models of solar output over the past 200 years. The IPCC uses a low variability model, like those on the right, in their calculations of human influence on climate and ignores the high variability models shown on the left. See: (Soon, Connolly, & Connolly, 2015) for a full discussion of the models.

Marcia Wyatt and Judith Curry (Wyatt & Curry, 2014) or WC14 believe that natural temperature variation due to long term natural cycles is not represented correctly in Figure 25(b). Their "Stadium Wave" (Wyatt, The "Stadium Wave", 2014) suggests that considerable natural warming was taking place in the 1980s and 1990s. If the long term (30 years or so) oscillations described in WC14 were incorporated into Figure 25(b) the amount of warming attributed to humans would be much less. Marcia Wyatt does consider variation in total solar irradiance to be a possible cause.

Any computer climate model must establish a track record before its output is used in calculations. The planet Earth is simply too complex and natural climate oscillations are poorly understood. If natural oscillations cannot be predicted they cannot be subtracted from observations to compute the human influence on climate. The debate is not whether humans influence climate, the debate is over how much we contribute and whether the additional warming is dangerous. The jury is still out. Certainly, the case for an impending catastrophe has not been made as this requires two speculative jumps. First, we need to assume that humans drive climate change, second, we need to assume this will lead to a catastrophe. One can predict a possible catastrophe if the most extreme model predictions are correct, but observations show they are not. Only INM-CM4 matches observations reasonably well and INM-CM4 does not predict anything remotely close to a catastrophe.

In the study of the process of evolution the problem is the same. Some believe that the dominant process is natural selection and epigenetic change is minor. Some believe the opposite. Everyone believes that both play a role. As in climate science, figuring out which process is dominant is tough.

Recent climate history (the "pause" in warming and the recent slow rate of warming) suggests that we have plenty of time to get our arms around this problem before doing anything drastic like destroying the fossil fuel industry and sending billions of people into poverty due to a lack of affordable energy. We owe a lot to cheap fossil fuels today. If the projections in WC14 are correct, the "pause" may go on for quite a while, giving us much more time.

In summary, science is a process of disproving ideas that purport to show how natural events occur and why. Science cannot be used to prove anything. Scientific ideas and hypotheses can be proposed, but they must be falsifiable. If no one can disprove an idea, it survives. If it remains viable over a significant period, then the idea becomes a theory.

Thus, climate scientists have not proven that humans control the climate with atmospheric emissions, nor could they ever do so. They also have not disproven that nature controls climate. This is their task, something they must do, if they expect to ever show humans are controlling it. There is abundant evidence that nature and solar variation play a large role in climate change. There is also quite a lot of evidence that greenhouse gases play a small role in influencing global warming as shown by Lindzen and Choi (Lindzen & Choi, 2011), Lewis and Curry (Lewis & Curry, 2018) and (Lewis & Curry, 2015). The median value and best estimate computed by Lewis and Curry is 1.5°C per doubling of CO_2 (Lewis & Curry, 2018). This is a little less than the sensitivity (~2°C) computed from the Russian INM-CM4 climate model (Clutz, 2015). Their value is much less than the sensitivity computed from the average of the other climate models (~3.1°C). Lindzen and Choi compute an even smaller value, roughly 0.44°C per doubling of CO_2 (ECS).

It cannot be said that these papers and other works by climate skeptics disprove the idea that humans have more control over Earth's climate than nature and the Sun, but they do cast considerable doubt on the idea. There is no data that supports the idea of an impending climate catastrophe of any kind. There are ways to create a climate model that shows problematic warming in the far future, but a model can be constructed to do anything you want.

We have tried to show how science works, from a scientist's perspective. Then we used this methodology to show the state of climate science in 2020. Climate scientists are vigorously debating the causes of climate change now and in the future. Alarmists have used models to predict an impending climate disaster. The skeptics have used observations to empirically calculate the effect of CO_2 on climate. The observations show the impact of CO_2 is much less than the models suggest. It seems unlikely that burning fossil fuels is dangerous.

Nothing is settled, nothing is proven, and nothing is disproven. This is a work in progress.

Consensus?

As we have discussed previously, the idea that politicians bring to the debate is that a "consensus" of scientists believe that humans control the climate, and this will lead to disaster. First, consensus has nothing whatever to do with science as we have explained. Second, the various studies, for example John Cook's (Cook, et al., 2013), that claim 97% (or some other large percentage) of scientists believe, "humans cause global warming" are vacuous. Virtually everyone, this author included, believe that. No survey is needed (Tol R. S., 2014). Given that CO_2 and methane are greenhouse gases, this is an obvious statement of fact. The key question, as we mention in the previous section, is how much warming do humans cause. Cook et. al. asked that question but did not report the results. Frank Hobbs (Hobbs, 2015) re-analyzed the same data and found that only 0.5% to 1.6% of the papers explicitly say humans were the primary cause of current global warming. Yet, we hear politicians say that 97% do, confusing "cause" with "primary cause."

Humans contribute to warming, but many believe the contribution is small, perhaps insignificant. Some climate scientists think the total feedback to CO_2 warming is negative reducing the CO_2 effect, Professor Richard Lindzen falls in this camp (Lindzen & Choi, 2011). The direct warming that CO_2 causes, absent all feedbacks, is about one degree C per doubling of CO_2. Others, like most of the IPCC authors, think the feedback will be positive and increase the warming. The IPCC, in AR5, *The Physical Science Basis*, page 60, state that it is extremely likely humans are responsible for more than half of the warming from 1951 to 2010, but this is based on models with well-known flaws (May, 2016i).

The Cook, et al. paper states the obvious and politicians, the news media and armchair climate alarmists all over the world translate its conclusions to some variation of "Humans cause *all* the warming and the warming will lead to disaster!" U.S. President Obama tweeted on May 16, 2013: "Ninety-seven percent of scientists agree: #climate change is real, man-made and dangerous." We can be sure that one-hundred percent of scientists believe climate change (whether natural or man-made) is real, far fewer believe it is all man-made as Obama implies, even fewer think it is dangerous (petitionproject.org, 2009).

The Cook, et al. paper is flawed. As we discussed in Chapter 2, Professor Richard Tol showed that Cook's sample is not representative of the scientific literature on climate change. The "97%" number is a proportion of a small subset of the papers they looked at; it is not a proportion of all climate scientists or papers. Further, they misrepresented the contents of numerous papers, according to the authors (Tol R. S., 2014) and (Tol R. , 2015b). Indeed, one of Richard Tol's papers was misclassified in the Cook study. David Legates and colleagues found that 23 of 64 papers that Cook and his team claim endorsed the standard definition of the consensus did not actually do so, that is 35% of the total (Legates, Soon, Briggs, & Monckton, 2015).

The Cook study has politicized the scientific debate. Nearly every debate over the science of climate change eventually degenerates to the alarmist side proclaiming some variation of: "I must be right, 97% of scientists agree with me." They will take the finding that 97% agree that "humans influence climate change," a true statement, and then surreptitiously add "humans are causing *most* of global warming and it will damage the planet."

Simply believing that a statement is true, without checking it, is not very scientific. Thomas Huxley, the famous English biologist, once said:

> "The [scientist] absolutely refuses to acknowledge authority ... skepticism is the highest of duties, blind faith the one unpardonable sin." (Huxley, 1866)

In the following chapter we will examine the origins of the idea that man-made CO_2 controls the climate and how government involvement has corrupted climate science and made it ineffective. A key weapon in this invasion is the just described and highly political "97% consensus" argument. True scientific debates on whether humans caused most of the climate change since 1951, as asserted by the IPCC in the AR5 report, are rare. There have been a few (May, 2015) and (May, Climate Change: The Great Debate, 2018d), but usually the alarmists prefer to avoid debating the science. They simply appeal to authority and declare that the science is settled, making a debate pointless.

Chapter 7: The Beginning

> "The whole point of science is to question accepted dogmas." Dr. Freeman Dyson to the *Boston Globe*, November 5, 2013 (Heartland Institute, 2015)
>
> "There is something fascinating about science. One gets such wholesale returns of conjecture out of such a trifling investment of fact." Mark Twain in *Life on the Mississippi*, (Twain, 1883, Ch. 17)

As described in the previous chapter, science is a methodology used to explain natural phenomena. The world cooled from 1944 to 1977 and many investigators tried to explain why. Then the world began to warm in 1977 and investigators tried to explain that. Around and around we go.

John Tyndall

John Tyndall was born in 1820 in Leighlin Bridge County Carlow, Ireland. Leighlin Bridge is called Leighlinbridge today. His father was the local constable. While attending the local schools he learned technical drawing and mathematics and after graduating was hired in 1839 as a draftsman by the Ordnance Survey of Ireland. In 1842 he was moved to Great Britain to work for the Ordnance Survey there.

In 1847, he accepted a position teaching mathematics and surveying at Queenwood College, a boarding school in Hampshire. A year later, he and his friend Edward Frankland decided to enroll in the University of Marburg in Germany to study physics and chemistry. While at the University of Marburg, Tyndall studied mathematics, laboratory science and magnetism. His early work on magnetism made his reputation and he was elected a fellow of the Royal Society in 1852 and this was quickly followed by an appointment as Professor of Natural Philosophy (physics) at the Royal Institution in London.

The Royal Institution was founded in 1799. Its purpose was to introduce new technologies and teach science to the public. The professors at the institution were expected to give lectures and demonstrations on their research topics. Edward Frankland was appointed to the Royal Institution at the same time.

Tyndall was a pioneering mountain climber and was one of the first team that climbed to the top of Weisshorn Mountain in the early afternoon of

August 19, 1861 (Jackson, 2018). The Weisshorn is fully within Switzerland and is 4,506 meters (14,783 ft.) high at the summit. Besides mountain climbing Tyndall studied glaciers. He contributed significantly to the mechanics of glacier movement and formation.

In 1859, Tyndall began his now famous work on the interaction of radiation with gases. Tyndall discovered that while the atmosphere is transparent to most incoming solar radiation, once the radiation is absorbed by Earth's surface, it is emitted in a form (now called infrared radiation or IR) that can be absorbed, and later emitted, by greenhouse gases, like carbon dioxide and water vapor. This delays the release of the energy from Earth's surface to outer space and warms the atmosphere, a process we now call the greenhouse effect. In Tyndall's words, "Thus the atmosphere admits of the entrance of the solar heat; but checks its exit, and the result is a tendency to accumulate heat at the surface of the planet" (Tyndall J. , 1859, p. 158). By today's standards he misuses the word "heat," he means thermal energy, but we excuse this, since he said it in 1859.

Josef Stefan would deduce the relationship between the frequency of Earth's emitted radiation and the temperature of the surface in 1879, using Tyndall's experimental results. Ludwig Boltzmann also derived the relationship between frequency and temperature from a theoretical perspective, and now the relationship is known as the Stefan-Boltzmann equation.

Tyndall was a skilled writer and wrote many popular books on science. He married Louisa Charlotte Hamilton, who was in her early thirties when he was 56 years old. Louisa was Tyndall's constant companion and helped him in his laboratory. She was a member of the very cream of English aristocracy and Tyndall was a poor man who lived in four rooms at the Royal Institution, but she joined him there without complaint.

The four rooms were poorly furnished, so a group of more than 300 subscribers, led by the Duke of Northumberland, gave them a silver plate and 300 guineas. Other friends donated some nice furniture and other things to "spruce" the place up for Louisa. They were married in Henry VIII's Chapel in Westminster Abbey on February 29, 1876 (Jackson, 2018, p. 351).

The marriage was a good one and they enjoyed each other's company. Louisa wrote in her diary that, "there is nothing I enjoy more than the stillness of that [laboratory] filled with the presence of my beloved" (Jackson, 2018, p. 358).

Tyndall was popular at the Royal Institution and among the scientific community at large. He was good friends with Louis Pasteur, and they were allies in the fight to convince the world that germs were dangerous, and that sterilization was important in hospitals. At the time many believed that bacteria spontaneously generated, but Tyndall's experiments had shown conclusively that "germs" could often survive hours of boiling and complete sterilization required a great deal of time.

Tyndall was also a contemporary of William Thomson (Lord Kelvin) and had some lively debates with him on radiation and heat. Michael Faraday, Thomas Huxley, Charles Darwin, Rudolf Clausius, Herman Helmholtz, Thomas Carlyle and Alfred Tennyson were all good friends with Tyndall.

Svante Arrhenius

Svante Arrhenius computed the sensitivity, called ECS or the equilibrium climate sensitivity, to the concentration of CO_2 and came up with a fairly large number, about 4°C per doubling of CO_2 in the atmosphere (Lapenis, 1998) and (Arrhenius S. , 1908, p. 53). Arrhenius' estimate is in the range of model-based estimates made today. Years later, Guy Callendar built a good record of CO_2 concentration and a decent record of global temperatures. He used this data to compute ECS empirically and came up with 2°C (Fleming, 2007, p. 72) and (Archer & Rahmstorf, 2009). This is close to the empirical estimate of 1.5°C made recently by Nic Lewis and Judith Curry mentioned in the previous chapter (Lewis & Curry, 2018). It is interesting that the difference between theoretical and observation-based estimates that exists today, is nearly the same as in 1938 when Callendar published his first estimate (Callendar, 1938).

Arrhenius was a Swedish physicist and one of the founders of the science of physical chemistry. He received the Nobel Prize for Chemistry in 1903 and was the first Swedish Nobel laureate.

Arrhenius was a child prodigy and taught himself to read at age three. He was an arithmetical prodigy at a young age. He attended the University of Uppsala but did his dissertation work at the Swedish Academy of Sciences. Once he completed it, he submitted his 150-page dissertation on electrolytic conductivity to the University. They were not impressed by the work and granted Arrhenius a fourth-class degree, but after his thesis defense it was upgraded to third-class. He continued working on the topic, adding to the thesis, and later published it. It was this work that earned him the Nobel Prize. His most important accomplishment was the recognition that solid salts disassociate into charged particles when dissolved in water. He also recognized that acids were fluids that produced hydrogen ions and bases were fluids that produce hydroxide ions.

Arrhenius' first estimate of ECS, published in 1896, was 5°C, he later revised it to 4°C in 1908 (Arrhenius S. , 1908, p. 53). He accomplished this by making detailed calculations based on infrared measurements of the moon by Frank Washington Very and Samuel Pierpont Langley at the Allegheny Observatory in Pittsburg, Pennsylvania. In addition to Very and Langley's measurements, Arrhenius utilized Léon Teisserenc de Bort's estimates of cloudiness for different latitudes, Knut Ångström's bulk absorption coefficients of water vapor and carbon dioxide, Alexander Buchan's charts of mean monthly temperatures over the globe and Arvid Högbom's ideas about the carbon cycle. So, he really pulled together a lot of different data and ideas and presented an impressive model.

Knut Ångström believed that the absorption of infrared radiation, in the bands that water vapor and CO_2 could absorb, were saturated and increasing their concentrations in the atmosphere would have little to no effect. Arrhenius disagreed and said that human emission of CO_2 would be strong enough to prevent the world from entering a new ice age (Arrhenius S. , 1908, pp. 53-54).

Guy Stewart Callendar

As can be seen in Figure 23, there was an earlier 20th century period of warming from 1910 to 1944. Just like in the modern warming period, scientists then wondered why the world was warming and proposed various possible reasons for it. One of the scientists was Guy Callendar. He was the first to convincingly demonstrate that the total Earth's land surface was warming in that period (Hawkins & Jones, 2013). Like today, Callendar suggested that carbon dioxide was responsible for much of the warming (Callendar, 1938). In fact, the idea that carbon dioxide can warm Earth has been called the "Callendar Effect" (Fleming, 2007). He followed Tyndall (Tyndall, 1861) and Arrhenius (Arrhenius, 1896) in reaching this conclusion, as both of them had previously suggested additional carbon dioxide in the atmosphere could have a warming effect because it was infra-red active.

To build his global temperature record, Callendar used data from 147 land-based weather stations. All the stations were between 60°N and 60°S. His temperature reconstruction matches the modern HadCRUT4 land-based 60°N and 60°S record quite well. Callendar's work was received with considerable skepticism at the time. Eventually, even Callendar's supporters gave up defending his ideas when it became apparent that the world was cooling in the 1950s. The cooling from 1944 to 1977 was seen, by most, as a refutation of Callendar's ideas, because CO_2 emissions continued to increase.

Figure 27. Guy Stewart Callendar in 1934. Source: University of East Anglia ana James R. Fleming (Fleming, 2007). Public domain photograph.

Besides creating a worldwide global temperature record, Callendar also established an accurate 19th century background concentration of carbon dioxide and argued the concentration was rising due to human combustion of fossil fuels. He established 290 ppm as the concentration of CO_2 in 1900, a value still used today. The idea that rising CO_2 concentrations were warming Earth, as Arrhenius had proposed in 1896, was still being debated when he did this work. In fact, in 1929, G. C. Simpson wrote,

"now generally accepted that variations in carbon dioxide in the atmosphere, even if they do occur, can have no appreciable effect on the climate." (Fleming, 2007, p. 69)

Earlier, as already mentioned, Knut Ångström had concluded that CO_2 and water vapor absorb radiation in the same spectral regions and the regions were saturated, so additional CO_2 should have no significant effect on temperature. But Callendar's work and publications, plus his evidence that global average temperature had been rising since 1910 revived it. He also carefully documented the worldwide use of fossil fuels and estimated the carbon dioxide uptake by plants and the oceans. He did all this work on his own, without pay.

His "day job" was first as a researcher at the British Electrical and Allied Industries Research Association (BEAIRA) where he worked for his father on the thermodynamics of steam. Later as a researcher for the U.K. Defense Department he invented the burners used in the FIDO fog dispersal system for airfields that became essential during World War II. He shares a patent for that work (Fleming, 2007, p. 47).

One other contribution, by this unassuming, quiet, and careful family man and researcher, was the documentation of glacial advances and retreats around the world. They showed the warming and cooling periods in the past. Callendar knew that most of the last few thousand years had been a period of cooling and that warming had only occurred sporadically. In his opinion, the recent warming, beginning about 1910, was beneficial and he suspected it was due, in part, to additional CO_2 (Fleming, 2007).

Callendar ended his famous 1938 paper with a risky prediction:

"The course of world temperatures during the next twenty years should afford valuable evidence as to the accuracy of the calculated effect of atmospheric carbon dioxide." (Fleming, 2007, p. 72) and (Callendar, 1938)

As we can see in Figure 23, global temperatures started to fall about 1944, just six years later. Callendar was still alive during the very cold winters of 1961 and 1962 and must have been disappointed, because it was clear by then that the world was getting much colder even as the CO_2 concentration was increasing in the atmosphere. But, in Fleming's biography we see no evidence of his ever saying so. In fact, he tried to make excuses by complaining about the global temperature computations and the movement of weather stations (Fleming, 2007, p. 83).

Between Arrhenius and Callendar all the elements necessary for the modern hypothesis of catastrophic anthropogenic global warming (CAGW) and modern climate models were established. This work was done between 80 and 120 years ago, yet their estimates of the possible impact of CO_2 on global temperatures are nearly the same as climate scientists compute today. Callendar's empirical estimate was 2°C (Fleming, 2007, p. 72) and Arrhenius' theoretical value was 4°C per doubling of CO_2 (ECS). Today Nic Lewis and Judith Curry, using modern data, empirically compute an ECS 1.5°C ±~0.4°C (Lewis & Curry, 2018). Using a theoretical model, the IPCC computes an ECS of 3°C, ± 1.5°C (IPCC, 2013, p. 68), a little less than Arrhenius' four degrees. As we discussed previously, there are many ways to computed ECS and the various calculations do not match, so these values are just the most commonly quoted empirical and theoretical values, and not necessarily correct (see Table 1 in Chapter 2).

Callendar did his work at no charge and on his own time, the same is true of Nic Lewis. Judith Curry and Svante Arrhenius were academics and paid modest salaries for their teaching and research. The IPCC has spent over 169 million Swiss Francs ($186 million U.S.) since 1988, not counting independent expenditures by member countries (IPCC, 2019). Yet we are still using the same values of ECS as 80 years ago, within the margin of error.

Modern Climate Science

The first modern theoretical estimates of ECS were reported in 1979 in the so-called "*Charney Report*" (Charney, et al., 1979). As already mentioned previously, the *Charney Report*, on page 2, estimates a theoretical ECS of 1.5°C to 4.5°C per doubling of the CO_2 atmospheric concentration, including an estimate of water vapor feedbacks, the effect of ice and their assumed uncertainties. Absent any water vapor feedback their computed value is 1°C per doubling of CO_2. They also supply a likely value of 2.4°C on page 9, although on page 2 they offer a value "near 3.0." The page 9 value is not far off from the empirical estimate made by Guy Callendar, but significantly higher than the 1.2°C to 1.95°C (best estimate 1.5°C) given by Nic Lewis and Judith Curry (Lewis & Curry, 2018).

The IPCC, in their AR5 report (IPCC, 2013), estimate ECS as lying between 1.5°C and 4.5°C and provide no best estimate. This estimate is precisely the same as the model-based estimate in the Charney Report made 34 years earlier. While the empirical, observation-based, estimates have narrowed to a range of about 1.2°C to 1.95°C recently, the theoretical range has not moved, despite thousands of government-funded scientists spending billions of dollars trying to do so. The data is very much the same today and churning it faster with powerful computers and billions of dollars doesn't seem to change the results. It works that way with manure also.

Digging deeply into AR5, as Monckton, et al. did in MSLB15, discussed in Chapter 2, we see that the elements of the theoretical calculation suggest that the range is narrowing, but in a downward direction. Given the political environment at the IPCC, one can easily suspect that the politicians do not want to admit the risks of CO_2-caused climate change are lessening. As more empirical estimates of the CO_2 effect appear and more theoretical work is done, one wonders how long the politicians can support the clearly incorrect range of 1.5°C to 4.5°C?

The 1980s was when the catastrophic man-made global warming catastrophe (CAGW) idea was developed. The alarmists have been beating the drum year-after-year ever since. In the United States, a Senate committee meeting, hosted by Senator Tim Wirth, on catastrophic climate change took place in the Washington, DC Dirksen Senate Office Building on June 23, 1988. It was a hot and humid day in swampy Washington, DC. The meeting was a watershed moment, in no small part due to Dr. James Hansen of NASA. In his presentation to the Congressional committee, he said:

"It is warmer in 1988 than at any time in the history of instrumental measurements."

"Altogether the evidence that the earth is warming by an amount which is too large to be a chance fluctuation and the similarity of the warming to that expected from the greenhouse effect represents a very strong case. In my opinion, ... the greenhouse effect has been detected, and it is changing our climate now."

"The present observed global warming is close to 0.4 degrees C, relative to 'climatology,' which is defined as the thirty-year (1951 – 1980) mean. ... we can state with about 99 percent confidence that current temperatures represent a real warming trend rather than a chance fluctuation over the 30-year period." (Hansen, 1988)

We will remember, from Chapter 3, that ExxonMobil believed that natural variability was ±0.5°C. They thought that a change had to be larger than that to be significant. Obviously, Hansen has narrowed this somehow. As we have already seen, the period from 1951 to 1977 was a cooling trend, by 1980 it was already on an upswing. An increase of 0.4°C is not much, so using that to determine that the "greenhouse effect" has been detected after a long period of cooling should have raised eyebrows and questions. Notice Hansen says, "greenhouse effect," when he means "human-caused greenhouse effect" or "enhanced greenhouse effect." There is a natural greenhouse effect, caused by natural CO_2 and other greenhouse gases, especially water vapor. This is the beginning of a deceptive tactic commonly used by the alarmists. To ignore natural causes of climate change, they equate "greenhouse effect" with "human-caused greenhouse effect." Also, they use "global warming" as synonymous to "human-caused global warming" and "climate change" is synonymous with "human-caused climate change." This sort of deceptive and manipulative language is still used today.

Senator Timothy E. Wirth said, after the meeting, which he chaired:

"As I read it, the scientific evidence is compelling: the global climate is changing as the earth's atmosphere gets warmer. Now, the Congress must begin to consider how we are going to slow or halt that warming trend and how we are going to cope with the changes that may already be inevitable." *New York Times* June 24, 1988

The first IPCC Report

The IPCC (Intergovernmental Panel on Climate Change) is an independent body founded under the auspices of the World Meteorological Organization and the United Nations Environment Programme. The IPCC states that its goal is:

"The [IPCC] is the international body for assessing the science related to climate change. The IPCC was set up in 1988 … to provide policymakers with regular assessments of the scientific basis of climate change, its impacts and future risks, and options for adaptation and mitigation." (IPCC, 2020)

The UNFCCC or the United Nations Framework Convention on Climate Change, was a convention held to introduce and finalize an international climate change treaty adopted on May 9th, 1992. It was held at the Earth Summit in Rio de Janeiro that same year. The treaty was ratified and went into force in 1994. The UNFCCC Secretariat was also created in 1992 to continue the mission of "supporting the global response to the threat of climate change." (UNFCCC, 2020b). It is not directly connected to the IPCC, but is the organization's cousin. It has a slightly different take on the IPCC mission:

"The Intergovernmental Panel on Climate Change (IPCC) assesses the scientific, technical and socioeconomic information relevant for the understanding of the risk of human-induced climate change." (UNFCCC, 2020)

According to the IPCC they investigate the risks of climate change without any mention of the cause. According to the UNFCCC Secretariat they are to investigate human-caused climate change, these statements are different. In a similar fashion the two bodies define "climate change" differently. The politically oriented UNFCCC Secretariat defines it as:

"[A] change in climate which is attributed directly or indirectly to human activity." (United Nations, 1992)

This contrasts with the IPCC definition of climate change, which is less political and more scientific:

"A change in the state of the climate that ... persists for an extended period, typically decades or longer. Climate change may be due to natural internal processes or external forcings, or to persistent anthropogenic changes in the composition of the atmosphere or in land use" (IPCC, 2012).

We can easily see that the UNFCCC Secretariat and the IPCC have a potential conflict. In fact, if the IPCC does not find that humans have a significant impact on climate, the UNFCCC Secretariat has no reason to exist. In the first IPCC report, published in 1990 and usually called "FAR" for the "IPCC First Assessment Report," they were unsure whether global warming was human-caused or natural, their conclusion was:

> "global-mean surface air temperature has increased by 0.3°C to 0.6°C over the last 100 years ... The size of this warming is broadly consistent with predictions of climate models, but it is also of the same magnitude as natural climate variability. ... The unequivocal detection of the enhanced greenhouse effect from observations is not likely for a decade or more." (IPCC, 1992, p. 6)

Given the wide range of opinions in the scientific community and the lack of solid evidence of human influence on climate, this was a logical conclusion. Bert Bolin was the chairman of the IPCC when FAR was being written and he was an independent-minded and hard-nosed Swedish meteorologist. He said James Hansen's congressional testimony in 1988 had exaggerated the significance of recent global warming. At this time, Margaret Thatcher was a full-blown climate alarmist and Bolin said she was "seriously misinformed" on the subject (Darwall, 2013, Kindle 3307). Later chairmen of the IPCC would not be so skeptical.

The FAR statement caused political problems for the UNFCCC Secretariat and others in government pushing climate alarmism. Enormous pressure was put on the scientists working on subsequent reports to attribute climate change to human activities by the Secretariat, alarmist environmental organizations, and politicians around the world.

The Rio de Janeiro Earth Summit

The United Nations Conference on Environment and Development in Rio de Janeiro in 1992 was organized and led by Maurice Strong who was appointed to be the U.N. Secretary General of the Conference. The political state-of-mind at the time can be seen with this quote from Senator Tim Wirth who attended the 1992 Earth Summit. He said the following four years earlier, in 1988:

"What we've got to do in energy conservation is try to ride the global warming issue. Even if the theory of global warming is wrong, to have approached global warming as if it is real, means energy conservation, so we will be doing the right thing anyway in terms of economic policy and environmental policy." (Sarewitz & Pielke Jr., 2000)

Senator Wirth would later become President Clinton's Under Secretary of State for Democracy and Global Affairs. He repeated most of the above statement again in 1995 at the SAR rewrite events (Bell, 2011, p. 102).

The 40,000 attendees, from 113 countries, at the conference were mostly true believers and thought they were saving the world. They called it the "Only one Earth" conference. The cost of reducing fossil fuel use clearly didn't bother the chairman, Maurice Strong, who later led the effort to put together the Kyoto Protocol. Strong was heard to say:

"If we don't change, our species will not survive... Frankly, we may get to the point where the only way of saving the world will be for industrial civilization to collapse." (National Review 9/1/1997) and (Goldberg, 2009)

Strong also said:

"Isn't the only hope for the planet that the industrialized civilizations collapse? Isn't it our responsibility to bring that about?" (Dewar, 1995)

Strong wanted the world to accept his idea of "sustainable development." He deliberately avoided running for political office to accomplish his goal, instead, according to Elaine Dewar, he decided to work through the United Nations. Working there, "he could raise his own money from whomever he liked, appoint anyone he wanted and control the agenda." She concluded "Strong was using the U.N. as a platform to sell a global environment crisis and the Global Governance Agenda." (Dewar, 1995, p. 330). To do this, in his view, the world needed to reduce resource consumption, especially of fossil fuels, which he claimed would not cause more poverty or lower the standard of living for anyone. He said in his opening speech at the conference:

"This Conference must establish the foundations for effecting the transition to sustainable development This can only be done through fundamental changes in our economic life and in international economic relations." (Strong, 1992)

Later in the opening speech, Strong said:

"patterns of production and consumption in the industrial world … are undermining the Earth's life-support systems; the explosive increase in population, largely in the developing world, that is adding a quarter of a million people daily; deepening disparities between rich and poor that leave 75 per cent of humanity struggling to live; and an economic system that takes no account of ecological costs or damage - one which views unfettered growth as progress. We have been the most successful species ever; we are now a species out of control. Our very success is leading us to a dangerous future.

The concentration of population growth in developing countries and economic growth in the industrialized countries has deepened, creating imbalances which are unsustainable, either in environmental or economic terms. Since 1972 world population has grown by 1.7 billion people, equivalent to almost the entire population at the beginning of this century. … Population must be stabilized, and rapidly. If we do not do it, nature will, and much more brutally." (Strong, 1992)

We now know that the rate of population growth is slowing and has slowed every year for decades. In percentage terms, population growth peaked in 1963 at 2.2% per year. In absolute terms, population growth peaked in 1989 at 88 million. Both are declining rapidly, and growth may hit zero by 2100. The world, especially the developing world, is becoming more affluent, and affluence lowers the birth rate. Strong has it backwards, "unfettered growth," leading to global affluence, is the cure, not the disease (May, 2018, pp. 32-36).

Another leader of the 1992 conference was Richard E. Benedick, who was a special advisor to Maurice Strong. He was a career diplomat and a U.S. deputy assistant secretary of state for environment, health, and natural resources. He supervised policy formation on climate change, stratospheric ozone, biotechnology, tropical forests, oceans, and other environmental and health issues for the United States. Benedick said:

> "A global warming treaty must be implemented even if there is no scientific evidence to back the [enhanced] greenhouse effect." (Bell, 2011, p. 102)

The Second Report, SAR

After SAR, all IPCC reports attributed most climate change and global warming to humans. SAR barely stepped over the threshold with the following conclusion:

> "The balance of evidence suggests a discernible human influence on global climate." (IPCC, 1996, p. 4)

Ronan Connolly and Michael Connolly (Connolly, 2019) explain that this statement was included in SAR because Benjamin Santer, the lead author of the SAR chapter on the attribution of climate change, presented some unpublished and non-peer-reviewed work in which he claimed to have identified a "fingerprint" of human influence on global warming. His evidence consisted of measurements that showed lower atmosphere (tropospheric) warming and upper atmosphere (stratospheric) cooling from 1963-1988. This qualitatively matched a prediction made by the climate models used for SAR. He did not connect these measurements to human emissions of CO_2, or to CO_2 at all, he simply said that they showed something like what the models predicted. From the paper, published the following year:

> "Our results suggest that the similarities between observed and model-predicted changes in the zonal-mean vertical patterns of temperature change over 1963-87 are unlikely to have resulted from natural internally generated variability of the climate system." (Santer B. , et al., 1996a)

Pretty weak evidence, and it was evidence that had not been peer-reviewed or even submitted for publication in 1995, when the decision to include it in SAR was made. Benjamin Santer and Tom Wigley originally wanted the conclusion to read "appreciable human influence," but Bert Bolin proposed "discernible" instead of "appreciable." Bolin's suggestion was adopted without objection (Darwall, 2013).

Santer's paper was eventually published in *Nature*, on July 4, 1996, it was first received by *Nature* April 9, 1996. SAR, *Climate Change 1995, The Science of Climate Change, Contribution of Working Group 1 to the Second Assessment Report of the Intergovernmental Panel on Climate Change*, (IPCC, 1996) was in final form and sent to the Cambridge University publishers in December 1995.

The fifth and final meeting of the IPCC SAR Working Group I was in Madrid, Spain from November 27 to 29, 1995, and was very contentious. They were debating, at the last minute, whether to change the already agreed underlying scientific reports in SAR so they matched the political *Summary for Policymakers* and "Technical Summary" as drafted by John Houghton, the senior editor and co-chairman of the volume with Gylvan Filho. According to Bernie Lewin, in his book *Searching for the Catastrophe Signal* (Lewin, 2017) the argument was largely between Dr. Mohammad Al-Sabban of Saudi Arabia and Dr. Benjamin Santer of Lawrence Livermore National Laboratory in the United States.

The key portion of the report that Santer wanted to change was Chapter 8. Santer was one of the lead authors of the chapter and had written the first draft in April, but now wanted to change it. The original April draft of the chapter is available, thanks to Bernie Lewin, and it concludes in part:

> "...no study to date has both detected a significant climate change and positively attributed all or part of that change to anthropogenic causes." (Lewin, 2017, p. 277)

Santer's original draft of Chapter 8 relied heavily on another unpublished paper that he and Tim Barnett wrote with Phil Jones, Raymond Bradley, and Keith Briffa. The paper is entitled "Estimates of low frequency natural variability in near-surface air temperature." It was later published in *The Holocene* (Barnett, Santer, Jones, Bradley, & Briffa, 1996). The paper forcefully makes the argument that long-term (i.e. low frequency) natural climate variability is not known accurately enough to detect any human climate change contribution with confidence. *The Holocene* received this article July 17, 1995 and it was not approved and published until January 1996. In the conclusions of the paper the authors write:

> The key message of this paper is that, *if* the[paleontological] data are reasonably correct and representative of large regions of the planet, then the *current* model estimates of natural variability cannot be used in rigorous tests aimed at detecting anthropogenic signals in the real world. (Barnett, Santer, Jones, Bradley, & Briffa, 1996), italics in the original.

Thus, they do not think that 1996 model estimates can detect human influence on climate. This conclusion was published a month after Santer and Houghton changed SAR to say that comparing a model to observations did just that. The conclusion of the final draft of SAR Chapter 8, agreed to by all 36 authors, contained the following:

> "we have no yardstick against which to measure the manmade effect. If long-range natural variability cannot be established, then we are back with the critique of Callendar in 1938, and we are no better off than Wigley in 1990." (Lewin, 2017, p. 277)

They compare where they are, in July of 1995, to Guy Callendar's classic 1938 paper and Tom Wigley's chapter on Detecting the Greenhouse Effect in FAR (IPCC, 1990, p. 244). In FAR, on page 244, Wigley and the other authors of Chapter 8 write, "Natural variability of the climate system could be as large as the changes observed to date, but there are insufficient data to be able to estimate its magnitude or its sign." Thus, they didn't know how large the natural forces are, or whether they are working to warm the planet or cool it.

When the authors agreed to the wording of SAR's Chapter 8 (page 409) in July, on the same subject, they still did not think they could detect a human influence on climate. John Houghton, the lead editor of the entire IPCC WG1 second assessment didn't care what the authors concluded. He insisted that the young Benjamin Santer change the chapter and bring it into agreement with his summary.

So, the agreed statement saying "we have no yardstick" quoted above, was removed and the statement below added, without consulting the other 35 authors of Chapter 8.

> "The body of statistical evidence in Chapter 8, when examined in the context of our physical understanding of the climate system, now points towards a discernable human influence on global climate." (IPCC, 1996, p. 439)

The agreement of all chapter authors had been reached in July of 1995 to say the opposite. Another paper of Santer's, published in *Climate Dynamics* in 1995, "Towards the detection and attribution of an anthropogenic effect on climate" (Santer B. , et al., 1995), states, "This analysis supports but does not prove the hypothesis that we have detected an anthropogenic climate change signal."

Santer's 1996 "fingerprint" paper, published after SAR came out, admits that they did not quantify the relative magnitude of natural and human influences on climate. They simply showed a statistically significant similarity between some observations and their model's predictions. As weak, and as new, as this unpublished study was, it was accepted as proof of a "discernable human influence" on climate change.

On November 27, 1995 Santer presented his work to the assembled group and John Houghton. Houghton formed an ad hoc committee to review Santer's work. The committee quickly voted to change Chapter 8 and bring it into line with the drafted *Summary for Policymakers*.

On the last day of the meeting, November 29th, the group debated the changes to the chapter. The Saudis and the Kuwaitis were insistent that the unpublished findings should be presented as preliminary. This had the advantage of being true, after all, the statements hinged on the unpublished and unreviewed fingerprint study.

The debate went on for many hours. The Saudis, led by Dr. Mohammad Al-Sabban, wanted the summary to revert to the agreed text and conclusions of the original chapter, as agreed to by the chapter authors. Most of the others disagreed. The majority prevailed and at 10:30PM, November 29th, the group settled on the final wording, "The balance of evidence suggests a discernable human influence on climate."

Word that unpublished and non-peer-reviewed work had caused the IPCC editors to change the agreed text of Chapter 8 got out. The changes turned critical statements on the detection of human influence on climate change 180 degrees. The statements went from (paraphrasing) "impossible to tell if it exists" to a "discernable human influence."

Frederick Seitz, who was the 17th president of the United States National Academy of Sciences from 1962-1969, was horrified by this action and wrote about it in the *Wall Street Journal* (Seitz, 1996), under the headline "A Major Deception On Global Warming." The late Seitz was a hugely influential scientist, but the IPCC lost his support and the support of hundreds of other influential scientists by caving to the politicians.

Bernie Lewin identified this 1995 meeting in Madrid as a key turning point in the climate change debate. Judith Curry agrees with his conclusion (Curry J. , 2018). The removal of agreed statements from a technical chapter to agree with unsubstantiated political opinions greatly hurt John Houghton's cause and reputation.

Seitz's allegations were contested (Avery, Try, Anthes, & Hallgren, 1996). An open letter to Benjamin Santer was published in the *Bulletin of the American Meteorological Society* (BAMS) supporting him. The letter explicitly mentions the article by Frederick Seitz in the *Wall Street Journal*. It states that the proper place to debate scientific issues is in peer-reviewed journals and not in the media where Seitz published his critical essay. This seems quite hypocritical, as peer-reviewed material was removed by the managing committee of the IPCC and replaced with the unpublished opinions of John Houghton and Benjamin Santer. In any case, the facts are the facts, the original approved draft of Chapter 8 exists, and it was changed by Houghton's supervising committee after review and without consulting most of the authors of the chapter. The facts are clear.

Benjamin Santer admitted changing the draft chapter eight at the behest of the governments but tried to insist that the changes didn't matter (Santer B. , 1996c). Rupert Darwall argues that if they didn't matter why did the governments want them changed? (Darwall, 2013, Kindle 6319). John

Houghton reports in *Nature* (Houghton, 1996) that one of the governments that pressured him to change Chapter 8 was the United States. He wrote that the U.S. found several inconsistencies and "that the chapter authors be prevailed upon to modify their text in an appropriate manner following the discussion in Madrid."

John Houghton wrote that "the IPCC is a scientific body charged with producing scientific assessments." (Houghton, 1996). It clearly is not. The governments funding the IPCC have the right to force these changes, but they can't change what the scientists write and claim the document is scientific. It is either a political document or a scientific document, it cannot be both.

Unfortunately, when Santer's fingerprint paper (Santer B. , et al., 1996) was finally published it ran into a firestorm of criticism. In particular, Dr. Patrick Michaels and Dr. Paul Knappenberger (Michaels & Knappenberger, 1996) pointed out that the tropospheric "hot spot" that comprised Santer et al.'s "fingerprint" of human influence disappeared if the 1963-1987 range was expanded to the full range of available data, 1958-1995. In other words, it appeared Santer, et al. had cherry-picked their "fingerprint."

There were other problems with Santer et al.'s interpretation. The warming and cooling trends that they identified may have been natural, as explained by Dr. Gerd R. Weber (Daly, 1997). The beginning of Santer, et al.'s selected period was characterized by volcanism and the end of the period by strong El Niños. The SAR Chapter 8 scandal left a lasting stain on the reputations of the IPCC, Benjamin Santer, and John Houghton.

Kyoto Agreement

Maurice Strong, the Canadian oil billionaire, was the Secretary-General of the 1992 United Nations Conference on Environment and Development. He also chaired the U.N. Climate Summit, the "Earth Summit" already mentioned, in Rio de Janeiro. The UNFCCC mission statement reads as follows:

"stabilize greenhouse gas concentrations in the atmosphere at a level that would prevent dangerous anthropogenic interference with the climate system." (UNFCCC, 2020)

As Dr. Roger Pielke Jr. has explained, the UNFCCC misdefined "Climate Change" as something caused by "greenhouse gas concentrations" (Pielke, 2005). Pielke believes, correctly, that this faulty definition has caused many problems. In the previous chapter, we saw that a large component of climate change may be natural, yet the mission of the UNFCCC Secretariat ignores this possibility and only focusses on the human contribution, which may be small and insignificant. It also assumes the human-caused portion of climate change is dangerous, even though no evidence supporting this idea exists.

If climate change creates problems in some parts of the world, adapting to it may be the best solution. But the UNFCCC mission statement does not include adaptation, it specifically directs the agency to "stabilize greenhouse gas concentrations," which may or may not be an important factor in climate change. By adopting such a restrictive mission statement, based on assumptions that are unsupported, the UNFCCC creates unnecessary division and conflict and it removes many possible solutions to climate-caused problems from consideration. Further, their definition subjugates all climate policy to energy policy. Yet, to adapt to climate change (whether natural or human-caused) energy will always be required. The UNFCCC produced a mission statement that dictates the actions they will take, and the actions work to reduce the very thing that may be needed to solve all climate related problems, energy.

The next big year in the human-caused global warming/climate change debate was 1998. This was the year Christine Stewart admitted to the *Calgary Herald* (the major newspaper in Calgary, Alberta, Canada) staff that there was an underlying agenda:

"No matter if the science of global warming is all phony…climate change [provides] the greatest opportunity to bring about justice and equality in the world." Christine Stewart, Canadian Minister of the Environment, speaking to the editors and reporters of the *Calgary Herald* in 1998.

This was not long after the Kyoto Protocol was adopted on December 11th, 1997. The protocol requests that "industrialized countries limit and reduce greenhouse gases in accordance with agreed individual targets" (UNFCCC, 2020). These measures would harm the global fossil fuel industry and cause many people to lose their jobs. What are the benefits? We turn again to Roger Pielke Jr., who writes:

> "[According to the IPCC] prevention of all future climate impacts is simply not a viable option. This is of course not an argument against mitigation activities, but frank recognition that under no scenario does conceivable mitigation policies alone fully address the problems to society posed by climate." (Pielke Jr. R. , 2005)

As Rupert Darwall points out, no official economic analysis was done before the Kyoto Protocol was proposed (Darwall, 2013, Kindle 7852). None of the participating countries had any idea what the treaty would cost them, either in jobs or standard of living. They also had no idea what the benefits would be. William Nordhaus, the famous Yale economist and Nobel laureate, called the Kyoto Protocol a "conceptual disaster; it has no coherence politically or economically or environmentally." (Yale University, 2007, pp. 131-132). Kyoto had little to do with climate change, it was mainly an enormous transfer of money from wealthy countries to poor countries.

The climate economist Dr. Bjorn Lomborg famously pointed out that even if Kyoto was fully implemented and more besides, the difference in temperature, in 2050, would only be an imperceptible 0.2°F (Lomborg, 2011). By boxing themselves in, with their restrictive mission statement, the UNFCCC was forced to tackle the most irrelevant part of a potential climate change problem, the human-caused part.

By February 4th, 2015, Christiana Figueres was the Executive Secretary of the UNFCCC and she said this:

> "This is the first time in the history of mankind that we are setting ourselves the task of intentionally, within a defined period of time to change the economic development model that has been reigning for at least 150 years, since the Industrial Revolution." (Zycher, 2015)

These anecdotes and quotes from the key political players show that the climate alarmists are less interested in "saving" us from climate change than in using the threat of a global climate crisis to create a global government. That government would then redistribute the wealth from developed countries to the developing world. By eliminating fossil fuels, they prevent the developing world from developing on their own, thus they need money from the developed world. What the climate warriors really want is a worldwide socialist government.

Their plans do transfer a lot of money and they will kill the fossil fuels industry which provides people a great deal of freedom. After all transporting energy as diesel or gasoline is much easier and cheaper than transporting the equivalent amount of energy in a lithium ion battery. We give up our cheap fossil fuels and they take our freedom.

The Third Report, TAR

The IPCC was embarrassed by the revelation that Santer et al. had fudged the data in their "fingerprint" paper, then used the unpublished paper to alter the SAR conclusions. Further, it was done with John Houghton's blessing and encouragement because he was pressured by the United States and other governments to keep the scientific content of the report aligned with the political message. SAR proclaimed that a human climate impact could be discerned, but the evidence subsequently evaporated.

They found another study to highlight in the third report, called TAR (IPCC, 2001). In 1998, Michael Mann, Raymond Bradley, and Malcolm Hughes published a Northern Hemisphere multiproxy temperature reconstruction of the past 600 years (Mann, Bradley, & Hughes, 1998), based mostly on tree rings. This paper is often abbreviated as MBH98. The reconstruction appeared to show that recent warming period was unusual, so it was easy to assume humans did it. As we showed in Chapter 5, this study was as deeply flawed as Santer's fingerprint study.

The MBH98 graph, only went back to 1400AD, Mann and Bradley extended it the next year to go back to 1000AD in a *Geophysical Research Letters* paper we will abbreviate as MB99 (Mann & Bradley, 1999). This extended graph is often called the "hockey stick" because of its shape. It is featured prominently on page 3 of the TAR *Summary for Policymakers* and is reproduced here as Figure 28.

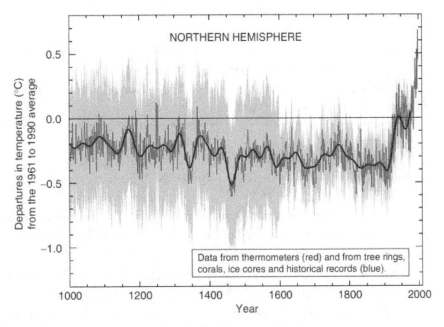

Figure 28. The version of the Mann, Bradley and Hughes temperature reconstruction used in the TAR Summary for Policymakers. Source: (IPCC, 2001b, p. 3). Public domain image, part of Figure 1 in TAR, The Scientific Basis.

The reconstruction in Figure 28 generated a firestorm of criticism. The Santer, et al. SAR Chapter 8 scandal was a campfire compared to the controversy over the hockey stick. Its prominent inclusion in TAR was also widely criticized. But, regardless of the criticism, the graph was used worldwide to increase the certainty that human greenhouse emissions were causing recent global warming. TAR contained the following conclusion, based upon the hockey stick:

> "In the light of new evidence and taking into account the remaining uncertainties, most of the observed warming over the last 50 years is likely to have been due to the increase in greenhouse gas concentrations." (IPCC, 2001, p. 699)

We have documented many of the problems with Mann's hockey stick and his conclusion that 20th century warming is unusual. Mann's conclusions, shown below, are also two of the principal conclusions of TAR (IPCC, 2001, p. 2). TAR refers to the hockey stick as their justification.

> "our results suggest that the latter 20th century is anomalous ... The 1990s was the warmest decade, and 1998 the warmest year, at moderately high levels of confidence." (Mann & Bradley, 1999)

The National Academy of Sciences specifically says they have low confidence in this conclusion. They consider the hypothesis that the 1990s were the warmest years and 1998 the warmest year in a millennium, less than "plausible" (National Research Council, 2006, p. 115). This is an odd way to put it, what is less than plausible? They seem to be euphemistically saying it is incorrect or without justification.

Professor Jonathon Jones, a physicist at Oxford University has written about the MB99 hockey stick. While looking up some detail about the Medieval Warm Period, he discovered the hockey stick and "this weird parallel universe of people who apparently did not believed [the MWP] had happened," and continued:

> "The hockey stick is an extraordinary claim which requires extraordinary evidence...the evidence is extraordinarily weak...its defenders were desperate to hide this fact...I'd always had an interest in pathological science, and it looked like I might have stumbled across a really good modern example...The Hockey Stick is obviously wrong. Everybody knows it is obviously wrong." (Steyn, 2015, Kindle loc. 731)

That pretty much summarizes the general opinion of the hockey stick by experts in the Medieval Warm Period (MWP) and the Little Ice Age (LIA). As Willie Soon and Sallie Baliunas pointed out in great detail (Soon & Baliunas, 2003), the absence of these prominent and well documented climatic anomalies showed the hockey stick was obviously wrong and to have it plastered all over the world was extremely annoying to those that knew this. The 1973 Nobel Prize winner Professor Ivar Giaever said, "Global Warming has become a new religion – because you can't discuss it and that is not right" (Steyn, 2015, Kindle loc. 595). Giaever likens modern climate science to a pseudoscience, an opinion Karl Popper would agree with. The advocates have this hypothesis that humans are causing dangerous climate change and see everything around them as confirming evidence.

At the time Michael Mann's hockey stick was chosen to be Figure 1 of the TAR *Summary for Policymakers*, Mann had just received his PhD. As many have noted, the ink was not yet dry on his diploma. In addition, he was made one of the lead authors of the very section of TAR that presented his hockey stick (see TAR chapter 2 and figure 2.20 on page 134). As a result, it was mostly up to him to validate his own work. In the words of Dr. Rob Van Dorland, an IPCC lead author:

> "It is strange that the climate reconstruction of Mann passed both peer review rounds of the IPCC without anyone ever really having checked it." (McKitrick, 2005)

John Christy was also a lead author of TAR Chapter 2. Later in 2011, after the TAR hockey stick was thoroughly debunked, he commented on it in testimony before the House Science, Space and Technology Committee. He said that many of the Chapter 2 staff were simply enamored by the hockey stick and wanted it to be true. He continued, "Skepticism was virtually non-existent." (Darwall, 2013, Kindle 6442).

Keith Briffa was a contributing author to the chapter. As we mentioned above, Briffa had closely studied bristlecone pine tree rings, especially those that Mann's reconstruction relied upon for the period from 1000AD to 1400AD. The committee reviewed his reconstruction beside Mann's. Briffa's clearly declined after 1960 and began diverging from temperature in the 1930s. The obvious question is, if they declined in the warmth of the twentieth century, how do we know they did not decline in the MWP? Briffa noted Mann's reconstruction was a nice tidy story, but believed the reality was much more complex (Darwall, 2013, Kindle 6477).

After Briffa's comments, it was decided to show both his reconstruction and Mann's in the chapter. But, somewhere in the editing process someone deleted Briffa's curve after 1960. The truncated curve is plotted with Mann's curve in TAR figure 2.21, page 134 and in our Figure 7. If anyone noticed the critical truncation, no one said anything according to John Christy. The data deletion was not mentioned in the caption or in the text. Briffa's discovery that tree rings diverged dramatically from temperatures after 1960 was prominently featured in *Nature*, in 1998 (Briffa, Schweingruber, Jones, Osborn, & Vaganov, 1998b), but ignored in TAR. A political decision was made to ignore peer-reviewed science from the most prestigious scientific journal in the world.

The MBH98 and MB99 papers were deeply flawed, the so-called hockey stick was never validated or reproduced prior to 1600AD, yet it was showcased in IPCC's TAR, with dissenting evidence hidden. It became so famous that it was taught to young children all over the world in elementary schools. It fit the IPCC political agenda, so they jumped all over it.

As discussed in Chapter 5, Willie Soon and Sallie Baliunas recognized that various proxy temperature records cannot be combined, statistically or otherwise, to make a hemispheric or global composite temperature reconstruction of any accuracy (Soon & Baliunas, 2003). However, when viewed individually, they can be used to answer the question of whether the 20th century is the warmest of the second millennium. They showed the MWP and LIA were global climatic events, and more importantly, they showed 20th century warming was not unusual.

Stephen McIntyre and Ross McKitrick thoroughly debunked the hockey stick with a series of papers published between 2003 and 2005. They showed the statistical methods used were inappropriate. Their work was reproduced and confirmed by the National Academy of Sciences (National Research Council, 2006, p. 90) and the Wegman Committee (Wegman, Scott, & Said, 2010).

"Why did the IPCC so quickly and uncritically accept the hockey stick?" asks Dr. Roy Spencer, "Because they wanted to believe it." They needed it as a political tool. They didn't check it in any way, it supported their agenda, so they just ran with it.

The Fourth Report, AR4

By the time the fourth report was written, the MBH98 hockey stick was discredited and in light of this, the lead author of the relevant chapter, Dr. Keith Briffa, admitted that recent warming was not unusual:

> "Some of the studies conducted since the Third Assessment Report (TAR) indicate greater multi-centennial Northern Hemisphere temperature variability over the last 1 kyr than was shown in the TAR, demonstrating a sensitivity to the particular proxies used, and the specific statistical methods of processing and/or scaling them to represent past temperatures. The additional variability shown in some new studies implies mainly cooler temperatures (predominantly in the 12th to 14th, 17th and 19th centuries), and only one new reconstruction suggests slightly warmer conditions in the 11th century, but well within the uncertainty range indicated in the TAR." (IPCC, 2007b, p. 436)

It is a weak admission of failure, as we might expect, but he acknowledges that the hockey stick was too flat and that temperatures during the Medieval Warm Period might have been as high or higher than today. This admission certainly took the wind out of the sails of TAR, so what can they do now? There was no direct data to support the idea that humans were causing global warming.

In the National Academy of Sciences report on Mann's hockey stick (National Research Council, 2006, p. 22) they list four lines of supposed evidence for human-caused global warming, but none are direct. All four are simply observations that match model output. The first claims that cooling in response to volcanic eruptions is consistent with that expected from climate models. This is circular since the models base their response on actual cooling due to volcanic eruptions. Circular reasoning is also used in the second point, that cooling due to increased ice cover during the last glacial maximum, 19,000 years ago, is consistent with model calculations. The calculations are based on ice cover observations.

The third and fourth items are that warming is global, the stratosphere has cooled, and the oceans have warmed. These are so general and can have so many causes, they are almost meaningless. Further, recent stratospheric cooling and ocean warming are probably due to natural factors and unrelated to humans or greenhouse gases. As explained above, Dr. Gerd R. Weber (Daly, 1997) reported that the beginning of Santer, et al.'s "fingerprint" period was characterized by volcanism and the end of the period by strong El Niños. It's a big world out there and very complex, general statements such as these are not evidence of anything.

It is interesting that the AR4 *Summary for Policymakers* was released February 2nd, 2007 (IPCC, 2007). It was the first part of AR4 released to the public, the rest of the report was released piecemeal after the summary, with the synthesis report coming out last on October 31st of the same year. The full report was not approved until November 17th, 2007, yet the *Summary for Policymakers* had been out for almost 10 months (Schlingemann & Foppiano, 2007). This seems backward. Andrew Turnbull, the past head of Her Majesty's civil service and a member of the House of Lords, quipped it was not a summary for policymakers, but a summary by policymakers (Darwall, 2013, Kindle 8949).

What needed to be changed in the rest of the report? Did they want to make sure that nothing in the 1,600 pages of the report conflicted with the political policymaker summary? Did they make political recommendations first and write up the science later? As the Queen of Hearts said in Louis Carroll's *Alice's Adventures in Wonderland*: "Sentence first-verdict afterwards" (Carroll, 1865). Even if this has an innocent explaination, the optics are terrible.

The IPCC decided to emphasize their climate models in AR4, rather than paleo-temperature reconstructions, atmospheric "fingerprints," or any other observational data. They found that if the models were run without any of the assumed human climate forcings the resulting computed global temperatures were flat. You can see this in Figure 25 from AR5 in Chapter 6 and in Figure 29b from AR4 below. Then they rerun the model with human climate forcings (human CO_2 emissions mainly) and the model temperatures will rise. Voila! We have shown human-caused global warming and didn't need observations! With this "proof" they triumphantly write:

"Most of the observed increase in global average temperatures since the mid-20th century is very likely due to the observed increase in anthropogenic greenhouse gas concentrations." (IPCC, 2007b, p. 10)

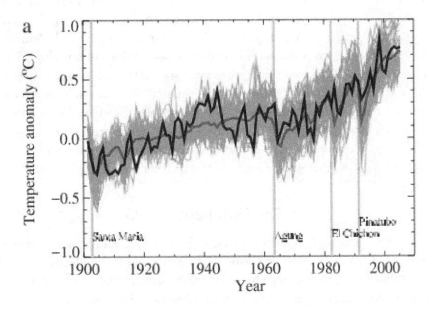

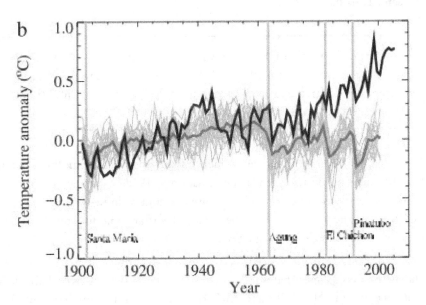

Figure 29. A comparison of climate model runs with computed human influences included (a) and without (b). The heavy black line are the observations. The heavy gray lines are model averages. Source: AR4 (IPCC, 2007b, p. 684). Used with permission.

In the climate simulations shown in Figure 29, the only natural forcings, that make any difference, are volcanic eruptions, since solar variations and ocean oscillations are assumed to net to zero over the period shown (May, 2016i) and (IPCC, 2013, p. 66). The volcanic eruptions are labeled. Perhaps for these reasons, or perhaps for unknown reasons, the rapid warming from 1910 to 1944 is very poorly matched in both Figure 29a and Figure 29b. Given the abundant literature supporting significant solar variability and significant natural ocean oscillations discussed in Chapter 6, plus the model/observation mismatch from 1910 to 1944, it is easy to doubt any calculation of human forcing made from the models shown in Figure 29. Thus, the entire conclusion given in AR4 and the similar conclusion reached with similar logic in AR5 are suspect.

The Fifth Report, AR5

AR5 is essentially a redo of AR4, they do the same thing and take the same approach. No new observational data supporting significant human involvement in climate change is presented, the same models are rerun with a few tweaks here and there and they reach essentially the same conclusion for the same reasons:

> "More than half of the observed increase in global mean surface temperature (GMST) from 1951 to 2010 is very likely due to the observed anthropogenic increase in greenhouse gas (GHG) concentrations." (IPCC, 2013, p. 869)

As far as computing human influence from observations, nothing much has changed since Guy Callendar's calculation in 1938 (Callendar, 1938). The model calculations of human influence are the same as in the Charney Report in 1979 (Charney, et al., 1979). The IPCC wheels are spinning madly and at great expense but gaining no traction.

Monckton, et al.'s MSLB15 paper makes it fairly clear that the newer climate models suggest that the theoretical sensitivity to CO_2 is probably less than suggested in both AR4 and AR5, but the reports are simply hiding this conclusion. The reports become more political and less scientific with each iteration.

TSI and the IPCC

We touched on solar variability as a factor in climate change in Chapter 6. There we saw that Willie Soon, Ronan Connolly and Michael Connolly (Soon, Connolly, & Connolly, 2015) had identified several valid, peer-reviewed solar activity reconstructions that could explain a lot of the warming since 1951 and earlier. These reconstructions were ignored by the IPCC.

As discussed in Chapter 1, Willie Soon is an astrophysicist at the Solar, Stellar and Planetary Sciences Division of the Harvard-Smithsonian Center for Astrophysics. He is a leading authority on the relationship between solar activity and Earth's climate.

At the time AR4 was being written, the accepted solar activity composite, as represented by TSI or Total Solar Irradiance, from satellite measurements, was the ACRIM composite. It was built by Richard Willson and his ACRIM team (Willson, 1997). It shows an increasing trend of solar activity from the 1980s to the 1990s. This supports the idea that at least some of the warming observed then was due to increasing solar activity. Scafetta and Willson in 2014 reported:

> "Our analysis provides a first order validation of the ACRIM TSI composite approach and its 0.037%/decade upward trend during solar cycles 21–22 [1986-1997]. The implications of increasing TSI during the global warming of the last two decades of the 20th century are that solar forcing of climate change may be a significantly larger factor than represented in the CMIP5 general circulation climate models." (Scafetta & Willson, 2014)

Sallie Baliunas and colleagues, in 1995, published evidence in *The Astrophysical Journal*, that our assumptions of the Sun's long-term variability are lower than the observed variability of other similar stars (Baliunas, et al., 1995). So Scafetta and Willson's idea had support in the existing literature. Nicola Scafetta is a professor at the University of Naples Federico II. Prior to that appointment he worked in the ACRIM satellite laboratory and was an adjunct professor at Duke University. He received his PhD in physics from the University of North Texas in 2001. Richard C. Willson is the principal investigator at the ACRIM laboratory in Coronado, California. He received his PhD in atmospheric physics at the University of California at Los Angeles in 1975.

Judith Lean was the lead author in charge of the relevant section of AR4 (Chapter 2.7, p. 188, "Natural Forcings"). Dr. Lean received her degree in atmospheric physics at the University of Adelaide, Australia in 1980. Later she became a Senior Scientist for Sun-Earth System Research at the U.S. Naval Research laboratory. Lean led the development of a rival TSI composite, called PMOD (Fröhlich & Lean, 1998). PMOD showed the opposite trend, it showed solar activity as static or declining and not increasing from 1986 to 1997. Claus Fröhlich and Judith Lean concluded:

> "these results indicate that direct solar total irradiance forcing is unlikely to be the cause of global warming in the past decade, the acquisition of a much longer composite solar irradiance record is essential for reliably specifying the role of the Sun in global climate change." (Fröhlich & Lean, 1998)

Fröhlich and Lean conclude that TSI is unlikely to have caused any global warming, then say they do not have enough data to be sure. As we will see the two groups used different techniques to reach their respective conclusions. The ACRIM group used an engineering approach and examined the raw data from the satellites. The PMOD group simply compared the computed TSI results from the satellites to a model of what they thought the satellite readings should be. Using the latter approach, it is no wonder they want a longer record.

The PMOD and ACRIM composites are complex because the satellite measurements must be scaled properly so they fit together end-to-end. The process is discussed in some detail in Scafetta and Willson's 2014 paper cited above and in their 2019 paper (Scafetta, Willson, Lee, & Wu, 2019). It is also discussed in Fröhlich and Lean, 1998 and in Kopp and Lean, 2011. This is a very important controversy and it directly affects the calculation of human influence on climate, yet it appears the decision to ignore the ACRIM composite and the more active TSI reconstructions, such as the Douglas Hoyt and Kenneth Schatten reconstruction shown in the upper left of Figure 26 in Chapter 6, was a political decision. In 2003, in an interview with Rebecca Lindsey of NASA, Judith Lean explained one of the reasons she developed PMOD.

> "The fact that some people could use [the ACRIM group's] results as an excuse to do nothing about greenhouse gas emissions is one reason, we felt we needed to look at the data ourselves. Since so much is riding on whether current climate change is natural or human-driven, it's important that people hear that many in the scientific community don't believe there is any significant long-term increase in solar output during the last 20 years." (Lindsey, 2003)

The PMOD and ACRIM total solar irradiance reconstructions are shown in Figure 30. The heavy gray straight line in each graph is at 1360.62 W/m² as noted in the figure. The ACRIM record shows an increase to 1996-1997 and a long-term increasing "secular" trend, which continues until about 2000 and then begins to slowly decrease (Scafetta, Willson, Lee, & Wu, 2019). This is best seen by comparing the solar cycle minima. The PMOD composite shows a pronounced and steady decreasing trend.

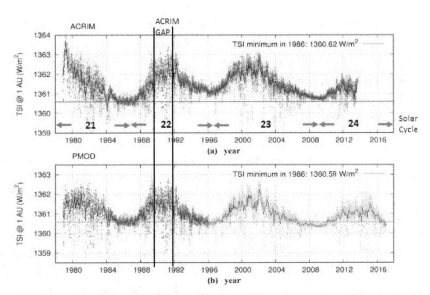

Figure 30. The ACRIM and PMOD TSI reconstructions. The trend of the ACRIM composite is up and the trend of the PMOD composite is flat to down. Focus on the solar minima. Source: Modified after (Scafetta, Willson, Lee, & Wu, 2019). Used with permission.

The Coupled Model Intercomparison Project (CMIP) modelers require a long-term TSI reconstruction as one of their input datasets. These reconstructions use sunspot records and many other proxies of solar activity, calibrated to modern satellite measurements, to extrapolate solar output as far back as 1700AD.

The choice of which TSI composite to use, either PMOD or ACRIM, affects the reconstruction significantly. In addition, the choice of what proxies to use is also important. The IPCC favors, and recommends the modelers use, the Wang, et al. 2005 reconstruction on the upper right of Figure 26 (Wang, Lean, & Sheeley, 2005). Soon, Connolly and Connolly favor the Hoyt and Schatten reconstruction as modified by Scafetta and Willson, it is on the upper left of Figure 26 (Scafetta & Willson, 2014).

The Wang, 2005 reconstruction shows less variation in solar output than most other reconstructions and the underlying long-term trend is flat. A similar, but newer reconstruction, by Greg Kopp and Judith Lean (Kopp & Lean, 2011) is compared to the Hoyt and Schatten reconstruction in Figure 31.

As explained by Ronan Connolly and Michael Connolly (Connolly, 2019), of the five models that contributed to the "natural forcings only" AR4 dataset illustrated in Figure 29(b), four used low variability solar reconstructions favored by Judith Lean. So, it is unsurprising that the natural forcings model does not match the obvious natural warming from 1910 to 1944. It is also not surprising that the "natural only" models in Figure 29(b) show no warming since 1951.

In AR5 the modelers also used solar reconstructions calibrated to Fröhlich and Lean's composite. The more active reconstructions, on the left of Figure 26, use more solar proxies than the "quieter" reconstructions. The quieter reconstructions rely heavily on sunspot numbers for their TSI reconstructions (Soon, Connolly, & Connolly, 2015). Thus, when there are no sunspots, they show no solar variation. Yet in periods of no sunspots, other indications of solar activity do show variability. See Figures 32, 33, and 34 to see this comparison for solar cycle 24. This causes the total variability and the long-term variability to be underestimated.

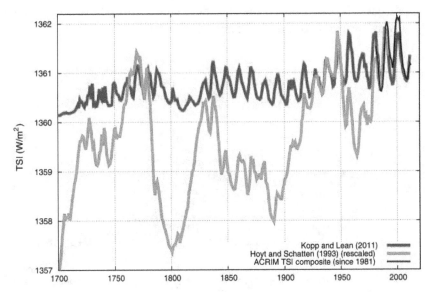

Figure 31. The Hoyt and Schatten TSI reconstruction, calibrated to the ACRIM TSI composite is shown in gray. The Kopp and Lean reconstruction, calibrated to the PMOD composite, is shown in very dark gray. The IPCC ignores the more active reconstructions in their attribution studies. Source: (Scafetta & Willson, 2014) figure 16. Used with Nicola Scafetta's kind permission.

By ignoring the more active TSI reconstructions, the IPCC have not considered a major source of uncertainty. Both the ACRIM- and PMOD-based reconstructions should have been used, or the reason for rejecting the ACRIM composite altogether explained to everyone's satisfaction. In addition, the use of more solar proxies, especially those that show variability when there are no sunspots, should be considered. Considering the full range of possible solar variation has not been done, this is clear from the discussion in (Scafetta & Willson, 2014) and in (Soon, Connolly, & Connolly, 2015). Two modern reconstructions, one from each camp, are compared in Figure 31, with both extended back to 1700AD. The difference between the two is significant and striking.

The attribution of "More than half" of climate change to humans in both AR4 and AR5 is based upon model results and both sets of models, natural only and human plus natural, assume that solar variability was net zero over the period. What would the calculation be if the Hoyt and Schatten reconstruction in Figure 31 were used? Soon, Connolly and Connolly (Soon,

Connolly, & Connolly, 2015) do that calculation. Since 1881 there has been about one-degree C of warming and they show that the Hoyt and Schatten TSI reconstruction can explain all but 0.12°C of that.

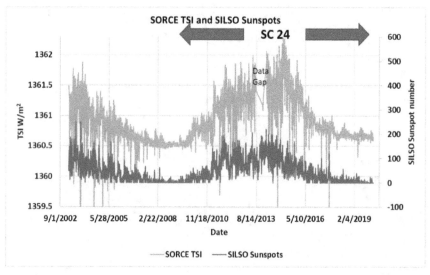

Figure 32. SORCE TSI compared to the SILSO sunspot record. Data from SORCE and SILSO.

As noted above when there are no sunspots, sunspot proxies imply there is no solar variation, but Figures 32, 33, and 34 show this is not the case. The more active reconstructions include proxies that are sensitive to the less active portions of the Sun and are less reliant on sunspot number (Scafetta, Willson and Lee, et al. 2019).

The figures show recent TSI measurements by the SORCE TSI instrument, which measured TSI continuously from 2003 until February of 2020, with one notable gap in 2013. The darker curve in the figures is the SILSO sunspot number (SILSO, 2020). Figure 32 is an overview of the whole record. Figure 33 shows the beginning of solar cycle 24 and Figure 34 shows the end. Periods of zero sunspots still show solar output variability.

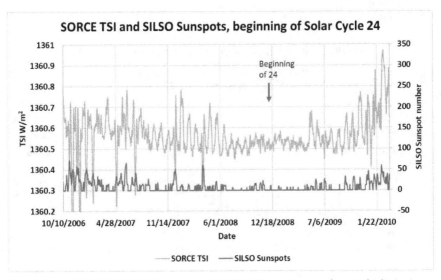

Figure 33. SORCE TSI compared to SILSO sunspot number at the beginning of solar cycle 24. Notice how variable TSI is when there are zero sunspots.

Studies of stars, similar to our Sun, show that it is in a relatively quiet period of its life (Lockwood, Skiff, Baliunas, & Radick, 1992). Lockwood, et al. write:

"This suggests that the Sun is in an unusually steady phase compared to similar stars, which means that reconstructing the past historical brightness record, for example from sunspot records, may be more risky than has been generally thought." (Lockwood, Skiff, Baliunas, & Radick, 1992)

Philip Judge, Ricky Egeland and Gregory Henry published another study of Sun-like stars in 2020 and found that extreme reconstructions, like the Hoyt and Schatten one seen in Figure 31, fall within the normal range for many other Sun-like stars (Judge, Egeland, & Henry, 2020). In Figure 35, from Philip Judge, et al., they have identified two specific extreme periods of solar change in Shapiro, et al.'s 2011 solar reconstruction (Shapiro, et al., 2011). Both changes in solar output fall within the range observed in other Sun-like stars. The right-hand change in Figure 35 occurs in half the stars they studied. Judge,

Egeland and Henry tell us that the IPCC estimates of solar forcing variability are an order of magnitude smaller than those observed in other Sun-like stars.

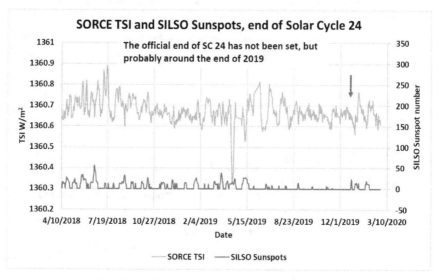

Figure 34. SORCE TSI compared to SILSO sunspot number at the end of solar cycle 24. The probable end of solar cycle 24 is noted by the arrow. Notice how variable TSI is when there are zero sunspots.

Since 1750, the IPCC estimates that humans have contributed 1.1 to 3.3 W/m² of radiative forcing through greenhouse gas emissions and the Sun has provided -0.3 to 0.1 W/m². Philip Judge, et al. show that neighboring Sun-like stars suggest that the solar forcing alone could vary as much as 3.1 W/m², very close to the total forcing required for the 20th century climate changes the IPCC now attributes to humans.

The Shapiro, et al. TSI reconstruction shown in Figure 35 is like the reconstruction by Hoyt And Schatten shown in Figure 31. Both have a range of four to five Watts/m². This is much larger than the range of two Watts/m² for the period that the IPCC prefers.

The use of models to "show" that humans are causing climate change is perfect for the politically motivated IPCC and the UNFCCC Secretariat. One of the key inputs to adjust in the IPCC models is solar variability. If it is invariant, which is unlikely for a variable star like the Sun, most of the warming can be attributed to humans.

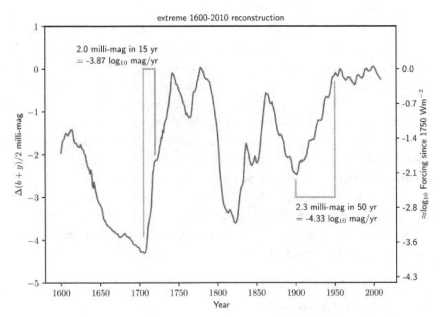

extreme 1600-2010 reconstruction

Figure 35. The solar reconstruction from Shapiro, et al., 2011. The two periods of rapid change in solar output identified are within the range observed by astronomers in other Sun-like stars. Source: (Judge, Egeland, & Henry, 2020). Used with Philip Judge's kind permission.

ACRIM v. PMOD

Whether the ACRIM or the PMOD composite is used to calibrate the solar proxies makes a difference (Fröhlich & Lean, 1998). It is not the sole reason for the difference between the two representative solar reconstructions shown in Figure 30, but it is a big part of it. Nicola Scafetta et al. (Scafetta, Willson, Lee, & Wu, 2019) take a look at the differences in the two composites and provide evidence that the ACRIM composite is preferred.

The most significant difference between the two composites is the overall TSI trend from 1986 to 1997, these are the minima before and after Solar Cycle 22, see Figure 30. The reason that they are so different is that they handle the so-called "ACRIM gap" differently. The ACRIM gap, from mid-1989 to late 1991, had no functioning high-quality TSI-measuring satellite. Only the Nimbus7/ERB and the ERBS/ERBE satellites were functioning, and they had opposite trends. The Nimbus7/ERB measurements trended up 0.26

W/m² per year and the ERBS/ERB trends down 0.26 W/m² per year (Scafetta, Willson and Lee, et al. 2019). This difference was enough that one of the satellites had to be wrong.

The PMOD group used solar proxies and a proxy model to attempt to show that the Nimbus7/ERB instrument had problems. During the gap, the PMOD group then significantly changed the TSI measurements of this instrument and changed the slope of the readings in the gap from positive to negative (Fröhlich & Lean, 1998). Then they further modified measurements from the accurate ACRIM1 and ACRIM2 instruments, claiming they had sensor problems. The PMOD modifications were made without consulting with the original satellite experiment science teams or examining the raw data. Their idea was that their solar proxy models were superior to the data and could be used to "fine-tune" the observations (Scafetta, Willson, Lee, & Wu, 2019) and (Fröhlich & Lean, 1998). Regarding the "corrections" the PMOD team made to the Nimbus7/ERB satellite data, the leader of the Nimbus7 team, Douglas Hoyt, wrote:

> "[The NASA Nimbus7/ERB team] concluded there was no internal evidence in the [Nimbus7/ERB] records to warrant the correction that [PMOD] was proposing. Since the result was a null one, no publication was thought necessary. Thus, Fröhlich's PMOD TSI composite is not consistent with the internal data or physics of the [Nimbus7/ERB] cavity radiometer." (Scafetta & Willson, 2014, Appendix A)

In Judith Lean's 1995 paper in *Geophysical Research Letters*:

> "Deviations of the SMM and UARS data from the reconstructed irradiances in 1980 and 1992, respectively, may reflect instrumental effects in the ACRIM data, since space-based radiometers are most susceptible to sensitivity changes during their first year of operation." (Lean, Beer, & Bradley, 1995)

Yes, Judith Lean is saying that her models "may reflect" that the instruments are wrong. Modifying the measurements to match an unvalidated model is not an accepted practice. Besides the original "corrections" to the satellite measurements made by Fröhlich and Lean, there are new "corrections" suggested by Claus Fröhlich (Fröhlich, Solar Irradiance Variability, 2003). Which set should we use? Scafetta, et al. comment on the "corrections:"

> "a proxy model study that highlights a discrepancy between data and predictions can only suggest the need to investigate a specific case. However, the necessity of adjusting the data and how to do it must still be experimentally justified. By not doing so, the risk is to manipulate the experimental data to support a particular solar model or other bias." (Scafetta, Willson, Lee, & Wu, 2019)

The ACRIM group and Douglas Hoyt believe that the upward trend in the Nimbus7/ERB data is more likely correct than the modeled downward trend created by the PMOD group. Further, the Nimbus7/ERB trend is supported by the more accurate ACRIM1 instrument. The downward trend of the ERBE instrument is in the opposite direction of the ACRIM trend and was caused by well-documented degradation of its sensors. The ACRIM team investigated the PMOD "corrections" to the ACRIM1 and ACRIM2 data and found that they were not justified.

Where is the IPCC?

The IPCC appears to have hit a dead end. They have been unable to find any observational direct evidence that humans contribute to climate change, much less measure the human impact on climate. They are reduced to creating models of climate and measuring the difference between models that include human forcings and those that do not. This done in both AR4 and AR5, the approach was similar and the results similar.

It appears that a significant problem with the AR4 and AR5 results was they used low variability solar variability reconstructions and ignored the equally well supported high variability reconstructions. This reduces the computed natural component of climate change and enlarges the computed human component. Part of the problem with the low variability reconstructions is they are "tuned" to the PMOD TSI composite, which is also based upon a proxy model. Thus, we have used a model to alter satellite measurements, then used the altered measurements to calibrate a proxy model. The proxy model is then projected back to 1700AD. Not very convincing.

What Nicola Scafetta, et al. did in their 2019 paper (Scafetta, Willson, Lee, & Wu, 2019) was reverse the PMOD process. They used the uncontroversial TSI observations before and after the ACRIM gap to build a model of the low-frequency component of the TSI record to fill in the gap. Their process explicitly allows for the models to be missing a slow varying component in the quiet sun regions. They tackled the ACRIM gap problem without using the Nimbus7/ERBS or ERBS/ERBE lower quality records. They simply evaluated how the proxy models reconstruct the ACRIM gap. The proxy models underestimated the TSI increase to the solar cycle 22 peak and overestimated the decline. There were also problems properly reconstructing solar cycles 23 and 24.

Scafetta, et al. then adjusted the models to correct the mismatch (rather than changing the data!) and produced a TSI composite that agreed well with the ACRIM composite and another composite created by Thierry Dudok de Wit (Dudok de Wit, et al. 2017). Both the new composite and the Dudok de Wit composite show an increasing trend from 1986 to 1997, like the ACRIM composite and unlike PMOD.

The new composite shows an increase in TSI of 0.4 W/m^2 from 1986 to 1996 and twice that much from 1980 to 2002. It decreases after 2002. This is like the ACRIM composite. The PMOD composite goes down from 1986 to 1996. Thus, PMOD appears to have been discredited by Scafetta, et al.

The debate on recent solar variability and how to properly correct satellite measured TSI is complex and we will not get into it further here. For this book we only needed to show that the decision of which solar reconstructions to use and which to ignore were political decisions, they were not scientific, and we have done that. For more detail. the interested reader is referred to several posts by the author: (May, How Constant is the Solar Constant?, 2018e), (May, Climate Change, Due to Solar Variability or Greenhouse Gases? Part A, 2018), and (May, Climate Change, due to Solar Variability or Greenhouse Gases, Part B, 2018c). The latter post, Part B, attempts to explain the differences between the ACRIM and PMOD composites. The interested reader is also directed to (Soon, Connolly, & Connolly, 2015), (Scafetta & Willson, 2014) and (Fröhlich & Lean, 1998).

The Political Advantages of the Climate Change Issue

Ambitious politicians love the climate change issue. It is global, it is easy to make a case that a global government is needed to tackle it, especially if they can tie it to human activities. After all, the only way to force worldwide cooperation is with a world government. The only thing that might get in their way is if it can be shown that climate change can be dealt with by local adaptation. In a *National Review* editorial, the editors write:

> "With global warming, the environmental movement thought it had hit the jackpot — a crisis sufficiently long-range that it could not be falsified and broad enough to justify massive political controls on resource use at a global level." (National Review Editors, 2010)

So, we see why politicians embraced the global warming issue, it was a global problem, to them that meant the solution had to be global.

Characterizing the current warming as an urgent and impending crisis is silly considering the scientific evidence we have today. There is no need to remove national boundaries, form a global government and abandon capitalism to "save the world." Climate changes, we all accept this, perhaps it is mostly man-made, perhaps it is mostly natural, we do not know. What we do know is that many communities may be affected by climate change. Sea level is rising about 1.8 to 3 millimeters per year (May, Glaciers and Sea Level Rise, 2017). This is not a large rate, perhaps seven inches to a foot in 100 years, much less than the daily tides. But, if it causes problems, seawalls can be built, people can move from dangerous areas or elevate their houses, it is a problem that can be dealt with locally, as it has for thousands of years. Why use a global solution?

Some think that if enough CO_2 is added to the atmosphere we will undergo out-of-control warming and the world will burn up. This cannot happen if the oceans exist. At every point in the oceans there is a temperature where heat (or more precisely, thermal energy) carried away as latent heat of evaporation exactly equals the energy striking the water from the Sun. The temperature varies depending upon latitude and cloud cover, but in the tropics where the Sun is close to directly overhead on a clear day, the temperature is around 30 to 32 degrees C (86°F) in the open ocean. This value was first computed by Reginald Newell and Thomas Dopplick in 1978 and 1979 (Newell & Dopplick, 1979). Since there is no such balancing temperature on land, the oceans can reach higher temperatures close to land bodies, perhaps up to 36 degrees C (97°F) at the surface. The ocean surface temperatures for the Indian Ocean and the western Pacific are shown in Figure 36. This area usually has the warmest ocean temperatures and no temperature contours above 30 degrees C can be seen. Close to land, in shallow water, we would probably see some in small areas, but at this scale they are not visible.

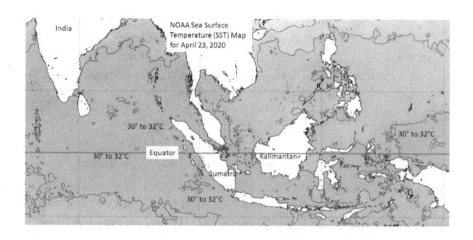

Figure 36. The NOAA sea surface temperature map from April 23, 2020. The contours seen on the map are mostly 30 degree C contours and the ocean areas within the closing 30-degree contours are labeled 30-32 degrees C. Any areas with temperatures above 32 degrees are too small to contour. This area of the western Pacific is usually one of the warmest areas of the world ocean. This illustration is after a public domain map.

The evaporation of water at the ocean surface warms the overlying air and increases the humidity, this is due to the evaporated water vapor carrying thermal energy from the ocean surface. The water vapor lowers the local air density because warm air with a lot water vapor has a lower density than dry air. Water vapor has a density of 0.8 g/liter and dry air has a density of 1.27 g/liter, both at standard conditions. This causes the air to rise, creating convection. The air rises to a level where clouds form, this is an altitude where water vapor, water droplets and/or ice can coexist. At this level, which varies in a complex fashion from place to place, the heat of evaporation (latent heat), carried from the ocean surface in water vapor, is released as the water vapor condenses to liquid droplets. This warms the air and the heat energy is either carried poleward or radiated to outer space. Most surface cooling is done in this way, via "convection." Very little thermal radiation is radiated directly to outer space from the surface.

Poleward from the tropics, the balancing temperature lowers from 30-32 degrees C because the energy striking the ocean from the Sun decreases, due to the oblique angle of incidence. Thus, as long as the oceans exist, we will not burn up due to climate change of any kind.

With fossil fuels or nuclear power, which the climate change alarmists want to eliminate, we can cool or heat our buildings if a community gets too hot or too cold. If we get more rain, we can improve our drainage or move out of flood plains. If it gets too dry, we can drill wells for water or move water via aqueducts. The point is each community needs to deal with its own problems. Climate change is not a problem that must be dealt with by a global government, as the U.N. would have us believe. The people affected and closest to the problem can deal with it in the most effective and efficient manner, as they always have. You don't swat flies with atomic bombs.

Just how much does government need to be involved with scientific research? We will examine this question next.

Chapter 8: How much government involvement in research?

> "Akin to, and largely responsible for the sweeping changes in our industrial-military posture, has been the technological revolution during recent decades.
>
> In this revolution, research has become central, it also becomes more formalized, complex, and costly. A steadily increasing share is conducted for, by, or at the direction of, the federal government.
>
> Today, the solitary inventor, tinkering in his shop, has been overshadowed by task forces of scientists in laboratories and testing fields. ...
>
> The prospect of domination of the nation's scholars by Federal employment, project allocation, and the power of money is ever present and is gravely to be regarded.
>
> Yet in holding scientific discovery in respect, as we should, we must also be alert to the equal and opposite danger that public policy could itself become the captive of a scientific-technological elite." President Dwight David Eisenhower's Farewell Address January 17, 1961 (Eisenhower, 1961)

President Eisenhower correctly predicted the future. We have reached the time he feared. Public policy has become the captive of a scientific-technological elite. The elite are controlled by federal bureaucrats and politicians. Both his fears were realized simultaneously, and a vicious circle of government/scientist co-dependency has developed. Government officials want predicted catastrophes that they can use to grab more power and scientists want a continuous supply of research dollars for themselves and their work. We've provided numerous examples of both problems in this book.

Should bureaucrats control research?

Federal money allows unelected bureaucrats to control scientific research. They dictate the projects, and often the outcomes. They use selective leaks to the press to embarrass any elected politicians who try and interfere with their control over research and outcomes. The bureaucrats trade in fear and relish it. Politicians who disagree with them are suppressing "science." The government money clearly does not improve the research, the theoretical estimates of the impact of man-made CO_2 have not narrowed in 41 years, despite billions in government spending. The empirical estimates are better, but these were not government funded. The funding did not improve science, it was not intended to improve the science, it was only for politics. This was certainly the case in the IPCC as we have seen.

They also use an ignorant and compliant news media, to demonize any privately funded scientific research as "corrupted" by "evil" corporations. The bureaucrats enlist the support of non-profit activists, supported by giant foundations, owned, and controlled by billionaires. These billionaires seek influence and political power. The non-profits lobby the press to get their version of the story out. Every company doing independent research is compared to an evil tobacco company and accused of lying to the public. We saw examples of this in Chapter 3.

This demonization is an attempt to deny corporations, farmers, and others a voice in debates over government regulations and environmental issues. An example is a report from the Union of Concerned Scientists (UCS), a left-wing advocacy non-profit organization that pretends to be scientific. It is well known for slanting its "research" to get desired results (Activist Facts, 2020). The report, *Heads They Win, Tails We Lose* (Grifo, Halpern, & Hansel, 2012), is a blatant attempt to suppress any scientific debate of government regulations by private corporations.

Grifo, et al. complain that there is "inappropriate influence of companies with a financial stake in the outcome." If the companies have a financial stake in the outcome, they *should* be involved in the regulatory debate, how can it be otherwise in a republic? These companies have a first amendment right to be involved. Grifo, et al. are demanding what President Eisenhower feared, "public policy could itself become the captive of a scientific-technological elite."

President Eisenhower had two fears, he was worried that scientists would take over public policy and that government officials would control scientific research and outcomes. We now have a devilish combination of the two.

Why have privately funded research?

The UCS fears that companies will be dishonest. They do not believe companies should use litigation to threaten their opponents into being silent, change their views, or destroy their reputations. They also fear that corporations will not be transparent (Grifo, Halpern, & Hansel, 2012, p. 45). Yet as we saw in Chapter 3, UCS did all these things when they attacked ExxonMobil.

In the 19th and pre-WWII 20th centuries, universities and private sector corporations and individuals worked closely together on research and academic programs. This was a good combination; universities tailored their degree programs and their research towards what industry needed. This supplied the corporations with well-trained employees and helped develop new products that changed the world.

The post-war explosion of federal funding of research is beginning to slow and simultaneously business funding has been increasing since about 2005. In our opinion this is a good trend. Although, federal spending on research is still almost double corporate spending (Mervis, 2017). As a result, university research is still more oriented toward government projects than business ventures and the government projects tend toward fearmongering projects like climate change, rather than projects that create new products and a better society. We believe government funding of research should be no more than corporate funding, and ideally zero because the government funding tends to be destructive and divisive.

Japan (Kazuyuki & Shingo, 2011) and China have many business oriented university projects with American companies. However, the projects in China are often with American companies like Microsoft or Google and are designed to steal U.S. technology (Song, 2008).

In the United States, liberal non-profit organizations, the news media, and some in government have driven a wedge between the natural collaboration between universities and business by demonizing the businesses and any funding they provide to universities. This has hurt the businesses, the universities and research in general. University climate change research is oriented toward creating elaborate scenarios that predict the end of the earth. The scenarios are used to try and eliminate millions of jobs in the fossil fuel industry. They want to create fear in the public and make them more manageable. This increases government power at the expense of the public's individual and property rights.

In the 1970s, the news media predicted we would all die due to global cooling as we saw in Chapter 6. Some scientists even blamed human emissions of CO_2 for the cooling. The media love a good disaster prediction to write about and if humans are to blame, the story is even better. Then warming began and again CO_2 was the reason. Now we are all going to die from CO_2-caused global warming. The shameless media didn't apologize or even blink, they published that as well. When global cooling begins again, as it inevitably will, count on the media to find a compliant scientist to blame CO_2.

It isn't just the government funding. Media attention motivates universities to come up with scary end-of-the-world stories, rather than products that improve our lives. Media attention means more government money. As government money begins to drive university research, the universities become more isolated from the businesses they are supposed to be training employees for.

University tuition and costs have gone up, but even accounting for increasing college costs, on average attending college is still worth it (Abel & Deitz, 2014). This may not be the case in the future, technology may erode the premium that college graduates can demand in the marketplace (Staton, 2014).

This is all happening as the United States has allowed our technology to be stolen by China and other countries. Onerous regulations, justified by sketchy and secret EPA funded research have forced high-paying, high value-add, manufacturing overseas. Other excessive regulations, often designed and justified with secret government scientific research, have been implemented that have made some extraction businesses (mining, oil, and gas) in the United States excessively expensive or impossible.

We are not only sending technology, manufacturing, and extraction overseas, we are simultaneously killing it in the Unites States and in Europe. As high value-add and high salaries leave, the value of a university education becomes less. Service industry jobs, such as mowing lawns, waitressing, or becoming a store clerk, pay less and these are the jobs laid off technology, manufacturing and extraction labor are forced into. These jobs do not require university degrees, but many with college degrees are forced into them when high paying jobs leave. The universities helped engineer the decline in western technology, manufacturing, and extraction and now they are engineering their own decline.

Businesses are far less likely to trust university educations as they become less involved in degree programs. Students are graduating with more debt as costs go up and make less income to pay it back. Many degrees have become valueless. It has been estimated that student debt exceeds 1.5 trillion dollars in the U.S. (Hanson, 2020). This debt slows home buying, marriage and child-rearing, the most important stimulants to our economy.

Victor Davis Hanson speculated in *National Review* that universities are sowing the seeds of their own obsolescence (Hanson, 2020). He is correct. To make universities more relevant to our nation, youth, and economy, we must drastically reduce or eliminate government funded university research.

Defense research, of necessity, must remain under government control and must be done in secret. But, except for defense, the government should withdraw from research funding. Universities need to reform and enlarge their relationships with private industry. Cutting off government funding of research would force this to occur. They must orient their research toward productive areas that create new products, improve our wellbeing, and expand the economy. Their faculties will be forced to move in the same direction and produce better workers for industry. The doom-and-gloom orientation of much of our university Earth science research today is poisonous and destructive.

The media have made scientists into gods that spout "truth" and "prove" things. Neither is possible, as we have seen, scientists only propose temporary ideas and then attempt to disprove them. Truths, or more accurately facts, only exist until disproven. Politicians choose scientists that "prove" things convenient to politicians. Witness the corruption of the scientists in the IPCC, as described in Chapter 7 and elsewhere in the book.

Socrates was a scientist who was killed by politicians in 399BC. Socrates believed that people should question everything. His discussions were full of questions, the questions led to more questions, it was his way of learning and teaching. He never proved anything, but he learned. Finally, by questioning the local gods and religion, he was killed. He defied the consensus with his skepticism and died for it (World History edu, 2020).

The public and the news media, who should be asking probing questions, have become convinced that they cannot understand science. They are reduced to asking scientists to spoon feed them sound bites. With a little work, most lay people can understand scientific papers and they should try. Relying on politicians, scientists, and the media to tell us what is happening is not acceptable. Scientists should write more that can be understood by lay people, as John Tyndall and Svante Arrhenius did. The news media are awful at writing about science because they often have no interest in what is true, they just want attention. We need to figure it out ourselves and remember these words from the great physicist Richard Feynman:

> "Science is the belief in the ignorance of experts." (Feynman, 1966)

Science is a method of uncovering the truth. It is a methodology, honed over millennia, that can be used to destroy what the majority thinks is true, but isn't. When a scientist stops challenging the consensus view, he is no longer a scientist.

The United States has a Constitution that protects individual rights. The bedrock under individual rights are property rights. One can own property and it cannot be taken away without fair compensation. The way around these individual rights is to use the EPA and scary, secret "scientific" findings that frighten people enough to give up their rights and their property for safety.

The best examples of this, are the climate change "scientific" findings described in this book. Any study that challenged the "imminent dangers" of man-made climate change was attacked. The news media abandoned their obligation to educate the public and show there was another interpretation of the data. The *PBS Newshour* once believed there are two sides to every story, but no longer. The news media were used as a tool to attack skeptical scientists personally, as we saw happened to Willie Soon and Sallie Baliunas. Other scientists attacked were William Happer, Fred Singer, David Legates, Roger Pielke Jr., Sherwood Idso, Craig Idso, Roy Spencer, Tim Ball, Frederick Seitz, John Christy, Richard Lindzen, Judith Curry, and Edward Wegman. There are many others as well.

All Computer Models are Wrong

We must have a healthy respect for what computer models can do and can't do. They tell us what might happen, with certain assumptions. They try and tell us what the risk of failure is and what the chances of success are. They help us plan. They are only very rarely correct, but a good model will help you better understand the problem.

When evaluating a model, whether it is a climate model or the models used to set policy during the COVID-19 pandemic, a simple peer-review is insufficient. Too often, in government decision making, the modeler will present his results to a panel of government bureaucrats and invited experts, and they ask questions. If the answers are satisfactory, the model results are accepted, and government policy is set. This is foolish, this sort of review is inadequate.

In the case of climate models, billions may be spent subsidizing wind and solar power installations and electric cars. In the case of Neil Ferguson's Imperial College COVID-19 model (Fund, 2020) trillion-dollar economies were shut down. But the models were wrong, which is normal. Billions and trillions were wasted. In the case of the COVID-19 model, there were coding errors (Dayaratna, 2020) and the model proved to be wildly inaccurate. Coding errors and many other problems with models can be identified if the code and data used are made publicly available and other researchers try to replicate the results. The standard should not be peer-review, the standard should be replicability for any research used to set public policy. This is especially true for expensive policies, like shutting down economies, subsidizing industries, and taking private property using environmental regulations. This recommendation is firmly presented by McIntyre and McKitrick (McIntyre & McKitrick, 2005c).

Lamar Smith's HONEST act is discussed in Chapter 4. Scott Pruitt made a similar rule that all studies used to justify EPA regulations must make their code and data publicly available or the studies cannot be used. These are critical rules to protect our future, regardless of the complaints from the UCS or *Scientific American*.

Had Dr. Neil Ferguson's (Imperial College modeler, see Dayaratna's and Lund's articles cited above) COVID-19 model been made available to other researchers, the errors in it would probably have been found and better policy decisions would have been made. Detailed review of properly documented computer models written by others can be accomplished in a few days to a few weeks, it is not a time-consuming process. When billions or trillions are at stake it is well worth it. All one needs to consider is that "all models are wrong," but some are useful (Box, 1976).

George E. P. Box, who ended his long and illustrious career as the Director of the Statistical Research Group at Princeton University, was a giant in statistical modeling and has a list of accomplishments far too long to list here. When Professor Box says "all models are wrong" we must take him seriously. To find out if a model is useful, even though it is wrong, we first need to replicate the results of interest independently. This is what McIntyre and McKitrick tried to do with Mann's hockey stick, but Mann would not give them enough of his code and data. This is unacceptable, as numerous investigations showed. Millions of dollars of U.S. government money were given to Michael Mann and his co-authors and colleagues to create the hockey stick, the code and data were not Mann's to withold.

Gary King, professor of political science at Harvard University, has written a lot about the importance of replication (King, 1995).

> "the only way to understand and evaluate an empirical analysis fully is to know the exact process by which the data were generated, and the analysis produced." (King, 1995)

Computer models, whether they are reconstructions of ancient climate, the prediction of future climate, or attempts to model the spread of disease, are based on the statistical manipulation of data. These types of studies, as King says, are impossible to understand or verify without replication. Unfortunately, many, if not most, government decision makers do not understand or appreciate the implications of this statement. Their attitude is, "I have to base my decision on something." Meaning they do not want to make the decision themselves; they want a computer model to do the work for them. They confuse model results with data and observations. Model results are projections and they can be anything the modeler wants them to be.

Once the model is replicated, the scientists must examine the model building process carefully and, knowing it is wrong, identify what is "importantly wrong," according to Box. He says, "It is inappropriate to be concerned about mice when there are tigers [around]." Next the model must be used to make a risky prediction. For example, a climate model might be used to predict global average surface temperatures some years ahead. After the years have passed, we can see how close it was.

As we saw in John Christy's graph in Chapter 6 (Figure 24), except for the Russian model INM-CM4, the CMIP models did not do very well. We also found that the array of models utilized by the IPCC came up with vastly different results. In fact, the spread of results exceeds the expected warming, this is important information and suggests the models are not capable of predicting future warming. The predictions are certainly not accurate enough to compute human influence on climate. The models should not be used for decision-making. If concern still exists about possible future warming, we can spend money trying to improve the models, but that is all that is warranted.

The IPCC revealed that their true purpose is to "sell" the idea of dangerous man-made global warming when they used Santer's clearly speculative "fingerprint" of human influence on climate in their second assessment and Mann's untested hockey stick in the third assessment as described in Chapter 7. To display these highly speculative ideas, so prominently, without replicating and thoroughly documenting them is disgraceful. It shows an unseemly desperation.

We also saw politicians from the countries supporting the IPCC insisting that the scientists writing SAR, the second IPCC report, change their scientific reports to match what the politicians wrote in their *Summary for Policymakers*. That the changes were made, at the insistence of politicians, was admitted to by Benjamin Santer (Santer B. , 1996c) and John Houghton (Houghton, 1996). There are no better examples of the corruption of science by politicians than the SAR Chapter 8 scandal and the hockey stick. If the politicians are writing and changing the science in the IPCC reports, the reports are political documents. They can be political or scientific, they cannot be both.

The billions spent by the IPCC and the member countries to research the causes of climate change has not increased our understanding of the impact of human emissions of CO_2. As we saw in Chapter 7, the 2013 AR5 IPCC report spent thousands of pages and millions, perhaps billions, of dollars explaining that the impact of CO_2 is the same as stated in the 1979 Charney report. In fact, the range of values of ECS given in AR5, 1.5°C to 4.5°C, is nearly the same as the difference between Guy Callendar's empirical estimate of 2°C in 1938 and Arrhenius' 1908 theoretical estimate of 4°C. Our understanding of the impact of CO_2 has not improved in over 80 years! It seems all the money went to propaganda.

Finally, in Chapter 3 we saw that state attorneys general (AGs), the UCS, and others used their considerable resources and power, not to fight for justice, but to try and attack and destroy a corporation, ExxonMobil, for political reasons. There was no accusation of a crime. It's not even clear the views of ExxonMobil were all that different from the views of the AGs. But, due to a perceived difference of opinion, these AGs used government resources to try and destroy a public company. It should be clear that the farther we keep scientific research away from government control, the better. It should also be clear that any abuse of the justice system, whether state or federal, for political gain should be severely punished.

Works Cited

Abel, J., & Deitz, R. (2014). Do the Benefits of College Still Outweigh the Costs? *Federal Reserve bank of New York, Current Issues*. Retrieved from https://www.newyorkfed.org/medialibrary/media/research/current_issues /ci20-3.pdf

Activist Facts. (2020). *Union of Concerned Scientists*. Retrieved from Activist Facts: https://www.activistfacts.com/organizations/145-union-of-concerned-scientists/

Allison, B., & Maloney, T. (2019, September 20). Billionaire Candidate Steyer Admits to Carbon 'Dregs' From His Hedge Fund Days. *Bloomberg*. Retrieved from https://www.bloomberg.com/news/articles/2019-09-20/steyer-invests-in-companies-he-says-are-part-of-the-problem

Almasy, S. (2014, February 17). John Kerry: Climate Change as big a threat as terrorism, poverty, WMDs. *CNN*. Retrieved from https://www.cnn.com/2014/02/16/politics/kerry-climate/index.html

andymaypetrophysicist.com. (2020, May 11). *Letters of support for Dr. Willie Soon*. Retrieved from andymaypetrophysicist.com: https://andymaypetrophysicist.files.wordpress.com/2020/05/soon15-april13-12lettersofsupportforwilliesoon.pdf

Archer, D., & Rahmstorf, S. (2009). *The Climate Crisis: An Introductory Guide to Climate Change*. Cambridge: Cambridge University Press. Retrieved from https://books.google.com/books?id=EyYgAwAAQBAJ&dq=+The+Clim ate+Crisis:+An+Introductory+Guide+to+Climate+Change&lr=

Arnold, R. (2016, May 9). *Facts Clear Astrophysicist Soon of Wrongdoing While Indicting Journalists Covering Climate Debate*. Retrieved from Wattsupwiththat.com: https://wattsupwiththat.com/2016/05/09/facts-clear-astrophysicist-soon-of-wrongdoing-while-indicting-journalists-covering-climate-debate/

Arrhenius, S. (1896). On the influence of carbonic acid in the air upon the temperature of the ground. *The London, Edinburgh, and Dublin Philosophical Magazine and Journal of Science, 41*, 237-276. Retrieved from https://www.tandfonline.com/doi/abs/10.1080/14786449608620846?jour nalCode=tphm16

Arrhenius, S. (1908). *Worlds in the Making*. (D. H. Borns, Trans.) New York: Harper and Brothers. Retrieved from https://archive.org/details/worldsinmakinge01arrhgoog/page/n7/mode/2up

Avery, S., Try, P., Anthes, R., & Hallgren, R. (1996, July 25). Open Letter to Ben Santer. *AMS*. Retrieved from https://journals.ametsoc.org/doi/pdf/10.1175/1520-0477-77.9.1961

Baliunas, S., Donahue, R., Soon, W., Horne, J., Frazer, J., Woodard-Eklund, L., . . . Rao, L. (1995). Chromospheric variations in main-sequence stars. *The Astrophysical Journal*, *438*, 269-287. Retrieved from http://adsabs.harvard.edu/full/1995ApJ...438..269B7

Ball, T. (2014). *The Deliberate Corruption of Climate Science*. Seattle: Stairway Press. Retrieved from https://www.amazon.com/Deliberate-Corruption-Climate-Science-ebook/dp/B00HXO9XGS/ref=tmm_kin_swatch_0?_encoding=UTF8&qid=&sr=

Banerjee, N. (2016, January 27). *Years After 'ExxonSecrets,' Activist Applauds New Spotlight on Old Nemesis*. Retrieved from Inside Climate news: https://insideclimatenews.org/news/25012016/years-after-exxon-secrets-kert-davies-applauds-new-spotlight-old-nemesis

Barnett, T., Santer, B., Jones, P., Bradley, R., & Briffa, K. (1996). Estimates of low frequency natural variability in near-surface air temperature. *The Holocene*, *6*(3). Retrieved from https://journals.sagepub.com/doi/abs/10.1177/095968369600600301

Barry, C. (2009, August 20). Plastic Breaks Down in Ocean, After All—And Fast. *National Geographic*. Retrieved from https://www.nationalgeographic.com/news/2009/8/plastic-breaks-down-in-ocean-after-all-and-fast/

Bast, J., & Spencer, R. (2014, May 26). The Myth of the Climate Change 97%. *Wall Street Journal*. Retrieved from https://www.wsj.com/articles/joseph-bast-and-roy-spencer-the-myth-of-the-climate-change-97-1401145980?mg=prod/accounts-wsj

Bates, C., & Rowell, A. (2019). *Tobacco Explained*. WHO. Retrieved from https://www.who.int/tobacco/media/en/TobaccoExplained.pdf?ua=1

Beaulieu, L. (2015, November 19). *How many Citations are actually a lot of Citations*. Retrieved from Ruminating: https://lucbeaulieu.com/2015/11/19/how-many-citations-are-actually-a-lot-of-citations/

Bedford, D., & Cook, J. (2013). Agnotology, Scientific Consensus, and the Teaching and Learning of Climate Change: A Response to Legates, Soon and Briggs.

Science and Education, 22. Retrieved from https://link.springer.com/article/10.1007/s11191-013-9608-3

Behringer, W. (2010). *A Cultural History of Climate.* Cambridge, UK: Polity Press. Retrieved from https://www.amazon.com/Cultural-History-Climate-Wolfgang-Behringer/dp/0745645291

Beitsch, R. (2020, January 14). Steyer claims he divested from fossil fuels a decade ago, but it's more complicated. *The Hill.* Retrieved from https://thehill.com/policy/energy-environment/478320-steyer-claims-he-divested-from-fossil-fuels-a-decade-ago-but-its

Bell, L. (2011). *Climate of Corruption: Politics and Power Behind the Global Warming Hoax.* Greenleaf Books. Retrieved from https://www.amazon.com/dp/B0097K964U/ref=dp-kindle-redirect?_encoding=UTF8&btkr=1

Belvedere, M. (2017, March 28). Like the new EPA chief, Southern Company's CEO doesn't see CO2 as main reason for climate change. *CNBC.* Retrieved from https://www.cnbc.com/2017/03/28/like-the-new-epa-chief-southern-companys-ceo-doesnt-see-co2-as-main-reason-for-climate-change.html

Benestad, R. (2016, January 21). A Mental Picture of the Greenhouse Effect. *Theoretical and Applied Climatology, 128*(3-4), 679-688. Retrieved from https://link.springer.com/article/10.1007/s00704-016-1732-y

Bindoff, N., & Stott, P. (2013). Detection and Attribution of Climate Change: From Global to Regional. In IPCC, *Climate Change 2013: The Physical Science Basis* (p. 1552). Cambridge. Retrieved from http://www.climatechange2013.org/images/report/WG1AR5_Chapter10_FINAL.pdf

Biondi, F., Perkins, D. L., Cayan, D. R., & Hughes, M. K. (1999, May 15). July temperature during the second millennium reconstructed from Idaho tree rings. *Geophysical Research Letters, 26*(10), 1445-1448. Retrieved from https://agupubs.onlinelibrary.wiley.com/doi/pdf/10.1029/1999GL900272

Black, R. (2009, December 3). Climate e-mail hack 'will impact on Copenhagen summit'. *BBC News.* Retrieved from http://news.bbc.co.uk/2/hi/sci/tech/8392611.stm

Bolar, L., & Steel, C. (2014, July 30). *The Chain of Environmental Command: How a Club of Billionaires and Their Foundations Control the Environmental Movement and Obama's EPA.* Retrieved from U.S. Senate Committee on Environment and Public Works:

https://www.epw.senate.gov/public/index.cfm/2014/7/post-53280dcb-9f2c-2e3a-7092-10cf6d8d08df

Booker, C. (2013). *The Real Global Warming Disaster*. Cornwall: Continuum International Publishing. Retrieved from https://www.google.com/books/edition/The_Real_Global_Warming_Dis aster/piDSBAAAQBAJ?hl=en&gbpv=0

Borger, J. (2001, March 29). Bush Kills global warming treaty. *The Guardian*. Retrieved from https://www.theguardian.com/environment/2001/mar/29/globalwarmin g.usnews

Box, G. E. (1976). Science and Statistics. *Journal of the American Statistical Association*, 791-799. Retrieved from http://www-sop.inria.fr/members/Ian.Jermyn/philosophy/writings/Boxonmaths.pdf

Bradley, R. (1999). *Paleoclimatology: Reconstructing Climates of the Quarternary*. Retrieved from https://www.google.com/books/edition/Paleoclimatology/eK47AgAAQ BAJ?hl=en&gbpv=1&printsec=frontcover

Brenan, M. (2019, September 26). Americans' Trust in Mass Media Edges Down to 41%. *Gallup*. Retrieved from https://news.gallup.com/poll/267047/americans-trust-mass-media-edges-down.aspx

Briffa, K. (1999, September 22). *From Michael Mann*. Retrieved from assassinationscience.com: http://www.assassinationscience.com/climategate/1/FOIA/mail/0938018 124.txt

Briffa, K., Jones, P., Schweingruber, F., & Osborn, T. (1998). Influence of volcanic eruptions on Northern Hemisphere summer temperature over the past 600 years. *Nature*. Retrieved from https://www.nature.com/articles/30943

Briffa, K., Schweingruber, F., Jones, P., Osborn, T., & Vaganov, E. (1998b). Reduced Sensitivity of recent tree-growth to temperature at high latitudes. *Nature*, 678-682. Retrieved from https://www.nature.com/articles/35596

Brooke, J. (2001, May 8). Story of Viking Colonies Icy Pompeii. Retrieved from https://www.nytimes.com/2001/05/08/science/story-of-viking-colonies-icy-pompeii-unfolds-from-ancient-greenland-farm.html

Brown, K. (2016, May 17). *New FOIA'd emails tell a very Different Story about how NY AG'S RICO Campaign Started Off*. Retrieved from EnergyInDepth, Climate and Environment: https://eidclimate.org/new-foiad-emails-tell-a-very-different-story-about-how-ny-ags-rico-campaign-started-off/

Brulle, R. (2013, December 21). Institutionalizing delay: foundation funding and the creation of U.S. climate change counter-movement organizations. *Climate Change, 122,* 681-694. Retrieved from https://link.springer.com/article/10.1007/s10584-013-1018-7#MOESM1

Brumfiel, G. (2006, June 28). Academy affirms hockey-stick graph. *Nature, 441,* pp. 1032-1033. Retrieved from https://www.nature.com/articles/4411032a#Sec1

Bruno, K. (2016, January 5). *email: Draft Agenda for a meeting on Exxon.* Retrieved from free beacon: http://freebeacon.com/wp-content/uploads/2016/04/scan0003.pdf

Brysse, K., Oreskes, N., O'Reilly, J., & Oppenheimer, M. (2012). Climate Change Prediction: Erring on the side of least drama? *Global Environmental Change.* doi:10.1016/j.gloenvcha.2012.10.008

Burkhardt, R. (2013, August). Lamarck, Evolution, and the Inheritance of Acquired Characters. *Genetics, 194,* 793-805. Retrieved from https://www.genetics.org/content/genetics/194/4/793.full.pdf

Callendar, G. S. (1938). The artificial production of carbon dioxide and its influence on temperature. *Q. J. R. Meteorol. Soc., 64,* 223-240. doi:10.1002/qj.49706427503

Cardinale, J. B., Gonzalez, A., Allington, G. R., & Loreau, M. (2018). Is local biodiversity declining or not? A summary of the debate over analysis of species richness time trends. *Biological Conservation,* 175-183. doi:https://doi.org/10.1016/j.biocon.2017.12.021

Carlin, A. (2015). *Environmentalism Gone Mad.* Mount Vernon: Stairway Press. Retrieved from https://www.amazon.com/Environmentalism-Gone-Mad-Activist-Discovered-ebook/dp/B00WFN8R50/ref=sr_1_1?dchild=1&keywords=Environmentalism+gone+mad&qid=1588094041&sr=8-1

Carroll, L. (1865). *Alice in Wonderland.* Retrieved from https://wordhistories.net/2019/07/14/sentence-first-verdict-afterwards/

Carter, J., MacKinney, T., Reed, G., & Goldman, G. (2020). *Presidential Recommendations for 2020 A Blueprint for Defending Science and Protecting the Public.* Union of Concerned Scientists. Retrieved from https://ucsusa.org/sites/default/files/2020-01/presidential-recommendations-for-2020_0.pdf

Cascone, S. (2020, April 21). Melting Ice Has Uncovered Hundreds of Ancient Viking Artifacts and a Previously Unknown Trade Route in Norway. *Art News.* Retrieved from https://news.artnet.com/art-world/melting-ice-reveals-ancient-viking-trade-route-1841139#:~:text=A%20trove%20of%20about%20800,a%20result%20of%20global%20warming.&text=In%20a%20melted%20ice%20patch,woolen%20mitten%2C%20and%20a%20tunic.

Cato, A. (2019, October 14). *Disclosure for thee, but not for me.* Retrieved from Daily Caller: https://www.washingtonexaminer.com/opinion/op-eds/disclosure-for-thee-but-not-for-me

CFAN. (2020, July 3). *Climate Forecast Applications Network.* Retrieved from Climate Forecast Applications Network: https://www.cfanclimate.net/products-tropical-cyclones

Charney, J., Arakawa, A., Baker, D., Bolin, B., Dickinson, R., Goody, R., . . . Wunsch, C. (1979). *Carbon Dioxide and Climate: A Scientific Assessment.* National Research Council. Washington DC: National Academies Press. doi:https://doi.org/10.17226/12181

Christiansen, B., & Ljungqvist, F. (2011, December 1). Reconstruction of the Extratropical NH Mean Temperature over the Last Millennium with a Method that Preserves Low-Frequency Variability. *AMS Journal,* 6013-6034. doi:10.1175/2011JCLI4145.1

Christiansen, B., & Ljungqvist, F. C. (2012). The extra-tropical Northern Hemisphere temperature in the last two millennia: reconstructions of low-frequency variability. *Climate of the Past, 8,* 765-786. doi:10.5194/cp-8-765-2012

Christy, J. (2016). *Testimony of John R. Christy.* Washington, D.C.: U.S. House Committee on Science, Space and Technology. Retrieved from https://docs.house.gov/meetings/SY/SY00/20160202/104399/HHRG-114-SY00-Wstate-ChristyJ-20160202.pdf

Clack, C. T., Qvist, S. A., Apt, J., Bazilian, M., Brandt, A., Caldeira, K., . . . Diakov, V. (2017). Evaluation of a proposal for reliable low-cost grid power with 100% wind, water and solar. *PNAS.* Retrieved from https://www.pnas.org/content/pnas/early/2017/06/16/1610381114.full.pdf

CLEAR. (1998). *Affiliations of Selected Global Warming Skeptics.* Environmental Working Group. Retrieved from http://www.documentcloud.org/documents/1700232-clear-affiliations-of-selected-global-warming.html

Climate Accountability Institute. (2019, October 8). *Carbon Majors.* Retrieved from Climate Accountability Institute: https://climateaccountability.org/carbonmajors.html

Climate Change Science Program. (2003). *Our Changing Planet.* Retrieved from https://www.carboncyclescience.us/sites/default/files/documents/2013/ocp2003.pdf

Climate Investigations Center. (2016, January 29). *CIC_v_DOE_court_filing.* Retrieved from cloudfront.net: https://d3n8a8pro7vhmx.cloudfront.net/climateinvestigations/pages/119/attachments/original/1454519977/CIC_First_Amended_Complaint.pdf?1454519977

Clutz, R. (2015, March 24). *Temperatures According to Climate Models.* Retrieved from Science Matters: https://rclutz.wordpress.com/2015/03/24/temperatures-according-to-climate-models/

Coles, P. (2019, April 15). Einstein, Eddington and the 1919 eclipse. *Nature.* Retrieved from https://www.nature.com/articles/d41586-019-01172-z

Columbia Law School. (2020, June 27). *18 U.S. Code § 241.Conspiracy against rights.* Retrieved from Columbia Law School: https://www.law.cornell.edu/uscode/text/18/241

Competitive Enterprise Institute. (2003, December). *Monthly Planet.* Retrieved from cei.org: https://cei.org/sites/default/files/CEI%20Staff%20-%202004%20December%20Edition%20of%20the%20Monthly%20Planet.pdf

Connolly, M., Connolly, R., Soon, W., Moore, P., & Connolly, I. (2018). *Analysis of Greenpeace's business model and philosophy.* Heartland. Retrieved from https://www.heartland.org/publications-resources/publications/analysis-of-greenpeace-business-model?fbclid=IwAR2zExmgrGIgmtqcdRPOfPNG9MqzT-Gm316A57hK_DmvSMkYxjGpDfdo0Y4

Connolly, R. (2019, September 23). *How the UN's climate change panel created a "scientific consensus" on global warming.* Retrieved from Medium: https://medium.com/@ronanconnolly/how-the-uns-climate-change-panel-created-a-scientific-consensus-on-global-warming-a062f5f54ab2

Cook, J., Nuccitelli, D., Green, S., Richardson, M., Winkler, B., Painting, R., . . . Skuce, A. (2013). Quantifying the consensus on anthropogenic global warming in the scientific literature. *Environmental Research Letters, 8.* Retrieved from https://iopscience.iop.org/article/10.1088/1748-9326/8/2/024024/pdf

Cook, R. (2009, December 29). *The lack of climate skeptics on PBS's Newshour.* Retrieved from American Thinker: https://www.americanthinker.com/blog/2009/12/the_lack_of_climate_sk eptics_o.html

Cook, R. (2015, February 26). *"Regurgitate Unsupportable Accusations, We Much?" Kert Davies is Back. Again.* Retrieved from Heartland: https://blog.heartland.org/2015/02/regurgitate-unsupportable-accusations-we-much-kert-davies-is-back-again/

Cook, R. (2020, March 30). *What does nearly $5 million buy?* Retrieved from GelbspanFiles.com: http://gelbspanfiles.com/?p=9968

Costella, J. (2010). *The Climategate Emails.* The Lavoisier Group. Retrieved from https://www.lavoisier.com.au/articles/greenhouse-science/climate-change/climategate-emails.pdf

Cózar, A., Echevarría, F., González-Gordillo, J. I., Irigoien, X., Úbeda, B., Hernández-León, S., . . . Duarte, C. M. (2014, July). Plastic debris in the open ocean. *PNAS.* Retrieved from https://www.pnas.org/content/111/28/10239.short

Crain, W. M., & Crain, N. V. (2014). *The Cost of Federal Regulation to the U.S. Economy, Manufacturing and Small Business.* National Association of Manufacturers. Retrieved from https://www.nam.org/the-cost-of-federal-regulation/

Crook, C. (2010, July 14). Climategate and the Big Green Lie. *The Atlantic.* Retrieved from https://www.theatlantic.com/politics/archive/2010/07/climategate-and-the-big-green-lie/59709/

Curry, J. (2009, November 22). *Curry: On the credibility of climate research.* Retrieved from Climate Audit: https://camirror.wordpress.com/2009/11/22/curry-on-the-credibility-of-climate-research/

Curry, J. (2014, May 20). *Climate scientists joining advocacy groups.* Retrieved from Climate, etc.: https://judithcurry.com/2014/05/20/climate-scientists-joining-advocacy-groups/

Curry, J. (2015, February 25). *Conflicts of interest in climate science.* Retrieved from Climate, Etc.: https://judithcurry.com/2015/02/25/conflicts-of-interest-in-climate-science/

Curry, J. (2017, October 6). *JC interview: hurricanse and global warming.* Retrieved from Climate, Etc.: https://judithcurry.com/2017/10/06/jc-interview-hurricanes-and-global-warming/

Curry, J. (2018, January 3). *Manufacturing consensus: the early history of the IPCC.* Retrieved from Climate, Etc.: https://judithcurry.com/2018/01/03/manufacturing-consensus-the-early-history-of-the-ipcc/

Curry, J. A., & Webster, P. J. (2012, October 28). *Climate Change: No Consensus on Consensus.* Retrieved from Climate, Etc.: https://judithcurry.com/2012/10/28/climate-change-no-consensus-on-consensus/

Cushman Jr., J. (1998, April 26). Industrial Group Plans to Battle Climate Treaty. *New York Times.* Retrieved from https://www.nytimes.com/1998/04/26/us/industrial-group-plans-to-battle-climate-treaty.html

Daly, J. L. (1997, June). *A Discernible Human Influence.* Retrieved from Still Waiting for Greenhouse: http://www.john-daly.com/sonde.htm

Daly, M. (2018, April 26). *Watch Live: EPA chief Scott Pruitt testifies before House panel amid ethics allegations.* Retrieved from PBS: https://www.pbs.org/newshour/nation/watch-live-epa-chief-scott-pruitt-testifies-before-house-energy-panel-amid-ethics-allegations

Daniels, E. (2019, October 31). *Tom Steyer on climate change, capitalism and his chat with the Clintons.* Retrieved from Politico: https://www.politico.com/news/2019/10/31/steyer-clintons-2020-climate-impeachment-062813

Darwall, R. (2013). *The Age of Global Warming: A History.* Quartet Books Limited. Retrieved from https://www.amazon.com/Age-Global-Warming-History/dp/0704373394

Darwin, C. (1859). *On the origin of Species.* Londn: John Murray, Ablemarle Street. Retrieved from http://www.gutenberg.org/files/1228/1228-h/1228-h.htm

Davies, K. (2020, May). *Who we are.* Retrieved from Climate Investigations Center: https://climateinvestigations.org/who_we_are/

Dayaratna, K. (2020, May 18). *Failures of an Influential COVID-19 Model Used to Justify Lockdowns.* Retrieved from The Heritage Foundation: https://www.heritage.org/public-health/commentary/failures-influential-covid-19-model-used-justify-lockdowns

Delingpole, J. (2009, December 24). Climategate: The Corrupton of Wikipedia. *The Telegraph.* Retrieved from http://www.informationliberation.com/?id=28353

deMenocal, P., Ortiz, J., Guilderson, T., & Sarnthein, M. (2000, July). Coherent High- and Low-Latitude Climate Variability During the Holocene Warm Period. *Science*, 2198-2202. Retrieved from https://www.researchgate.net/publication/12453679_Coherent_High-_and_Low-Latitude_Climate_Variability_During_the_Holocene_Warm_Period

Deng, W., Liu, X., Chen, X., Wei, G., Zeng, T., Xie, L., & Zhao, J. (2016, December 21). A comparison of the climates of the Medieval Climate Anomaly, Little Ice Age, and Current Warm Period reconstructed using coral records from the northern South China Sea. *JGR Oceans, 122*(1). Retrieved from https://agupubs.onlinelibrary.wiley.com/doi/full/10.1002/2016JC012458

Dennis, B., Mufson, S., & Clement, S. (2019, September 13). American increasing see climate change as a crisis, poll shows. *Washington Post*. Retrieved from https://www.washingtonpost.com/climate-environment/americans-increasingly-see-climate-change-as-a-crisis-poll-shows/2019/09/12/74234db0-cd2a-11e9-87fa-8501a456c003_story.html

Denton, G., & Karlén, W. (1973, August). Holocene Climatic Variations - Their Pattern and Possible Cause. *Quaternary Research, 3*(2). doi:doi.org/10.1016/0033-5894(73)90040-9

Dewar, E. (1995). *The Cloak of Green.* J. Lorimer. Retrieved from https://books.google.com/books/about/Cloak_of_green.html?id=RN8JA QAAMAAJ

Doran, P. (2009, January 20). Examining the Scientific Consensus on Climate Change. *EOS, 90*(3). Retrieved from https://www.webcitation.org/65ry87IoX

Dornelas, M., Gotelli, N. J., McGill, B., Shimadzu, H., Moyes, F., Sievers, C., & Magurran, A. E. (2014). Assemblage Time Series Reveal Biodiversity Change but Not Systematic Loss. *Science, 344*(6181), 296-299. Retrieved from http://science.sciencemag.org/content/344/6181/296

Dressler, A., & North, G. R. (2013, October 6). Climate change is real and denial is not about the science. *MySanAntonio*. Retrieved from https://www.mysanantonio.com/opinion/commentary/article/Climate-change-is-real-and-denial-is-not-about-4866529.php

Easterbrook, G. (1992, July 6). Has environmentalism blown it? Green Cassandras. *New Republic, 207*(2), pp. 23-25.

eelegal. (2016, May). *GMU and UCS emails*. Retrieved from eelegal.org: https://eelegal.org/wp-content/uploads/2016/05/img20160205_17361082.pdf

Ehrlich, P. (1968). *The Population Bomb*. Buccaneer Books. Retrieved from https://www.amazon.com/Population-Bomb-Paul-Ehrlich-1995-12-01/dp/B01JXQJGRO/ref=tmm_hrd_swatch_0?_encoding=UTF8&qid=1516638475&sr=8-1

EIA. (2020, May 7). *U.S. energy facts explained*. Retrieved from U.S. Energy Information Administration: https://www.eia.gov/energyexplained/us-energy-facts/

Eisenhower, D. D. (1961, January 17). *Farewell Address to the Nation*. Retrieved from mcadams.posc.edu: http://mcadams.posc.mu.edu/ike.htm

Elsevier. (2020). *Undisclosed conflicts of interest*. Retrieved from Elsevier: https://www.elsevier.com/editors/perk/undisclosed-conflicts-of-interest

Environment and Ecology. (2020). *Gaia*. Retrieved from Environment and Ecology: http://environment-ecology.com/gaia.html

EPA. (2003). *EPA's Draft Report on the Environment Technical Document*. EPA. Retrieved from https://nepis.epa.gov/Exe/ZyNET.exe/30005E2Z.txt?ZyActionD=ZyDocument&Client=EPA&Index=2000%20Thru%202005&Docs=&Query=&Time=&EndTime=&SearchMethod=1&TocRestrict=n&Toc=&TocEntry=&QField=pubnumber%5E%22600R03050%22&QFieldYear=&QFieldMonth=&QFieldDay=&UseQFi

EPA. (2009). *EPA: Greenhouse Gases Threaten Public Health and the Environment*. Press Release. Retrieved from https://yosemite.epa.gov/opa/admpress.nsf/0/08D11A451131BCA585257685005BF252

EPA. (2019, October 22). *About Waters of the United States*. Retrieved from EPA: https://www.epa.gov/nwpr/about-waters-united-states

EPA. (2020, May 25). *Clean Air Act Requirements and History*. Retrieved from EPA: https://www.epa.gov/clean-air-act-overview/clean-air-act-requirements-and-history

EPA. (2020b, July 4). *Clean Water Rule: Definition of "Waters of the United States"*. Retrieved from Federal Register: https://www.federalregister.gov/documents/2015/06/29/2015-13435/clean-water-rule-definition-of-waters-of-the-united-states

EPA. (2020c, July 4). *Affordable Clean Energy Rule*. Retrieved from EPA: https://www.epa.gov/stationary-sources-air-pollution/affordable-clean-energy-rule#:~:text=Proposed%20Affordable%20Clean%20Energy%20Rule,fired%20electric%20utility%20generating%20units.

Epstein, A. (2014). *The Moral Case for Fossil Fuels.* Penguin Publishing Group. Retrieved from https://www.amazon.com/Moral-Case-Fossil-Fuels-ebook/dp/B00INIQVJA/ref=sr_1_1?s=digital-text&ie=UTF8&qid=1516628309&sr=1-1&keywords=The+Moral+Case+for+fossil+fuels

Epstein, A. (2016, April 14). *Philosopher Alex Epstein champions fossil fuels at the Senate EPWC -- complete testimony and Q&A.* Retrieved from Youtube: https://www.youtube.com/watch?v=R5KoYJ64vjA&feature=youtu.be

Essex, C. (2010, June 7). *Letter of support for Dr. Willie Soon.* Retrieved from andymaypetrophysicist.com: https://andymaypetrophysicist.files.wordpress.com/2020/05/essex_lettero fsupportforwilliesoon_57_scientists.pdf

ExxonMobil. (2016). *Exxon Internal Documents.* Retrieved from andymaypetrophysicist.com: https://andymaypetrophysicist.files.wordpress.com/2020/03/internal_me mos.zip

ExxonMobil. (2018a). *Cause No. 096-297222-18, Tarrant County District Court, Petitioner's Objections and Response.* Retrieved from https://jnswire.s3.amazonaws.com/jns-media/9b/d2/781207/ExxonStudy.pdf

ExxonMobil. (2018b). *Tarrant County Court, cause no. 096-297222-18, Verified petition and depositions.* Retrieved from https://www.courthousenews.com/wp-content/uploads/2018/01/ExxonDepositions.pdf

ExxonMobil. (2019). *2019 Outlook for Energy: A perspective to 2040.* Retrieved from ExxonMobil: https://corporate.exxonmobil.com/-/media/Global/Files/outlook-for-energy/2019-Outlook-for-Energy_v4.pdf

Feynman, R. (1966). What is Science? National Teachers Association.

Flannery, B. P. (2001). An Industry Perspective on Carbon Management. In N. R. Council, *Carbon Mamagement: Implications for R&D in the Chemical Sciences* (pp. 44-57). National Academy Press.

Flannery, B. P., Callegari, A. J., Hoffert, M. I., Hseih, C. T., & Wainger, M. D. (1985). CO2 Driven Equator-To-Pole Paleotemperatures: Predictions of an Energy Balance Climate Model with and without a Tropical Evaporation Buffer. In E. T. Sundquist, & W. S. Broecker, *The Carbon Cycle and Atmospheric CO2: Natural Variations Archean to Present, Volume 32.* Retrieved from https://agupubs.onlinelibrary.wiley.com/doi/10.1029/GM032p0070

Fleming, J. R. (2007). *The Callendar Effect: The Life and Work of Guy Stewart Callendar (1898–1964), the Scientist Who Established the Carbon Dioxide Theory of Climate Change*. Boston, Mass.: American Meteorological Society. Retrieved from http://www.colby.edu/sts/callendar_effect_ebook.pdf

Frank, P. (2016, April 19). *Systematic Error in Climate Measurements: The surface air temperature record*. Retrieved from Wattsupwiththat.com: https://wattsupwiththat.com/2016/04/19/systematic-error-in-climate-measurements-the-surface-air-temperature-record/

Frazee, G., & Finnegan, M. (2020, January 23). *Remembering Jim Lehrer*. Retrieved from PBS News Hour: https://www.pbs.org/newshour/nation/remembering-jim-lehrer

Freedman, A. (2018, March 17). *What you learn by giving 200 Senate speeches on climate change*. Retrieved from Mashable: https://mashable.com/2018/03/17/sheldon-whitehouse-200-climate-change-speeches/

Freedman, D. (2013, September 1). The Truth about Genetically Modified Food. *Scientific American*. Retrieved from https://www.scientificamerican.com/article/the-truth-about-genetically-modified-food/

Fröhlich, C. (2003). *Solar Irradiance Variability*. AGU. Retrieved from https://scholar.google.com/scholar?hl=en&as_sdt=0%2C44&q=Fr%C3%B6hlich%2C+C.+Solar+irradiance+variability.+In+Geophysical+Monograph+141%3A+&btnG=

Fröhlich, C., & Lean, J. (1998). The Sun's Total Irradiance: Cycles, Trends and Related Climate Change Uncertainties since 1976. *Geophysical Research Letters, 25*(23). Retrieved from https://agupubs.onlinelibrary.wiley.com/doi/pdf/10.1029/1998GL900157

Frumhoff, P. (2016, May 11). *Scientists, Legal Scholars Brief State Prosecutors on Fossil Fuel Companies' Climate Accountability*. Retrieved from Union of Concerned Scientists: https://blog.ucsusa.org/peter-frumhoff/scientists-state-prosecutors-fossil-fuel-companies-climate-accountability

Frumhoff, P. (2016b, May 6). *follow up to April 25 HLS-UCS Meeting*. Retrieved from Climate Litigation Watch: https://climatelitigationwatch.org/wp-content/uploads/2019/05/Frumhoff-blog-admission-post-docs.pdf

Fund, J. (2014, March 31). Gaia Retreats: Environmentalist Has Second Thoughts. *National Review*. Retrieved from https://www.nationalreview.com/corner/gaia-retreats-environmentalist-has-second-thoughts-john-fund/

Fund, J. (2020, May 6). 'Professor Lockdown' Modeler Resigns in Disgrace. *National Review*. Retrieved from https://www.nationalreview.com/corner/professor-lockdown-modeler-resigns-in-disgrace/

Funk, C., & Hefferon, M. (2019, November 25). *U.S. Public Views on Climate and Energy*. Retrieved from Pew Research Center: https://www.pewresearch.org/science/2019/11/25/u-s-public-views-on-climate-and-energy/

GAO. (1996). *Regulatory Burden*. United States General Accounting Office. Retrieved from https://www.gao.gov/products/GGD-97-2

Garneau, R. (2017, March 2). At Last, Greenpeace Admits to 'Rhetorical Hyperbole'. *National Review*. Retrieved from https://www.nationalreview.com/2017/03/greenpeace-environmental-groups-sued-resolute-forest-products-ontario-quebec/

Garret, B. (2014). The Constutional Standing of Corporations. *University of Pennsylvania Law Review*. Retrieved from https://scholarship.law.upenn.edu/cgi/viewcontent.cgi?article=9460&context=penn_law_review

Gell, A. (2014, June 4). The Inside Story Of How Greenpeace Built A Corporate Spanking Machine To Turn The Fortune 500 Into Climate Heroes. *Business Insider*. Retrieved from https://www.businessinsider.com/greenpeace-fortune-500-deforestation-global-warming-2014-6?IR=T

Getler, M. (2009, December 17). *The Mailbag*. Retrieved from PBS Ombudsman: http://www.pbs.org/ombudsman/2009/12/the_mailbag_21.html

Geyer, R. (1993). *A Global Warming Forum: Scientific, Economic and Legal Overview*. Retrieved from https://www.amazon.com/Global-Warming-Forum-Scientific-Economic/dp/0849344190

Giaschi, J. C. (2019, August 22). *Decision in Mann v Ball*. Retrieved from Supreme Court of British Columbia: https://principia-scientific.org/wp-content/uploads/2019/09/mann-judgement-canada.pdf

Gillis, J., & Krauss, C. (2015, November 5). Exxon Mobil Investigated for Possible Climate Change Lies by New York Attorney General. *New York Times*. Retrieved from https://www.nytimes.com/2015/11/06/science/exxon-mobil-under-investigation-in-new-york-over-climate-statements.html?hp&action=click&pgtype=Homepage&module=first-column-region&region=top-news&WT.nav=top-news&_r=1

Gillis, J., & Schwartz, J. (2015, February 21). Deeper Ties to Corporate Cash for Doubtful Climate Researcher. *New York Times*. Retrieved from https://www.nytimes.com/2015/02/22/us/ties-to-corporate-cash-for-climate-change-researcher-Wei-Hock-Soon.html

Global Warming Petition Project. (2007). *Global Warming Petition Project*. Retrieved from Global Warming Petition Project: http://www.petitionproject.org/index.php

Goldberg, C. (1997, September 16). Downsizing Activism: Greenpeace Is Cutting Back. *New York Times*. Retrieved from https://www.nytimes.com/1997/09/16/us/downsizing-activism-greenpeace-is-cutting-back.html

Goldberg, J. (2009, June 18). Fossil Future. *National Review*. Retrieved from https://www.nationalreview.com/magazine/2009/07/06/fossil-future/

Goodess, C. (2003, November). Stormy Times for Climate Research. *Scientists for Global Responsibility*. Retrieved from https://web.archive.org/web/20110525042645/http:/www.sgr.org.uk/resources/stormy-times-climate-research

Gore, A. (1992). *The Earth in the Balance, Forging a new Common Purpose*. Eathscan. Retrieved from https://www.google.com/books/edition/Earth_in_the_Balance/ZOwJAQAAMAAJ?hl=en&gbpv=0

Gough, M. (2003). *Politicizing Science: The Alchemy of Policymaking*. Stanford: Hoover Institution Press. Retrieved from https://www.amazon.com/Politicizing-Science-Policymaking-Institution-Publication-ebook/dp/B001E5E4TS/ref=sr_1_1?dchild=1&keywords=Politicizing+Science&qid=1588096070&sr=8-1

Gray, L. (2013). David Attenborough – Humans are plague on Earth. *The Telegraph*. Retrieved from http://www.telegraph.co.uk/news/earth/earthnews/9815862/Humans-are-plague-on-Earth-Attenborough.html

Graybill, D., & Idso, S. (1993). Detecting the aerial fertilization effect of atmospheric CO2 enrichment in tree-ring chronologies. *AGU, 7*(1). Retrieved from https://agupubs.onlinelibrary.wiley.com/doi/abs/10.1029/92GB02533

Greenpeace. (2016). *Annual Reports*. Retrieved from Greenpeace: https://www.greenpeace.org/archive-international/en/about/how-is-greenpeace-structured/reports/

Greenpeace. (2020). *ExxonMobil Climate Denial Funding 1998-2014*. Retrieved from Exxonsecrets.org: https://exxonsecrets.org/html/index.php

Grifo, F., Halpern, M., & Hansel, P. (2012). *Heads They Win, Tails We Lose, How Corporations Corrupt Science at the Public's Expense*. Union of Concerned Scientists. Retrieved from https://www.ucsusa.org/sites/default/files/2019-09/heads-they-win-report.pdf

Groseclose, T., & Milyo, J. (2005, November). A Measure of Media Bias. *Quarterly Journal of Economics, 120*(4). Retrieved from http://www.stat.columbia.edu/~gelman/stuff_for_blog/Media.Bias.pdf

GWPF. (2019). *The GWPF: History and Mission*. Retrieved from The Global Warming Policy Foundation: https://www.thegwpf.org/who-we-are/

Gwynne, P. (1975, April 28). The Cooling World. *Newsweek*. Retrieved from https://www.scribd.com/doc/225798861/Newsweek-s-Global-Cooling-Article-From-April-28-1975#download

Hahne-Waldscheck, B. (2012, May 8). I'm ashamed of that today! *EIKE - European Institute for Climate and Energy*. Retrieved from https://www.eike-klima-energie.eu/2012/05/08/dafuer-schaeme-ich-mich-heute/

Hamlin, L. (2017, June 21). *Renewable energy cost and reliability claims exposed and debunked*. Retrieved from Wattsupwiththat.com: https://wattsupwiththat.com/2017/06/21/renewable-energy-cost-and-reliability-claims-exposed-and-debunked/

Hannon, R. (2018, March 28). *Modern Warming - Climate Variability or Climate Change*. Retrieved from Wattsupwiththat.com: https://wattsupwiththat.com/2018/03/28/modern-warming-climate-variablity-or-climate-change/

Hannon, R. (2020, May 27). *The Yin and Yang of Holocent Polar Regions*. Retrieved from andymaypetrophysicist.com: https://andymaypetrophysicist.com/2020/05/27/the-yin-and-yang-of-holocene-polar-regions/

Hansen, J. (1988, June 23). *Congressional Testimony of Dr. James Hansen June 23, 1988*. Retrieved from sealevel.info: https://www.sealevel.info/1988_Hansen_Senate_Testimony.html

Hansen, K. (2017, July 28). *Plastics Yet Again*. Retrieved from Wattsupwiththat.com: https://wattsupwiththat.com/2017/07/28/plastics-yet-again/

Hanson, V. D. (2020, July 2). Universities Sowing the Seeds of Their Own Obsolescence. *National Review*. Retrieved from https://www.nationalreview.com/2020/07/universities-sowing-the-seeds-of-their-own-obsolescence/?fbclid=IwAR2V04SdUfamxwmCEhYkU7QljC9-5KlRz25YZjmla3TJKJFWcYo3pPsWffw

Happer, W. (2011, June). The Truth about Greenhouse Gases. *First Things*. Retrieved from https://www.firstthings.com/article/2011/06/the-truth-about-greenhouse-gases

Harder, A., Barrett, D., & Olson, B. (2016, April 13). Exxon Fires Back at Climate-Change Probe. *Wall Street Journal*. Retrieved from https://www.wsj.com/articles/exxon-fires-back-at-climate-change-probe-1460574535

Haughey, N. (1997, January 13). Emergency Greenpeace meeting ends in stand off. *Irish Times*. Retrieved from https://www.irishtimes.com/news/emergency-greenpeace-meeting-ends-in-stand-off-1.21278

Hawkins, E., & Jones, P. (2013, June 21). Notes and Correspondence On increasing global temperatures: 75 years after Callendar. *Royal Meteorological Society, 139*, 1961-1963. Retrieved from https://rmets.onlinelibrary.wiley.com/doi/pdf/10.1002/qj.2178

Hazen, D. (1997, August 28). *It's Not Easy Being Green(Peace)*. Retrieved from Albion Monitor: http://www.albionmonitor.com/9709a/greenpeace.html

Heartland Institute. (2015, April 21). *Willie Soon: Astrophysicist and a Geoscientist Based in Cambridge, Ma.* Retrieved from Heartland.org: https://www.heartland.org/topics/climate-change/willie-soon/index.html

Heede, R. (2014). Tracing anthropogenic carbon dioxide and methane emissions to fossil fuel and cement producers, 1854–2010. *Climatic Change, 122*. Retrieved from https://link.springer.com/article/10.1007/s10584-013-0986-y

Hemingway, M. (2015, June 2). *Senator: Use RICO Laws to Prosecute Global Warming Skeptics*. Retrieved from Washington Examiner: https://www.washingtonexaminer.com/weekly-standard/senator-use-rico-laws-to-prosecute-global-warming-skeptics

Henig, J. (2009, December 10). *Climategate*. Retrieved from FactCheck.org: https://www.factcheck.org/2009/12/climategate/

Heritage Foundation. (2020, May 24). *Property rights - Country rankings*. Retrieved from The Global Economy: https://www.theglobaleconomy.com/rankings/herit_property_rights/

Hobbs, F. (2015, December 20). *What is there a 97% consensus about?* Retrieved from Climate, Etc.: https://judithcurry.com/2015/12/20/what-is-there-a-97-consensus-about/

Horner, C. (2018). *Law Enforcement for Rent.* Competitive Enterprise Institute. Retrieved from https://cei.org/AGclimatescheme

Horner, C. (2019, May 4). *UCLA Litigation Docs Affirm Origin of UCS, Harvard Scramble to Rebut revelation of "Secret Meeting" for AGs.* Retrieved from Climate Litigation Watch: https://climatelitigationwatch.org/ucla-litigation-docs-affirm-origin-of-ucs-harvard-scramble-to-pre-but-revelation-of-secret-meeting-for-ags-prospective-funders/

Houghton, J. (1996, August 22). Justification of Chapter 8. *Nature, 382,* 665. Retrieved from https://www.nature.com/articles/382665a0.pdf?origin=ppub

Huang, S. P., Pollack, H. N., & and Shen, P.-Y. (2008). A late Quaternary climate reconstruction based on borehole heat flux data, borehole temperature data, and the instrumental record. *Geophys. Res. Let., 35.* Retrieved from https://agupubs.onlinelibrary.wiley.com/doi/full/10.1029/2008GL034187

Hufbauer, C. R. (1992, September 13). Global Warming: What my Father Really said. *Washington Post.* Retrieved from https://www.washingtonpost.com/archive/opinions/1992/09/13/global-warming-what-my-father-really-said/5791977b-74b0-44f8-a40c-c1a5df6f744d/

Huxley, T. H. (1866). On the advisableness of improving natural knowledge. *Fortnightly Review.* Retrieved from http://public-library.uk/pdfs/9/260.pdf

Idso, C. (2011). *Estimates of Global Food Production in the Year 2050.* Center for the Study of Carbon Dioxide and Global Change. doi:10.1.1.405.6313

Idso, S. (1984). What if Increases in Atmospheric CO2 Have an Inverse Greenhouse Effect? *Journal of Climatology, 4,* 399-409. Retrieved from https://pubag.nal.usda.gov/download/54926/PDF

Inhofe, J. (2006, June 23). *Inhofe says NAS Report reaffirms 'Hockey Stick' is broken.* Retrieved from U.S. Senate Committee on Environment and Public Works: https://www.epw.senate.gov/public/index.cfm/press-releases-republican?ID=BF2A375E-9FAE-46F3-92B2-F8EA005CD8F1

Inside Politics. (2005, June 17). *Bush/Gore Grades and SAT scores.* Retrieved from Inside Politics: http://www.insidepolitics.org/heard/heard32300.html

Institute of Global Environment and Society. (2014). *IRS Form 990*. Retrieved from Guidestar: https://pdf.guidestar.org/PDF_Images/2014/521/761/2014-521761388-0b7d49e1-9.pdf

IPCC. (1990). *Climate Change, The IPCC Scientific Assessment*. Cambridge: Cambridge University Press. Retrieved from https://www.ipcc.ch/site/assets/uploads/2018/03/ipcc_far_wg_I_full_report.pdf

IPCC. (1992). *Climate Change: The IPCC 1990 and 1992 Assessments*. Canada: IPCC. Retrieved from https://www.ipcc.ch/report/climate-change-the-ipcc-1990-and-1992-assessments/

IPCC. (1996). *SAR, Climate Change 1995, The Science of Climate Change*. Cambridge: Cambridge University Press. Retrieved from file:///F:/Climate_Change/IPCC_Reports/SAR/ipcc_sar_wg_I_full_report.pdf

IPCC. (2001). *Climate Change 2001: The Scientific Basis [TAR]*. New York: University Press. Retrieved from https://www.ipcc.ch/site/assets/uploads/2018/03/WGI_TAR_full_report.pdf

IPCC. (2001b). *Summary for Policymakers*. Cambridge: Cambridge University Press. Retrieved from https://www.ipcc.ch/site/assets/uploads/2018/07/WG1_TAR_SPM.pdf

IPCC. (2007b). *IPCC press release*. Retrieved from IPCC: https://www.ipcc.ch/2007/

IPCC. (2007b). *WG1: Climate Change 2007: The Physical Science Basis (AR4)*. Cambridge University Press. Retrieved from https://www.ipcc.ch/site/assets/uploads/2018/05/ar4_wg1_full_report-1.pdf

IPCC. (2012). *Glossary of terms. In: Managing the Risks of Extreme Events and Disasters to Advance Climate Change Adaptation*. Cambridge: Cambridge University Press. Retrieved from https://archive.ipcc.ch/pdf/special-reports/srex/SREX-Annex_Glossary.pdf

IPCC. (2013). In T. Stocker, D. Qin, G.-K. Plattner, M. Tignor, S. Allen, J. Boschung, . . . P. Midgley, *Climate Change 2013: The Physical Science Basis. Contribution of Working Group I to the Fifth Assessment Report of the Intergovernmental Panel on Climate Change*. Cambridge: Cambridge University Press. Retrieved from https://www.ipcc.ch/pdf/assessment-report/ar5/wg1/WG1AR5_SPM_FINAL.pdf

IPCC. (2014c, April 2). *Coordinating Lead Authors, Lead authors, and review editors.* Retrieved from IPCC Working Group II Contribution to AR5: http://www.ipcc-wg2.org/AR5/images/uploads/WGII-AR5_Authors.pdf

IPCC. (2019). *IPCC Trust Fund Programme and Budget.* IPCC. Retrieved from https://www.ipcc.ch/site/assets/uploads/2019/01/080320190344-Doc2-Budget.pdf

IPCC. (2020). *IPCC Factsheet: What is the IPCC?* Retrieved from IPCC: https://www.ipcc.ch/site/assets/uploads/2018/02/FS_what_ipcc.pdf

IRS. (2020, May 5). *Tax Exempt Organization Search Bulk Data Downloads.* Retrieved from irs.gov: https://www.irs.gov/charities-non-profits/tax-exempt-organization-search-bulk-data-downloads

Istvan, R. (2015, March 1). *Lessons from the 'Irreducibly Simple' kerfuffle.* Retrieved from Climate, Etc.: https://judithcurry.com/2015/03/01/lessons-from-the-irreducibly-simple-kerfuffle/

Jackson, R. (2018). *The Ascent of John Tyndall.* Oxford: Oxford Univerisity Press. Retrieved from https://www.amazon.com/Ascent-John-Tyndall-Mountaineer-Intellectual/dp/0198788959

Jacobson, M., Delucchi, M., Cameron, M., & Frew, B. (2015, December 8). Low-cost solution to the grid reliability problem with 100% penetration of intermittent wind, water, and solar for all purposes. *PNAS.* doi:https://doi.org/10.1073/pnas.1510028112

Jepson, G., Mayr, E., & Simpson, G. (1949). *Genetics, paleontology, and evolution.* Princeton University Press. Retrieved from https://www.cabdirect.org/cabdirect/abstract/19511603281

Jha, G. (2014, August 5). Bihar village rejects solar-powered micro-grid and demands 'real' electricity. *Daily Mail.* Retrieved from https://www.dailymail.co.uk/indiahome/indianews/article-2717149/Bihar-village-rejects-solar-powered-micro-grid-demands-real-electricity.html

Johnson, D. (2019, December 5). *Environmental Group Misrepresented Itself As A Nonprofit In Order To Stick Taxpayers With The Bill For Its Open Records Requests.* Retrieved from Daily Caller: https://dailycaller.com/2019/12/05/climate-investigations-center-misrepresented-nonprofit-taxpayers-bill/

Jones, D. (1993, September 24). *S. Fred Singer Deposition.* Retrieved from OSS: http://www.ossfoundation.us/projects/environment/global-warming/myths/revelle-gore-singer-lindzen/documents/S-F-Singer_Deposition.pdf/view

Jones, J., & Ritter, Z. (2018, January 17). *Americans See More News Bias; Most Can't Name Neutral Source.* Retrieved from Gallup: https://news.gallup.com/poll/225755/americans-news-bias-name-neutral-source.aspx

Judge, P., Egeland, R., & Henry, G. (2020, March 1). Sun-like Stars Shed Light on Solar Climate Forcing. *The Astrophysical Journal, 891*(1). Retrieved from https://iopscience.iop.org/article/10.3847/1538-4357/ab72a9/meta

Kasprak, A. (2019, March 12). *Did Patrick Moore, a Doubter of Anthropogenic Climate Change, Co-Found Greenpeace?* Retrieved from Snopes: https://www.snopes.com/fact-check/patrick-moore-climate-doubter/

Kazman, S. (2011, March 17). How Washington Ruined Your Washing Machine. *Wall Street Journal.* Retrieved from https://www.wsj.com/articles/SB10001424052748704662604576202212717670514

Kazuyuki, M., & Shingo, M. (2011). *Examining the University Industry Collaboration Policy in Japan: Patent Analysis.* Rieti. Retrieved from https://www.rieti.go.jp/jp/publications/dp/11e008.pdf

Kenny, M. O. (2019, March 15). *Top Five Unbiased Fact-Checking Websites For Finding The Truth.* Retrieved from Lazy Truth: http://www.lazytruth.com/top-five-unbiased-fact-checking-websites-for-finding-the-truth/

Kheshgi, H., & White, B. (2001). Testing Distributed Parameter Hypotheses for the Detection of Climate Change. *Journal of Climate, 14*, 3464-3481. Retrieved from https://journals.ametsoc.org/doi/pdf/10.1175/1520-0442(2001)014%3C3464%3ATDPHFT%3E2.0.CO%3B2

King, G. (1995, September). Replication, Replication. *Political Science and Politics.* Retrieved from https://gking.harvard.edu/files/gking/files/replication.pdf

Kliegman, J. (2014, May 13). *Marco Rubio says humans are not causing climate change.* Retrieved from Politifact: https://www.politifact.com/factchecks/2014/may/13/marco-rubio/marco-rubio-says-humans-are-not-causing-climate-ch/

Knies, J., Cabedo-Sanz, P., Belt, S., Baranwal, S., Fietz, S., & Rosell-Mele, A. (2014). The emergence of modern sea ice cover in the Arctic Ocean. *Nature Communications, 5.* doi:https://doi.org/10.1038/ncomms6608

Kopp, G., & Lean, J. (2011, January 14). A new, lower value of total solar irradiance: Evidence and climate significance. *Geophysical Research Letters, 38*(1). Retrieved from https://agupubs.onlinelibrary.wiley.com/doi/full/10.1029/2010GL045777

Kovacs, W. (2020, April 2). Massachusetts v. EPA: After 13 years, it's time for climate policy review. *The Hill.* Retrieved from https://thehill.com/opinion/energy-environment/490813-mass-v-epa-after-13-years-its-time-for-climate-policy-review

Lamarck, J. B. (1801). Système des animaux sans vertèbres... *précédé du Discours d'ouverture de l'an VIII de la République.*

Lamarck, J. B. (1802). Recherches sur l'organisation des corps vivans et particulièrement sur son origine, sur la cause de ses développemens et des progrès de sa composition, et sur celle qui, tendant continuellement à la détruire dans chaque individu, amène nécessairement sa.

Lamb, H. H. (1965). The Early Medieval Warm Epoch and its Sequel. *Palaeogeography, Palaeoclimatology, Palaeoecology.* Retrieved from http://citeseerx.ist.psu.edu/viewdoc/download?doi=10.1.1.455.9147&rep=rep1&type=pdf

Lancaster, J. J. (2006, July 6). *The Cosmos Myth.* Retrieved from OSS: http://www.ossfoundation.us/projects/environment/global-warming/myths/revelle-gore-singer-lindzen

Lapenis, A. G. (1998). Arrhenius and the Intergovernmental Panel on Climate Change. *Eos, 79*(23).

Lean, J., Beer, J., & Bradley, R. (1995). Reconstruction of solar irradiance since 1610: Implications for climate change. *Geophysical Research Letters.* Retrieved from https://agupubs.onlinelibrary.wiley.com/doi/abs/10.1029/95GL03093

Legates, D. (2003, August 25). Global warming smear targets. *Washington Times.* Retrieved from https://www.washingtontimes.com/news/2003/aug/25/20030825-090130-5881r/

Legates, D. R., Eschenbach, W., & Soon, W. (2014, May 27). Arctic albedo changes are small compared with changes in cloud cover in the tropics. *PNAS.* Retrieved from https://www.pnas.org/content/111/21/E2157.short

Legates, D., Soon, W., & Briggs, W. (2013, March 23). Learning and Teaching Climate Science: The Perils of Consensus Knowledge Using Agnotology. *Science and Education.* Retrieved from http://www.landandwaterusa.com/WillieSoon/2013_WillieSoon/3-27LegatesSoonBriggs13-SCED-Agnotology.pdf

Legates, D., Soon, W., Briggs, W., & Monckton, C. (2015). Climate Consensus and 'Misinformation': A Rejoinder to Agnotology, Scientific Consensus, and the

Teaching and Learning of Climate Change. *Science and Education, 24*, 299-318. doi:10.1007/s11191-013-9647-9

Lewin, B. (2017). *Searching for the Catastrophe Signal.* Global Warming Policy Foundation. Retrieved from https://www.amazon.com/Searching-Catastrophe-Signal-Origins-Intergovernmental/dp/0993118992

Lewis, N., & Curry, J. (2015). The implications for climate sensitivity of AR5 forcing and heat uptake estimates. *Climate Dynamics, 45*, 1009-1023. Retrieved from https://search.proquest.com/openview/2f4994e4ab3a28571ecdff2edb3aeb13/1?pq-origsite=gscholar&cbl=54165

Lewis, N., & Curry, J. (2018, April 23). The impact of recent forcing and ocean heat uptake data on estimates of climate sensitivity. *Journal of Climate.* Retrieved from https://journals.ametsoc.org/doi/10.1175/JCLI-D-17-0667.1

Lieberman, B. (2000, July 1). *Say Goodbye to Your Washing Machine.* Retrieved from CEI: https://cei.org/news-letters-cei-planet/say-goodbye-your-washing-machine

Lieberman, B. (2019, May 14). *Can Trump Save Your Air Conditioner from the Deep State?* Retrieved from Competitive Enterprise Institute: https://cei.org/blog/can-trump-save-your-air-conditioner-deep-state

Lieberman, B. (2020, January 29). *Department of Energy Finalizes Process Rule for Appliance Efficiency Standards Process Rule for Appliance Efficiency Standards.* Retrieved from Competitive Enterprise Institute: https://cei.org/blog/department-energy-finalizes-process-rule-appliance-efficiency-standards

Lindsey, R. (2003, August 1). *Under a Variable Sun.* Retrieved from Earth Observatory: https://web.archive.org/web/20150908095752/http://earthobservatory.nasa.gov/Features/VariableSun/printall.php

Lindzen, R. (2015, March 4). The Political Assault on Climate Skeptics. *Wall Street Journal.* Retrieved from https://www.wsj.com/articles/richard-s-lindzen-the-political-assault-on-climate-skeptics-1425513033

Lindzen, R., & Choi, Y.-S. (2011, August 28). On the Observational Determination of Climate Sensitivity and Implications. *Asia-Pacific Journal of Atmospheric Sciences, 47*(377). Retrieved from https://link.springer.com/article/10.1007/s13143-011-0023-x#citeas

Liu, M. (2018, March 23). *Great Pacific Garbage Patch now three times the size of France.* Retrieved from CNN: https://www.cnn.com/2018/03/23/world/plastic-great-pacific-garbage-patch-intl/index.html

Lockwood, G., Skiff, B., Baliunas, S., & Radick, R. (1992, December 17). Long-term solar brightness changes estimated from a survey of Sun-like stars. *Nature, 360*, 653-655. Retrieved from https://www.nature.com/articles/360653a0

Lomborg, B. (2011, December 12). Global Warming and Adaptability. *Wall Street Journal.* Retrieved from https://www.wsj.com/articles/SB100014240529702034133045770863619 84880468

Lomborg, B. (2015, September 18). Trade-Offs for Global Do-Gooders. *Wall Street Journal.* Retrieved from https://www.wsj.com/articles/trade-offs-for-global-do-gooders-1442589938

Lomborg, B. (2016, May 5). No one ever says it, but in many ways global warming will be a good thing. *The Telegraph.* Retrieved from https://www.telegraph.co.uk/news/2016/05/05/no-one-ever-says-it-but-in-many-ways-global-warming-will-be-a-go/

Lomborg, B. (2016b, November). Impact of Current Climate Proposals. *Global Policy, 7*(1), 109. Retrieved from Bjorn Lomborg, Get the facts straight: https://onlinelibrary.wiley.com/doi/epdf/10.1111/1758-5899.12295

Luxon, E. M., & Wong, W. H. (2017, February 14). Agenda-Setting in Greenpeace and Amnesty: The Limits of Centralisation in International NGOs. *Global Society,* 479-509. Retrieved from https://www.tandfonline.com/doi/abs/10.1080/13600826.2016.1277190?journalCode=cgsj20

Malakoff, D. (2003, August 8). Bush Bashed for Use of Science. *Science.* Retrieved from https://www.sciencemag.org/news/2003/08/bush-bashed-use-science

Mann, M. (2011). *Notice of Civil Claim.* Supreme Court of British Columbia. Retrieved from https://www.desmogblog.com/sites/beta.desmogblog.com/files/Mann-Ball%20Libel%20Claim.pdf

Mann, M. (2012). *Complaint and reason for Steyn and National Review lawsuit.* Washington DC: Superior Court of the District of Columbia. Retrieved from https://legaltimes.typepad.com/files/michael-mann-complaint.pdf

Mann, M. (2020, May 15). *Curriculum Vitae.* Retrieved from Michael E. Mann: http://www.meteo.psu.edu/holocene/public_html/Mann/about/cv.php

Mann, M. E. (2012). *The Hockey Stick and the Climate Wars, Dispatches from the Front Lines.* New York: Columbia. Retrieved from https://www.amazon.com/Hockey-Stick-Climate-Wars-Dispatches/dp/0231152558

Mann, M. E., Bradley, R. S., & Hughes, M. K. (1998). Global-scale temperature patterns and climate forcing over the past six centuries. *Nature, 392,* 779-787. Retrieved from https://www.nature.com/articles/33859

Mann, M. E., Zhang, Z., Rutherford, S., Bradley, R. S., Hughes, M. K., & Shindell, D. (2009, November 27). Global Signatures and Dynamical Origins of the Little Ice Age and Medieval Climate Anomaly. *Science, 27.* Retrieved from https://science.sciencemag.org/content/326/5957/1256.abstract

Mann, M., & Bradley, R. (1999, March 15). Northern Hemisphere Temperatures during the Past Millennium: Inferences, Uncertainties and Limitations. *Geophysical Research Letters, 26*(6), 759-762. doi: https://doi.org/10.1029/1999GL900070

Mann, M., & Gleick, P. (2015, March 31). Climate change and California drought in the 21st century. *PNAS.* doi:10.1073/pnas.1503667112

Mann, M., Amman, C., Bradley, R., & Briffa, K. (2003, July 8). On Past Temperatures and Anomalous Late-20th Century Warmth. *EOS, 84*(27). Retrieved from https://agupubs.onlinelibrary.wiley.com/doi/pdf/10.1029/2003EO27000 3

Mann, M., Zhang, Z., Hughes, M., Bradley, R., Miller, S., Rutherford, S., & Ni, F. (2008). Proxy-based reconstructions of hemispheric and global surface temperature variations over the past two millennia. *PNAS.* Retrieved from https://www.pnas.org/content/105/36/13252.short

Marcott, S. A., Shakun, J. D., Clark, P. U., & Mix, A. C. (2013, March 8). A Reconstruction of Regional and Global Temperature for the Past 11,300 Years. *Science,* 1198-1201. Retrieved from https://science.sciencemag.org/CONTENT/339/6124/1198.abstract

Marcott, S., Shakun, J., Clark, P., & Mix, A. (2013c). Supplementary Materials for A Reconstruction of Regional and Global Temperature for the Past 11,300 Years. *Science.* Retrieved from http://science.sciencemag.org/content/suppl/2013/03/07/339.6124.1198 .DC1

Mass, C. (2017, August). *Global Warming and Hurricane Harvey.* Retrieved from Cliff Mass Weather Blog: https://cliffmass.blogspot.com/2017/08/global-warming-and-hurricane-harvey.html?m=1

May, A. (2015, August 23). *A Summary of the APS Workshop on Climate Change.* Retrieved from andymaypetrophysicist.com: https://andymaypetrophysicist.com/a-summary-of-the-aps-workshop-on-climate-change/

May, A. (2015b, November 26). *Climate and Human Civilization over the last 18,000 years, updated.* Retrieved from https://andymaypetrophysicist.com/climate-and-human-civilization-over-the-last-18000-years/

May, A. (2016d). CO2, Good or Bad. Retrieved from https://andymaypetrophysicist.com/co2-good-or-bad/

May, A. (2016h, October 8). *The Economist, Fossil Fuel Subsidies and Climate Disaster.* Retrieved from andymaypetrophysicist.com: https://andymaypetrophysicist.com/the-economist-fossil-fuel-subsidies-and-climate-disaster/

May, A. (2016i, December 21). *Detection and Attribution of man-made climate change.* Retrieved from andymaypetrophysicist.com: https://andymaypetrophysicist.com/detection-and-attribution-of-man-made-climate-change/

May, A. (2016j, January 3). *Greenpeace Crimes and Lies.* Retrieved from andymaypetrophysicist.com: https://andymaypetrophysicist.com/greenpeace-crimes-and-lies-2/

May, A. (2016k, September 27). *Solar Variability and the Earth's Climate.* Retrieved from andymaypetrophysicist.com: https://andymaypetrophysicist.com/solar-variability-and-the-earths-climate/

May, A. (2016m, August 6). *Politifact or Politi-fiction.* Retrieved from andymaypetrophysicist.com: https://andymaypetrophysicist.com/politifact-or-politi-fiction/

May, A. (2016p). *The Exxon Climate Papers.* Retrieved from andymaypetrophysicist.com: https://andymaypetrophysicist.com/did-exxon-lie-about-the-dangers-of-climate-change-or-are-they-being-silenced-through-intimidation/

May, A. (2017, December 28). *Glaciers and Sea Level Rise.* Retrieved from andymaypetrophysicist.com: https://andymaypetrophysicist.com/2017/12/28/glaciers-and-sea-level-rise/

May, A. (2017h, June 9). *A Holocene Temperature Reconstruction Part 4: The global reconstruction.* Retrieved from https://andymaypetrophysicist.com/2017/06/09/a-holocene-temperature-reconstruction-part-4-the-global-reconstruction/

May, A. (2017k, March 18). *Exergy and Power Plants.* Retrieved from andymaypetrophysicist.com: https://andymaypetrophysicist.com/exergy-and-power-plants/

May, A. (2018). *Climate Catastrophe! Science or Science Fiction?* American Freedom Publications LLC. Retrieved from https://www.amazon.com/CLIMATE-CATASTROPHE-Science-Fiction-ebook/dp/B07CPHCBV1/ref=sr_1_1?ie=UTF8&qid=1535627846&sr=8-1&keywords=climate+catastrophe+science+or+science+fiction

May, A. (2018, May 2). *Climate Change, Due to Solar Variability or Greenhouse Gases? Part A.* Retrieved from andymaypetrophysicist.com: https://andymaypetrophysicist.com/2018/05/02/climate-change-due-to-solar-variability-or-greenhouse-gases-part-a/

May, A. (2018c, May 3). *Climate Change, due to Solar Variability or Greenhouse Gases, Part B.* Retrieved from andymaypetrophysicist.com: https://andymaypetrophysicist.com/2018/05/03/climate-change-due-to-solar-variability-or-greenhouse-gases-part-b/

May, A. (2018d). *Climate Change: The Great Debate.* The Woodlands, Texas, USA: Andy May. Retrieved from https://andymaypetrophysicist.files.wordpress.com/2018/09/the-great-debate-report1.pdf

May, A. (2018e, September 19). *How Constant is the Solar Constant?* Retrieved from andymaypetrophysicist.com: https://andymaypetrophysicist.com/2018/09/19/how-constant-is-the-solar-constant/

May, A. (2020a, January 3). *Earth's Ice Ages.* Retrieved from andymaypetrophysicist.com: https://andymaypetrophysicist.com/2020/01/03/earths-ice-ages/

May, A. (2020b, April 18). *IPCC Politics and Solar Variability.* Retrieved from andymaypetrophysicist.com: https://andymaypetrophysicist.com/2020/04/18/ipcc-politics-and-solar-variability/

May, A. (2020b, March 23). *Key Documents in the Exxon-Mobil lawsuit by state Attorneys Geneeral.* Retrieved from andymaypetrophysicist.com: https://andymaypetrophysicist.com/2020/03/23/key-documents-in-the-exxon-mobil-lawsuit-by-state-attorneys-general/

Mayewski, P. A., Rohling, E., Stager, J., Karlen, W., Maasch, K., Meeker, D., . . . Steig, E. (2004, November). Holocene Climate Variability. *Quaternary Research, 62*(3), 243-255. Retrieved from https://www.sciencedirect.com/science/article/pii/S0033589404000870

McDermott, J. (2019, April 11). *Sen. Whitehouse targets dark money to address climate change.* Retrieved from The Washington Times: https://www.washingtontimes.com/news/2019/apr/11/sen-whitehouse-targets-dark-money-to-address-clima/

McFarlane, A. (2018, November 19). *The 1870s Global Cooling Consensus was not a Myth.* Retrieved from Watts Up With That: https://wattsupwiththat.com/2018/11/19/the-1970s-global-cooling-consensus-was-not-a-myth/

McGurn, W. (2019, September 23). A Climate of Lawsuits. *WSJ.* Retrieved from https://www.wsj.com/articles/a-climate-change-for-lawsuits-11569279287

McIntosh, E. (2019, June 14). Michael E. Mann took climate change deniers to court. They apologized. *Grist.* Retrieved from https://grist.org/article/michael-e-mann-took-climate-change-deniers-to-court-they-apologized/

McIntyre, S. (2010). Climategate: A Battlefield Perspective. *Heartland Conference.* Chicago: Heartland. Retrieved from http://www.climateaudit.info/pdf/mcintyre-heartland_2010.pdf

McIntyre, S. (2011, May 29). *Keith's Science Trick, Mike's Nature Trick and Phil's Combo.* Retrieved from Climate Audit: https://climateaudit.org/2011/03/29/keiths-science-trick-mikes-nature-trick-and-phils-combo/

McIntyre, S. (2014, September 6). *The Original Hide-the-Decline.* Retrieved from Climate Audit: https://climateaudit.org/2014/09/06/the-original-hide-the-decline/

McIntyre, S. (2015, September 28). *Shukla's Gold.* Retrieved from Climate Audit: https://climateaudit.org/2015/09/28/shuklas-gold/

McIntyre, S., & McKitrick, R. (2003, November 1). Corrections to the Mann et. al. (1998) Proxy Data Base and Northern Hemispheric Average Temperature Series. *Energy and Environment.* Retrieved from https://journals.sagepub.com/doi/abs/10.1260/095830503322793632

McIntyre, S., & McKitrick, R. (2005). Hockey sticks, principal components, and spurious significance. *Geophysical Research Letters, 32.* doi:10.1029/2004GL021750

McIntyre, S., & McKitrick, R. (2005c). The M&M Critique of the MBH98 Northern Hemisphere Climate Index: Update and Implications. *Energy and Environment, 16*(1). Retrieved from http://citeseerx.ist.psu.edu/viewdoc/download?doi=10.1.1.96.8159&rep=rep1&type=pdf

McKitrick, R. (2005, April 4). What is the Hockey Stick Debate About. *APEC Study Group, Australia.* Retrieved from http://www.geo.utexas.edu/courses/387H/PAPERS/conf05mckitrick.pdf

Mendizabal, I., Keller, T., Zeng, J., & Yi, S. (2014, July). Epigenetics and Evolution. *54*(1). doi:https://doi.org/10.1093/icb/icu040

Mervis, J. (2017, March 9). *Data check: U.S. government share of basic research funding falls below 50%.* Retrieved from Science: https://www.sciencemag.org/news/2017/03/data-check-us-government-share-basic-research-funding-falls-below-50

Met Office. (2013). *The recent pause in global warming (2): What are the potential causes.* MET office. Retrieved from https://www.metoffice.gov.uk/binaries/content/assets/metofficegovuk/pdf/research/climate-science/climate-observations-projections-and-impacts/paper2_recent_pause_in_global_warming.pdf

Met Office Hadley Centre. (2017). HadCRUT 4 Data: download. Retrieved from https://www.metoffice.gov.uk/hadobs/hadcrut4/data/current/download.html

Met Office Hadley Centre datasets. (2020, July 22). *Met Office Hadley Centre datasets, HadSST 4.0 download.* Retrieved from Met Office: https://www.metoffice.gov.uk/hadobs/hadsst4/data/download.html

Michaels, P., & Knappenberger, P. (1996). Human effect on global climate? *Nature,* 522-523. Retrieved from https://www.nature.com/articles/384522b0

Mitchell, C. (2019, August 20). *Failure of Climate Communications and Law to Register.* Retrieved from Daily Caller: https://cdn01.dailycaller.com/wp-content/uploads/2019/08/20190820095056.pdf

Moberg, A. (2020, July). *Paleoclimatology Data.* Retrieved from NOAA: https://www.ncdc.noaa.gov/data-access/paleoclimatology-data

Moberg, A., Sonechkin, D., Holmgren, K., Datsenko, N., & Karlen, W. (2005). Highly variable Northern Hemisphere temperatures reconstructed from low- and high-resolution proxy data. *Nature, 433,* 613-617. Retrieved from https://www.nature.com/articles/nature03265

Mohleji, S., & Pielke Jr., R. (2014, November). Reconciliation of Trends in Global and Regional Economic Losses from Weather Events: 1980–2008. *Natural Hazards Review, 15*(4).

Monckton, C., Soon, W., Legates, D., & Briggs, W. (2015, January). Why Models run hot: results from an irreducibly simple climate model. *Science Bulletin, 60*(1), 122-135. doi:https://doi.org/10.1007/s11434-014-0699-2

Montford, A. (2010). *The Hockey Stick Illusion.* Stacey International Publishing. Retrieved from https://www.amazon.com/Hockey-Stick-Illusion-Andrew-Montford-ebook/dp/B0182I73BA/ref=sr_1_1?dchild=1&keywords=The+Hockey+Stick+Illusion&qid=1590414534&sr=8-1

Montford, A. (2015, February 22). *Another witchhunt.* Retrieved from Bishop Hill: http://bishophill.squarespace.com/blog/2015/2/22/another-witchhunt.html

Morano, M. (2015, September 3). *'It's All Wrong': UN IPCC Lead Author Dr. Richard Tol slams media for false claims about alleged 97% consensus.* Retrieved from Climate Depot: https://www.climatedepot.com/2015/09/03/its-all-wrong-un-convening-lead-author-dr-richard-tol-slams-media-for-false-claims-about-alleged-97-consensus/

Morano, M. (2015, September 20). *Update: Scientist leading effort to prosecute climate skeptics under RICO 'paid himself & his wife $1.5 million from govt climate grants for part-time work'.* Retrieved from Climate Depot: https://www.climatedepot.com/2015/09/20/update-leader-of-effort-to-prosecute-skeptics-under-rico-paid-himself-his-wife-1-5-million-from-govt-climate-grants-for-part-time-work/

Mundahl, E. (2018, September 25). *Meet the Man Behind the Global Warming Lawsuits Racket.* Retrieved from InsideSources: https://www.insidesources.com/whos-at-the-bottom-of-the-climate-change-lawsuit-racket-it-looks-like-matt-pawa/

Munk, W., & Frieman, E. (1992). Let Roger Revelle Speak for Himself. *Oceanography, 5*(2), 125. Retrieved from https://tos.org/oceanography/article/let-roger-revelle-speak-for-himself

National Research Council. (2006). *Surface Temperature Reconstructions for the Last 2,000 Years.* Washington, DC: The National Academies Press. doi:https://doi.org/10.17226/11676

National Review. (2020, February 27). No, Michael Mann, You Aren't Going to 'Ruin' this 'Filthy Organization'. *National Review.* Retrieved from https://www.nationalreview.com/2020/02/no-michael-mann-you-arent-going-to-ruin-this-filthy-organization/

National Review Editors. (2010, February 10). *Climate Götterdämmerung*. Retrieved from National Review: https://www.nationalreview.com/2010/02/climate-g-tterd-mmerung-editors/

National Science Foundation. (2011). *Closeout Memorandum*. National Science Foundation. Retrieved from https://www.nsf.gov/oig/case-closeout/A09120086.pdf

Nature. (2020). Epigenetics. *Nature*. Retrieved from https://www.nature.com/subjects/epigenetics

Nature.com. (2018). Availability of data, material and methods. *Nature*. Retrieved from https://www.nature.com/authors/policies/availability.html

New York Times. (2015, November 6). A Range of Opinions on Climate Change at Exxon Mobil. *New York Times*. Retrieved from https://www.nytimes.com/interactive/2015/11/06/science/exxon-mobil-global-warming-statements-climate-change.html

New York Times. (2015, February 15). *Funding that Climate Researcher Failed to Disclose*. Retrieved from New York Times: https://www.nytimes.com/interactive/2015/02/21/science/document-climate.html

Newell, R., & Dopplick, T. (1979). Questions Concerning the Possible Influence of Anthropogenic CO2 on Atmospheric Temperature. *J. Applied Meterology, 18*, 822-825. Retrieved from http://journals.ametsoc.org/doi/pdf/10.1175/1520-0450(1979)018%3C0822%3AQCTPIO%3E2.0.CO%3B2

Nisbet, M. (2018, May 22). Strategic philanthropy in the post-Cap-and-Trade years: Reviewing U.S. climate and energy foundation funding. *WIRES Climate Change, 9*(4). doi:https://doi.org/10.1002/wcc.524

NOAA. (2020). *What are El Nino and La Nina?* Retrieved from noaa.gov: https://oceanservice.noaa.gov/facts/ninonina.html

Nordhaus, W. (1990). Global CO2 Emissions Reductions: The Impacts of Rising Energy Costs. In H. Aaron, *Setting National Priorities: Policy for the Nineties* (pp. 185-211). Retrieved from https://www.osti.gov/biblio/5062180

Nordhaus, W. (2007). *Professor Revelle explained that higher levels of CO2 would create what he called the greenhouse effect, which would cause the earth to grow warmer*. New Haven , Connecticutt: Yale University. Retrieved from http://www.econ.yale.edu/~nordhaus/homepage/OldWebFiles/DICEGAMS/dice_mss_072407_all.pdf

Norero, D. (2018, June 20). *Unfairly demonized GMO crops can help fight malnutrition.* Retrieved from Cornell Alliance for Science: https://allianceforscience.cornell.edu/blog/2018/06/unfairly-demonized-gmo-crops-can-help-fight-malnutrition/

North, G. R. (2013). *Climate Change Data for the Future of Engineered River Basins.* Retrieved from https://www.harcresearch.org/sites/default/files/Climate%20Change%20Data%20for%20the%20Future%20of%20Engineered%20River%20Basins.pdf

North, G., Biondi, F., Bloomfield, P., Christy, J., Cuffey, K., Dickson, R., . . . Otto-Bliesner, B. (2006). *High Confidence' That Planet Is Warmest in 400 Years; Less Confidence in Temperature Reconstructions Prior to 1600.* Retrieved from https://www.nationalacademies.org/news/2006/06/high-confidence-that-planet-is-warmest-in-400-years-less-confidence-in-temperature-reconstructions-prior-to-1600

Oosthoek, K. J. (2015, June 5). *Little Ice Age.* Retrieved from Environmental History Resources: https://www.eh-resources.org/little-ice-age/

Open Science Collaboration. (2015, August). Estimating the reproducibility of psychological science. *Science, 349*(6251). Retrieved from http://science.sciencemag.org/content/349/6251/aac4716

Oreskes, N. (2004, December 3). The Scientific Consensus on Climate Change. *Science, 306*(5702). Retrieved from https://science.sciencemag.org/content/306/5702/1686/

Oreskes, N., & Conway, E. (2010). *Merchants of Doubt.* New York: Bloomsbury Press. Retrieved from https://www.google.com/books/edition/Merchants_of_Doubt/fpMh3nh3JI0C?hl=en&gbpv=1&printsec=frontcover

Oskin, B. (2013, May 31). Carbon Dioxide Greening Deserts. *Live Science.* Retrieved from https://www.livescience.com/37055-greenhouse-gas-desert-plants-growing.html

Pages2K. (2019, July 24). Consistent multidecadal variability in global temperature reconstructions and simulations over the Common Era. *Nature Geoscience.* Retrieved from https://www.nature.com/articles/s41561-019-0400-0

Patrick, W. (2019, February 21). 24 Media Organizations Oppose Defamation Suit Waged by Climate Scientist. *Epoch Times.* Retrieved from https://www.theepochtimes.com/24-media-organizations-oppose-defamation-suit-waged-by-climate-scientist_2810374.html

Pawa, M. (2016, January 8). *Agenda*. Retrieved from eidclimate.org: https://eidclimate.org/wp-content/uploads/2017/10/Rockefeller-ExxonKnew-Strategy-Meeting-Memo-Jan-2016.pdf

Pennsylvania State University. (2010). *RA-1O Final Investigation Report Involving Dr. Michael E, Mann*. Retrieved from https://www.psu.edu/ur/2014/fromlive/Final_Investigation_Report.pdf

Peterson, T., Connolley, W., & Fleck, J. (2008, September 1). The Myth of the 1970s Global Cooling Scientific Consensus. *BAMS*. Retrieved from https://journals.ametsoc.org/bams/article/89/9/1325/59455

petitionproject.org. (2009). *Global Warming Petition Project*. Retrieved from http://www.petitionproject.org/index.php

Pielke Jr., R. (2005). Misdefining "climate change": consequences for science and action. *Environmental Science and Policy, 8*, 548-561. Retrieved from https://www.uvic.ca/research/centres/globalstudies/assets/docs/publications/RPielke.pdf

Pielke Jr., R. (2010). *The Climate Fix, What Scientists and Politicians won't tell you about global warming*. New York, New York, USA: Basic Books. Retrieved from link: http://sciencepolicy.colorado.edu/publications/special/climate_fix/index.html

Pielke Jr., R. (2015, February 25). *I am under "Investigation"*. Retrieved from The Climate Fix: https://theclimatefix.wordpress.com/2015/02/25/i-am-under-investigation/

Pielke Jr., R. (2017). *Statement of Dr. Roger Pielke, Jr. to the Committee on Science, Space and Technology of the U.S. House of Representatives*. U.S. House of Representatives, Washington, DC. Retrieved from https://science.house.gov/imo/media/doc/Pielke%20Testimony1.pdf

Pielke Jr., R. (2017b, November 15). A Litigious Climate Threatens Scientific Norms. *Wall Street Journal*. Retrieved from https://www.wsj.com/articles/a-litigious-climate-threatens-scientific-norms-1510789511

Pierrehumbert, R. (2011, January). Infrared radiation and planetary temperature. *Physics Today*, pp. 33-38. Retrieved from http://faculty.washington.edu/dcatling/555_PlanetaryAtmos/Pierrehumbert2011_RadiationPhysToday.pdf

Pierson, B. (2019, December 10). Exxon Mobil scores win in New York climate change lawsuit. *Reuters*. Retrieved from https://www.reuters.com/article/us-exxon-mobil-lawsuit/exxon-mobil-scores-win-in-new-york-climate-change-lawsuit-idUSKBN1YE1ZU

Pile, B. (2013, July 23). *What's behind the battle of received wisdoms?* Retrieved from University of Nottingham: http://blogs.nottingham.ac.uk/makingsciencepublic/2013/07/23/whats-behind-the-battle-of-received-wisdoms/

PNAS. (2020, May 13). *Editorial & Journal Policies.* Retrieved from PNAS: https://www.pnas.org/page/authors/journal-policies

Popper, K. R. (1962). *Conjectures and Refutations, The Growth of Scientific Knowledge.* New York: Basic Books. Retrieved from http://ninthstreetcenter.org/Popper.pdf

Property Rights Alliance. (2019). *Countries.* Retrieved from International Property Rights Index: https://www.internationalpropertyrightsindex.org/countries

Qiu, L. (2015, August 28). *Rick Santorum.* Retrieved from Politifact: https://www.politifact.com/factchecks/2015/sep/02/rick-santorum/santorum-un-climate-head-debunked-widely-cited-97-/

Rasmussen. (2016, August 9). *Most Still Oppose Government Prosecution of Global Warming Critics.* Retrieved from Rasmussen Reports: https://www.rasmussenreports.com/public_content/politics/current_events/environment_energy/most_still_oppose_government_prosecution_of_global_warming_critics

Rasmussen. (2017, January 26). *50% Say There Are Too Many Government Regulations on Business.* Retrieved from Rasmussen Reports: https://www.rasmussenreports.com/public_content/business/general_business/january_2017/50_say_there_are_too_many_government_regulations_on_business

Rasmussen. (2019, September 26). *33% say New York Times is usually accurate.* Retrieved from Rasmussen Reports: https://www.rasmussenreports.com/public_content/politics/general_politics/september_2019/33_say_new_york_times_is_usually_accurate

Rasmussen. (2019, November 14). *Most Say Media Working with Democrats to Impeach Trump.* Retrieved from Rasmussen Reports: https://www.rasmussenreports.com/public_content/politics/trump_administration/november_2019/most_say_media_working_with_democrats_to_impeach_trump

Rasmussen. (2019, December 5). *Voters Blame Humans for Climate Change But Spare Air Travel, Meat Consumption.* Retrieved from Rasmussen Reports: https://www.rasmussenreports.com/public_content/politics/partner_surveys/voters_blame_humans_for_climate_change_but_spare_air_travel_meat_consumption

Rasmussen. (2020, July 17). *63% Say Most News Organizations Are Politically Biased.* Retrieved from Rasmussen Reports: https://www.rasmussenreports.com/public_content/politics/general_polit ics/july_2020/63_say_most_news_organizations_are_politically_biased

Regalado, A. (2006, June 23). Panel Study Fails To Settle Debate On Past Climates. *Wall Street Journal.* Retrieved from https://www.wsj.com/articles/SB115098487133887497

Revelle, R., & Suess, H. E. (1957). Carbon Dioxide Exchange Between Atmosphere and Ocean and the Question of an Increase of Atmospheric CO2 during the Past Decades. *Tellus.* doi:https://doi.org/10.3402/tellusa.v9i1.9075

Revkin, A. (2005, June 8). Bush Aide Softened Greenhouse Gas Links to Global Warming. *New York Times.* Retrieved from https://www.nytimes.com/2005/06/08/politics/bush-aide-softened-greenhouse-gas-links-to-global-warming.html

Reynolds, G. H. (2016, April 11). Dear attorneys general, conspiring against free speech is a crime: Glenn Reynolds. *USA Today.* Retrieved from https://www.usatoday.com/story/opinion/2016/04/11/attorney-generals-conspire-free-speech-schneiderman-harris-exxon-cei-column/82878218/

Richard, K. (2016, September 13). *Massive Cover-up Exposed: 285 Papers From 1960s-'80s Reveal Robust Global Cooling Scientific 'Consensus'.* Retrieved from notrickszone.com: http://notrickszone.com/2016/09/13/massive-cover-up-exposed-285-papers-from-1960s-80s-reveal-robust-global-cooling-scientific-consensus/#sthash.7O4otojA.dpbs

Ridley, M. (2013, October 19). Why climate change is good for the world. *The Spectator.* Retrieved from https://www.spectator.co.uk/article/why-climate-change-is-good-for-the-world

Rinne, G. (2019, March 14). *Six years later, Resolute lawsuit against Greenpeace continues.* Retrieved from tbnewswatch.com: https://www.tbnewswatch.com/local-news/six-years-later-resolute-lawsuit-against-greenpeace-continues-1319638

Risky Business Project. (2020). *The Economic Risks of Climate Change in the United States.* Retrieved from Risky Business: https://riskybusiness.org/report/national/

Rose, C. (2010). *How to Win Campaigns.* Routledge. Retrieved from https://www.amazon.com/How-Win-Campaigns-Chris-Rose/dp/1849711143

Rosenthal, Y., Linsley, B., & Oppo, D. (2013, November 1). Pacific Ocean Heat Content During the Past 10,000 years. *Science*. Retrieved from http://science.sciencemag.org/content/342/6158/617

Royal Society. (2020, May 25). *History of the Royal Society*. Retrieved from The Royal Society: https://royalsociety.org/about-us/history/

Russell, M. (2010, July). *The Independent Climate Change Review*. Retrieved from http://www.cce-review.org/pdf/FINAL%20REPORT.pdf

Sanchez, I. (2003, September 12). *Warming Study Draws Fire*. Retrieved from The Crimson: https://www.thecrimson.com/article/2003/9/12/warming-study-draws-fire-a-study/

Santer, B. (1996c, June 25). No Deception in Global Warming Report. *Wall Street Journal*. Retrieved from https://www.wsj.com/articles/SB835642517444561000

Santer, B. D., Wigley, T. M., Barnett, T. P., & Anyamba, E. (1996b). Detection of climate change and attribution of causes. In *Climate Change 1995 (IPCC)*.

Santer, B., Taylor, K., Penner, J., Wigley, T. M., Johns, T. C., Jones, P. D., & Karoly, D. J. (1996a, July 4). A search for human influences on the thermal structure of the atmosphere. *Nature, 382*, 39-46. Retrieved from https://www.nature.com/articles/382039a0

Santer, B., Taylor, K., Wigley, T., Penner, J., Jones, P., & Cubasch, U. (1995). Towards the detection and attribution of an anthropogenic effect on climate. *Climate Dynamics, 12*, 77-100. doi:https://doi.org/10.1007/BF00223722

Sarewitz, D., & Pielke Jr., R. (2000, July). Breaking the Global Warming Gridlock. *The Atlantic*. Retrieved from https://www.theatlantic.com/magazine/archive/2000/07/breaking-the-global-warming-gridlock/304973/

Scafetta, N., & Willson, R. (2014). ACRIM total solar irradiance satellite composite validation versus TSI proxy models. *Astrophysics and Space Science, 350*(2), 421-442. Retrieved from https://link.springer.com/article/10.1007/s10509-013-1775-9

Scafetta, N., Willson, R., Lee, J., & Wu, D. L. (2019). Modeling Quiet Solar Luminosity Variability from TSI Satellite Measurements and proxy Models during 1980-2018. *Remote Sensing, 11*. Retrieved from https://www.mdpi.com/2072-4292/11/21/2569

Schleeter, R. (2020, July 30). *Greenpeace USA Commends the Environmental Justice for All Act*. Retrieved from Greenpeace:

https://www.greenpeace.org/usa/news/greenpeace-usa-commends-the-environmental-justice-for-all-act/

Schlingemann, S., & Foppiano, F. (2007, November 17). *Press Conference for the release of the IPCC Synthesis Report*. Retrieved from IPCC: https://www.ipcc.ch/site/assets/uploads/2018/04/press-conference-18-october-2007.pdf

Schulte, K. (2008). Scientific consensus on climate change? *Energy and Environment.* Retrieved from https://journals.sagepub.com/doi/abs/10.1260/095830508783900744

Schwartz, J. (2016a, March 29). Exxon Mobil Climate Change Inquiry on New York Gains Allies. *New York Times.* Retrieved from https://www.nytimes.com/2016/03/30/science/new-york-climate-change-inquiry-into-exxon-adds-prosecutors.html

Schwartz, J. (2016b, April 14). Pressure on Exxon Over Climate Change Intensifies With New Documents. *New York Times.* Retrieved from https://www.nytimes.com/2016/04/14/science/pressure-on-exxon-over-climate-change-intensifies-with-new-documents.html?_r=2

Scotese, C. (2015). *Some thoughts on Global Climate Change: The Transition from Icehouse to Hothouse.* PALEOMAP Project. Retrieved from https://www.researchgate.net/profile/Christopher_Scotese3/project/Earth-History-The-Evolution-of-the-Earth-System/attachment/575023e708aec90a33750af1/AS:368505070342144@1464869863189/download/Some+Thoughts+on+Global+Climate+Change v21ar+copy.pdf

Seitz, F. (1996, June 12). A Major Deception on Global Warming. *Wall Street Journal.* Retrieved from https://www.wsj.com/articles/SB834512411338954000

Severinghaus, J. P., Sowers, T., Brook, E. J., Alley, R. B., & Bender, M. L. (1998, January 8). Timing of abrupt climate change at the end of the Younger Dryas interval from thermally fractionated gases in polar ice. *Nature, 391,* pp. 141-146. Retrieved from http://shadow.eas.gatech.edu/~jean/paleo/Severinghaus_1998.pdf

Shapiro, A., Schmutz, W., Rozanov, E., Schoell, M., Haberreiter, M., Shapiro, A. V., & Nyeki, S. (2011, May). A new approach to the long-term reconstruction of the solar irradiance leads to large historical solar forcing. *Astronomy and Astrophysics, 529.* Retrieved from https://www.aanda.org/index.php?Itemid=129&access=doi&doi=10.1051/0004-6361/201016173&option=com_article

Shepherd, T. (2019, October 12). Climate Change Reporting Website Obscures Its Funding with Dark Money Network. *Washington Free Beacon*. Retrieved from https://freebeacon.com/issues/climate-change-reporting-website-obscures-its-funding-with-dark-money-network/

Shollenberger, B. (2012, March 7). *A detailed review of Mann's book: The Hockey Stick and the Climate Wars as it relates to the Wegman report to Congress*. Retrieved from Wattsupwiththat.com: https://wattsupwiththat.com/2012/03/07/a-detailed-review-of-manns-book-the-hockey-stick-and-the-climate-wars-as-it-relates-to-the-wegman-report-to-congress/?ak_action=reject_mobile

Shukla, J. (2015, September 1). *Letter to President Obama, Attorney General Lynch, and OSTP Director Holdren*. Retrieved from Internet Archive, Wayback Machine: https://web.archive.org/web/20150920110942/http://www.iges.org/letter/LetterPresidentAG.pdf

Shulman, S. (2012). *Establishing Accountability for Climate Change Damages: Lessons from Tobacco Control*. La Jolla: Climate Accountablity Institute and the Union of Concerned Scientists. Retrieved from https://climateaccountability.org/pdf/Climate%20Accountability%20Rpt%20Oct12.pdf

Shultz, N. (2003, October 28). Researchers question key global-warming study. *USA Today*. Retrieved from https://usatoday30.usatoday.com/news/opinion/editorials/2003-10-28-schulz_x.htm

SILSO. (2020, August 10). *Sunspot Number*. Retrieved from Sunspot Index and Long-term Solar Observations: http://www.sidc.be/silso/datafiles

Simberg, R. (2012, July 13). *The Other Scandal in Unhappy Valley*. Retrieved from Compretitive Enterprise Institute: https://cei.org/blog/other-scandal-unhappy-valley

Singer, S. F. (2003). The Revelle-Gore Story: Attempted political suppression of science. In M. Gough, *Politicizing Science* (p. 313). Hoover Institution Press. Retrieved from https://www.amazon.com/Politicizing-Science-Policymaking-Institution-Publication-ebook/dp/B001E5E4TS/ref=sr_1_1?dchild=1&keywords=Politicizing+Science&qid=1587729383&sr=8-1

Singer, S. F., Revelle, R., & Starr, C. (1991). What To Do about Greenhouse Warming: Look Before you Leap. *Cosmos: A Journal of Emerging Issues, 1*(1). Retrieved from https://www.semanticscholar.org/paper/What-To-Do-about-

Greenhouse-Warming%3A-Look-Before-Singer-
Revelle/a10b19cbbdeebb465dbd442b6a345188fd1250e2

Smith, B. (2020, January 20). Celebrate the Citizens United Decade. *Wall Street Journal*. Retrieved from https://www.wsj.com/articles/celebrate-the-citizens-united-decade-11579553962

Smith, L. (2017, March 30). *H.R. 1430 - HONEST Act*. Retrieved from Congress.Gov: https://www.congress.gov/bill/115th-congress/house-bill/1430/text

Smithsonian Astrophysical Observatory. (2012). *FOIA Request Documents*. Retrieved from PDF: https://s3.amazonaws.com/s3.documentcloud.org/documents/1531939/foia-response-willie-soon-2012.pdf

Smithsonian Institution. (2020, May 11). *Records Requests*. Retrieved from Smithsonian: https://www.si.edu/ogc/records-requests

Smythies, J., Edelstein, L., & Ramachandran, V. (2014). Molecular mechanisms for the inheritance of acquired characteristics—exosomes, microRNA shuttling, fear and stress: Lamarck resurrected? *Frontiers in Genetics, 5*. doi:10.3389/fgene.2014.00133

Sobczyk, N., & Koss, G. (2018, August 22). *Conservatives warn endangerment finding fight is 'still alive'*. Retrieved from E&E News: https://www.eenews.net/stories/1060094933

Soltis, D., & Soltis, P. (1989, August). Allopolyploid Speciation in Tragopogon: Insights from Chloroplast DNA. *Botany, 76*(8). Retrieved from https://bsapubs.onlinelibrary.wiley.com/doi/epdf/10.1002/j.1537-2197.1989.tb15096.x

Sonderegger, P., & Owens, S. (2019). *Waters of the United States' Rule from EPA, Corps May Make Real Estate Development More Easily Achievable and Less Costly*. Retrieved from American Bar Association: https://www.americanbar.org/groups/real_property_trust_estate/publications/ereport/rpte-ereport-winter-2019/_waters-of-the-united-states-rule-from-epa--corps-may-make--real/#:~:text=In%202015%2C%20under%20the%20Obama,any%20body%20of%20water%20within

Song, L. (2008). *Innovation Together: Microsoft Research Asia Academic Research Collaboration*. Springer. Retrieved from https://books.google.com/books?id=tVBcDyCX1rUC&pg=PR9&lpg=PR9&dq=China+University+and+corporation+joint+research+results&source=bl&ots=sI_BOEyVQV&sig=ACfU3U1sMmMz3h4dDs_wbWLzYR4

7nlU6Cg&hl=en&sa=X&ved=2ahUKEwjsifnHtrHqAhUSZKwKHTbbBs
IQ6AEwAnoECAcQAQ#v=onepa

Soon, W., & Baliunas, S. (2003). Proxy climatic and environmental changes of the past 1000 years. *Climate Research*, 89-110. Retrieved from https://www.int-res.com/abstracts/cr/v23/n2/p89-110/

Soon, W., & Legates, D. (2010). Avoiding Carbon Myopia: Three Considerations for Policy Makers Concerning Manmade Carbon Dioxide. *Ecology Law Currents, 37.* Retrieved from https://heinonline.org/HOL/LandingPage?handle=hein.journals/ecolwcu r37&div=3&id=&page=

Soon, W., Baliunas, S., & Legates, D. (2003c, July 8). Comment on "On Past Temperatures and Anomalous Late-20th Century Warmth". *Eos, 84*(44), 473-476. Retrieved from https://agupubs.onlinelibrary.wiley.com/doi/abs/10.1029/2003EO440007

Soon, W., Baliunas, S., Idso, C., Idso, S., & Legates, D. (2003b). Reconstructing Climatic and Environmental Changes of the Past 1000 years: A Reappraisal. *Energy and Environment, 14*(2&3). Retrieved from https://journals.sagepub.com/doi/abs/10.1260/095830503765184619

Soon, W., Connolly, R., & Connolly, M. (2015). Re-evaluating the role of solar variability on Northern Hemisphere temperature trends since the 19th century. *Earth Science Reviews, 150,* 409-452. Retrieved from https://www.sciencedirect.com/science/article/pii/S0012825215300349

Spencer, L., Bollwerk, J., & Morais, R. (1991, November). The Not So Peaceful World of Greenpeace. *Forbes.* Retrieved from http://luna.pos.to/whale/gen_art_green.html

Spencer, R. (2020, April 1). *UAH Global Temperature Update for march 2020: +0.48 deg. C.* Retrieved from Global Warming: http://www.drroyspencer.com/2020/04/uah-global-temperature-update-for-march-2020-0-48-deg-c/

Srolovic, L. (2016, March 30). *email: Re Wall Street Journal.* Retrieved from eelegal: https://eelegal.org/wp-content/uploads/2016/04/NY-OAG-wants-Pawa-to-not-confirm-participation-to-WSJ.pdf

Staton, M. (2014). The Degree is Doomed. *Harvard Business Review.* Retrieved from https://hbr.org/2014/01/the-degree-is-doomed

Stearns, P. (2012, February 22). *George Mason University* . Retrieved from USA Today: http://i.usatoday.net/communitymanager/_photos/science-fair/2012/02/22/GMU-STATEMENT-WALSCHx-large.jpg

Stevens, P. (2019, December 11). Exxon found not guilty in New York climate-change securities fraud trial, ending 4-year saga. *CNBC*. Retrieved from https://www.cnbc.com/2019/12/10/exxon-did-not-mislead-investors-a-new-york-judge-ruled-on-tuesday.html

Steyn, M. (2015). *A Disgrace to the Profession*. Stockade Books. Retrieved from https://www.amazon.com/%2522A-Disgrace-Profession%2522-Steyn-editor/dp/0986398330/ref=sr_1_1_twi_pap_2?s=books&ie=UTF8&qid=1440265074&sr=1-1&keywords=a+disgrace+to+the+profession

Strong, M. (1992, June 3). *Opening statement to the Rio Summit*. Retrieved from MauriceStrong.net:
http://www.mauricestrong.net/index.php?option=com_content&view=article&id=165&Itemid=86

Struck, D. (2014, January 10). How the "Global Cooling" Story Came to Be. *Scientific American*. Retrieved from https://www.scientificamerican.com/article/how-the-global-cooling-story-came-to-be/

Supran, G., & Oreskes, N. (2017, August 2017). Assessing ExxonMobil's climate change communications (1977-2014). *Environmental Research Letters, 12*(8). Retrieved from https://iopscience.iop.org/article/10.1088/1748-9326/aa815f?_sm_au_=iVV24w1JV7kRbjMJ

Svoboda, M. (2019, January 21). *Meet the Press' climate change episode shows a better way to cover the issue*. Retrieved from Yale Climate Connections: https://www.yaleclimateconnections.org/2019/01/nbc-meet-the-press-goes-long-on-climate-change/

Swift, A. (2017, October 11). *Americans' Views on Government Regulation Remain Steady*. Retrieved from Gallup: https://news.gallup.com/poll/220400/americans-views-government-regulation-remain-steady.aspx

Swift, A. (2017, April 5). *Six in 10 in U.S. See Partisan Bias in News Media*. Retrieved from Gallup: https://news.gallup.com/poll/207794/six-partisan-bias-news-media.aspx

Thompson, P. J. (2017, March 3). Greenpeace admits its attacks on forest products giant were 'non-verifiable statements of subjective opinion'. *Financial Post*. Retrieved from https://business.financialpost.com/news/greenpeace-admits-its-attacks-on-forest-products-giant-were-non-verifiable-statements-of-subjective-opinion

Tol, R. (2009). The Economic Effects of Climate Change. *Journal of Economic Perspectives, 23*(2), 29-51. Retrieved from https://www.aeaweb.org/articles?id=10.1257/jep.23.2.29

Tol, R. (2014b). Correction and Update: The Economic Effects of Climate Change. *Journal of Economic Perspectives, 28*(2), 221-226. Retrieved from https://www.aeaweb.org/articles?id=10.1257/jep.28.2.221

Tol, R. (2014c, May 20). UN climate change expert reveals bias in global warming report. *Fox News*. Retrieved from https://www.foxnews.com/opinion/un-climate-change-expert-reveals-bias-in-global-warming-report

Tol, R. (2015, March 29). *PPPS: Cook's missing papers.* Retrieved from Richard Tol: Ocasional thoughts on all sorts: http://richardtol.blogspot.com/2015/03/ppps-cooks-missing-papers.html

Tol, R. (2015b, March 25). *Global warming consensus claim does not stand up (author's cut).* Retrieved from Richard Tol Occasional thoughts on all sorts: http://richardtol.blogspot.com/2015/03/now-almost-two-years-old-john-cooks-97.html

Tol, R. (2015c). *Economic Impacts of climate change.* University of Sussex. Retrieved from https://www.sussex.ac.uk/webteam/gateway/file.php?name=wps-75-2015.pdf&site=24

Tol, R. S. (2014, October). Quantifying the consensus on anthropogenic global warming in the literature: A re-analysis. *Energy Policy*, 701-705. doi:https://doi.org/10.1016/j.enpol.2014.04.045

Tollefson, J. (2015, February 21). *Documents spur investigation of climate sceptic.* Retrieved from Nature: https://www.nature.com/news/documents-spur-investigation-of-climate-sceptic-1.16972?WT.mc_id=TWT_NatureNews

Tuttle, I. (2016, May 13). *Emails between Pro-RICO Climate Scientists Made Public.* Retrieved from National Review: https://www.nationalreview.com/corner/climate-change-rico-letter-george-mason-university-professors-emails/

Twain, M. (1880). *The Complete Works of Mark Twain, Mark Twains Speeches Vol. 24.* New York: Harper and Bros. Retrieved from http://archive.org/stream/completeworksofm24twai/completeworksofm24twai_djvu.txt

Twain, M. (1883). *Life on the Mississippi.* Boston: James R. Osgood and Company. Retrieved from https://www.gutenberg.org/files/245/245-h/245-h.htm#linkc17

Tyndall, J. (1859). On the transmission of heat of different qualities through gases of different kinds. *Notices of the Proceedings at the Meetings of the Royal Institution of Great Britain. 3.* Royal Institution. Retrieved from https://play.google.com/store/books/details?id=Hxc_AQAAMAAJ&rdid =book-Hxc_AQAAMAAJ&rdot=1

Tyndall, J. (1861). On the absorption and radiation of heat by gases and vapours, and on the physical connexion of radiation, absorption, and conduction. *The London, Edinburgh, and Dublin Philosophical Magazine and Journal of Science, 22*, 169-194.

U. S. Senate Committee on Environment and Public Works. (2006). *Statement of David Deming, PH.D., University of Oklahoma, College of earth and energy.* Retrieved from https://www.govinfo.gov/content/pkg/CHRG-109shrg52324/html/CHRG-109shrg52324.htm

U.S. Federal Register. (2019, October 22). *EPA.* Retrieved from EPA: https://www.epa.gov/sites/production/files/2019-09/documents/wotus_rin-2040-af74_final_frn_prepub2.pdf

U.S. Government Accountability Office (GAO). (2016). *Climate Change Funding and Management.* Retrieved from https://www.gao.gov/key_issues/climate_change_funding_management/issue_summary

U.S. House of Representatives. (2007). *Political Interference with Climate Change Science Under the Bush Administration.* Congress, Committee on Oversight and Government Reform. Retrieved from https://www.hsdl.org/?abstract&did=481710

UNFCCC. (2020). *Climate: Get the big picture.* Retrieved from United Nations Framework Convention on Climate Change: https://unfccc.int/resource/bigpicture/

UNFCCC. (2020). *Cooperation with the IPCC.* Retrieved from United Nations Climate Change: https://unfccc.int/topics/science/workstreams/cooperation-with-the-ipcc

UNFCCC. (2020, April 8). *What is the Kyoto Protocol?* Retrieved from United Nations Climate Change, Process and meetings: https://unfccc.int/kyoto_protocol

UNFCCC. (2020b, August 8). *About the Secretariat.* Retrieved from United Nations Climate Change: https://unfccc.int/about-us/about-the-secretariat

Union of Concerned Scientists. (2020, May 18). *History.* Retrieved from Union of Concerned Scientists: https://ucsusa.org/about/history

Union of Concerned Scientists. (2020b, May 18). *Union of Concerned Scientists, American Oversight Sue for Records Related to USDA Relocation.* Retrieved from Union of

Concerned Scientists: https://ucsusa.org/about/news/union-concerned-scientists-american-oversight-sue-records-related-usda-relocation

Union of Concerned Scientists. (2020c, January 29). *Presidential Recommendations for 2020.* Retrieved from Union of Concerned Scientists: https://ucsusa.org/resources/presidential-recommendations-2020

Union of Concerned Scientists. (2020d, August 17). *Climate Change.* Retrieved from Union of Concerned Scientists: https://www.ucsusa.org/climate

United Nations. (1992). *UNITED NATIONS FRAMEWORK CONVENTION ON CLIMATE CHANGE.* New York: United Nations. Retrieved from https://unfccc.int/files/essential_background/background_publications_h tmlpdf/application/pdf/conveng.pdf

University of Virginia. (2020, May 28). *What is Academic Fraud.* Retrieved from Honor Committee: https://honor.virginia.edu/academic-fraud

Valdmanis, R., Jensen, F., & Paul, S. (2014, May 13). From black to green: U.S. billionaire's 'Road to Damascus'. *Reuters.* Retrieved from https://www.reuters.com/article/us-usa-steyer-coal-insight/from-black-to-green-u-s-billionaires-road-to-damascus-idUSBREA4C06B20140513

Vergano, D. (2011, May 26). University investigating prominent climate science critic. *USA Today.* Retrieved from http://content.usatoday.com/communities/sciencefair/post/2010/10/we gman-plagiarism-investigation-/1#.XuvqjmhKiUl

Vian, T., & Crable, E. (2017). Corruption and the Consequences for Public Health. In S. Quah, & W. Cockerham, *International Encyclopedia of Public Health* (pp. 168-176). Retrieved from https://www.sciencedirect.com/science/article/pii/B97801280367850009 16

Vinós, J. (2017, April 30). *Nature Unbound III: Holocene climate variability (Part A).* Retrieved from Climate Etc.: https://judithcurry.com/2017/04/30/nature-unbound-iii-holocene-climate-variability-part-a/

Vinós, J. (2018, August 14). *Nature Unbound X - The Next Glaciation.* Retrieved from Climate, Etc.: https://judithcurry.com/2018/08/14/nature-unbound-x-the-next-glaciation/

Volodin, E., Dianskii, N., & Gusev, A. (2010). Simulating present-day climate with the INMCM4.0 coupled model of the atmospheric and oceanic general circulations. *Atmos. Ocean. Physics, 46,* 414-431. doi:https://doi.org/10.1134/S000143381004002X

Wadman, M. (2018, April 26). Famed cancer biologist allegedly sexually harassed women for decades. *Science.* Retrieved from https://www.sciencemag.org/news/2018/04/famed-cancer-biologist-allegedly-sexually-harassed-women-decades#

Waldman, S., & Bravender, R. (2018, March 16). Pruitt Expected to Limit Science Used to Make EPA Pollution Rules. *Scientific American.* Retrieved from https://www.scientificamerican.com/article/pruitt-expected-to-limit-science-used-to-make-epa-pollution-rules/

Walker, J. (1998, April 3). *Draft Global Client Science Communications Team.* Retrieved from Document Cloud: https://assets.documentcloud.org/documents/784572/api-global-climate-science-communications-plan.pdf

Wall Street Journal Editorial Board. (2009, December 8). The tip of the Climategate Iceberg. *Wall Street Journal.* Retrieved from https://www.wsj.com/articles/SB100014240527487043424045745766832116723794

Walrath, S. (2018, August 22). *Obscure Activist Emerges as key Player in Climate Litigation Campaign.* Retrieved from Energy in Depth, Climate and Environment: https://eidclimate.org/obscure-activist-emerges-as-key-player-in-climate-litigation-campaign/

Walrath, S. (2019, April 11). *How the Rockefellers Manufactured the Climate Liability Campaign.* Retrieved from Energy in Depth, Climate and Environment: https://eidclimate.org/how-the-rockefellers-manufactured-the-climate-liability-campaign/

Walrath, S. (2019b, October 14). *Climate Investigations Center Utilizes Dark Money Network to Obscure its Funders.* Retrieved from Energy in Depth, Climate and Environment: https://eidclimate.org/climate-investigations-center-utilizes-dark-money-network-to-obscure-its-funders/

Wang, Y. M., Lean, J., & Sheeley, N. R. (2005, May 20). Modeling the Sun's Magnetic Field and Irradiance since 1713. *The Astronomical Journal, 625,* 522-538. Retrieved from https://iopscience.iop.org/article/10.1086/429689/pdf

Watts, A. (2015, February 26). *Anatomy of a climate witch-hunt letter from U.S. Representative Raúl M. Grijalva.* Retrieved from Wattsupwiththat: https://wattsupwiththat.com/2015/02/26/anatomy-of-a-climate-witch-hunt-letter-from-u-s-representative-raul-m-grijalva/

Watts, A. (2016, May 13). *BREAKING: CEI Defeats RICO-20 Ringleader Shukla In FOIA Lawsuit – Emails to be are made public.* Retrieved from

Wattsupwiththat.com:
https://wattsupwiththat.com/2016/05/13/breaking-cei-defeats-rico-20-ringleader-shukla-in-foia-lawsuit-emails-to-be-made-public/

Weart, S. (2007, July). *Roger Revelle's Discovery*. Retrieved from The Discovery of Global Warming: https://history.aip.org/climate/Revelle.htm

Webster, P. (1984). The Carbon Dioxide/Climate Controversy: Some Personal Comments on Two Recent Publications. *Climatic Change, 6*, 377-390. Retrieved from https://link.springer.com/article/10.1007/BF00212629

Wegman, E., Scott, D., & Said, Y. (2010). *Ad Hoc Committee Report on the Hockey Stick Global Climate Reconstruction*. U.S. Congress. Science and Public Policy Institute. Retrieved from http://scienceandpublicpolicy.org/wp-content/uploads/2010/07/ad_hoc_report.pdf

Weingart, S. (2012, September 24). *How many citations does a paper have to get before it's significantly above baseline impact for the field?* Retrieved from scottbot.net: http://www.scottbot.net/HIAL/index.html@p=22108.html

Weinkle, J., Maue, R., & Pielke Jr., R. (2012, July 9). Historical Global Tropical Cyclone Landfalls. *AMS*. doi:https://doi.org/10.1175/JCLI-D-11-00719.1

Wheeler, A. (2020, February 25). *Science Advisory Board Engagement Process for Review of Regulatory Actions*. Retrieved from EPA: https://yosemite.epa.gov/sab/sabproduct.nsf/WebBOARD/RegReviewProcess/$File/SAB%20Engagement%20Process%20re%20Regulatory%20Actions.pdf

White House Press Secretary. (2011, July 29). *President Obama Announces Historic 54.5 mpg Fuel Efficiency Standard*. Retrieved from White House: https://obamawhitehouse.archives.gov/the-press-office/2011/07/29/president-obama-announces-historic-545-mpg-fuel-efficiency-standard

White, A. (2011, January 4). *Oceanic "garbage patch" not nearly as big as portrayed in media*. Retrieved from Oregon State University: https://today.oregonstate.edu/archives/2011/jan/oceanic-%E2%80%9Cgarbage-patch%E2%80%9D-not-nearly-big-portrayed-media

Whitehouse, S. (2015, May 29). The fossil-fuel industry's campaign to mislead the American people. *Washington Post*. Retrieved from https://www.washingtonpost.com/opinions/the-fossil-fuel-industrys-campaign-to-mislead-the-american-people/2015/05/29/04a2c448-0574-11e5-8bda-c7b4e9a8f7ac_story.html

Whitehouse, S. (2019b, April 11). *Whitehouse Introduces Disclose Act to Restore American's Trust in Democracy*. Retrieved from Sheldon Whitehouse: https://www.whitehouse.senate.gov/news/release/whitehouse-introduces-disclose-act-to-restore-americans-trust-in-democracy

Wilcox, C. (2011, December 18). *Evolution: Watching Speciation Occur | Observations*. Retrieved from Scientific American: https://blogs.scientificamerican.com/science-sushi/evolution-watching-speciation-occur-observations/

Willson, R. (1997). Total Solar Irradiance Trend During Solar Cycles 21 and 22. *Science, 277*(5334), 1963-1965. Retrieved from https://science.sciencemag.org/content/277/5334/1963

Willson, R., & Mordvinov, A. (2003). Secular total solar irradiance trend during solar cycles 21-23. *Geophysical Research Letters, 30*(5). Retrieved from https://agupubs.onlinelibrary.wiley.com/doi/epdf/10.1029/2002GL016038

World History edu. (2020, April 10). *Socrates: His Beliefs and Philosophy*. Retrieved from World History EDU.com: https://www.worldhistoryedu.com/socrates-his-beliefs-and-philosophy/

Wyatt, M. (2014). *The "Stadium Wave"*. Retrieved from Wyatt on Earth: http://www.wyattonearth.net/thestadiumwave.html

Wyatt, M., & Curry, J. (2014, May). Role for Eurasian Arctic shelf sea ice in a secularly varying hemispheric climate signal during the 20th century. *Climate Dynamics, 42*(9-10), 2763-2782. Retrieved from https://link.springer.com/article/10.1007/s00382-013-1950-2#page-1

Yale University. (2007). Yale Symposium on the Stern Review. Retrieved from http://piketty.pse.ens.fr/files/SternReviewYaleSymposium2007.pdf

Yan, H., Wei, W., Soon, W., An, Z., Zhou, W., Liu, Z., . . . Carter, R. (2015, March 9). Dynamics of the intertropical convergence zone over the western Pacific during the Little Ice Age. *Nature Geoscience, 8*, 315-320. Retrieved from https://www.nature.com/articles/ngeo2375

Yeatman, W. (2016, December 28). Can Any Branch of Government Oversee the EPA? *Competitive Enterprise Institute*. Retrieved from https://cei.org/blog/can-any-branch-government-oversee-epa

Zycher, B. (2015, February 10). The climate Comintern speaks. *The Hill*. Retrieved from https://thehill.com/blogs/pundits-blog/energy-environment/232229-the-climate-comintern-speaks

Table of Figures

Index

F

G

M

National Association of Manufacturers, 158

National Black Chamber of Commerce, 116

National Center for Atmospheric Research, xii, 65, 188

National Environmental Trust, 44

National Geographic, 202

National Research Council, 52, 58, 61, 175, 184, 186, 188, 194

National Review, 77, 174, 176, 184, 259

National Science Foundation, 129, 185

natural selection, 206, 213

NBC, 174

NCAR, xii

Neoglacial, 26

Neuendorf, Kimberly, 139
    ExxonKnew, 139

New Republic, 18

New York, 137, 139

New York Supreme Court
    ExxonKnew, 140

New York Times, 43, 47, 67, 73, 80, 81, 85, 122, 141, 142, 202
    Attacks Philip Cooney, 59
    Attacks Willie Soon, 48, 61, 73, 74, 75, 76, 77, 80, 85, 86

New Zealand, 53, 160

Newell, Reginald, 259

Newfoundland, 52, 182

Newsom, Gavin, 138

Newsweek, 18, 202

Newton, Isaac, 205

Nightline, 20

Nimbus7/ERB, 255, 257

Nimbus7/ERBS, 258

NOAA, 202
    endangerment finding, 152

Nordhaus, William, 17

North America, 54, 58

North Pacific, 183

North Pacific gyre, 121

North, Gerald, 177, 188, 190, 195, 196
    NAS Investigation, 188

Norwegian Meteorological Institute, 31

Notrickszone.com, 199

NSF
    defined, 129

Nychka, Douglas, 188

NYU, 137

O

O'Brien, Rindy, 122

O'Donovan, Kevin, 55

Obama administration, 73

Obama, Barak, 73, 124, 149, 151, 154, 215
    97% consensus, 215
    Shukla letter, 129
    transparency, 153

Office of Research and Development, 150

Only one Earth, 228

Oppo, Delia, 183

ORD
    defined, 150

Ordnance Survey of Ireland, 217

Oregon, 137

Oregon State University, 121

Oreskes, Naomi, 105, 131, 133, 143
    ExxonKnew, 140
    loses in court, 139, 140

Otto-Bliesner, Bette, 188, 195

Our Next Economy, 41

Our Next Economy, LLC, 67

OurEarth, 83

Oxford Journal, 206

T

U

V

W

X

Y

About the Author

Andy May is a writer, blogger and author living in The Woodlands, Texas. He was born in Lawrence, Kansas, but never really appreciated how interesting Kansas history was until he researched his second book. He enjoys golf and traveling in his spare time. He is also an editor for the climate blog Wattsupwiththat.com, where he has published numerous posts and is the author or co-author of seven peer-reviewed papers on various geological, engineering and petrophysical topics. He has also written about computers and computer software. His personal blog is andymaypetrophysicist.com.

He retired from a 42-year career in petrophysics in 2016. Most of his petrophysical work was for several oil and gas companies worldwide. He has worked in exploring, appraising and developing oil and gas fields in the U.S., Argentina, Brazil, Indonesia, Thailand, China, the U.K. North Sea, Canada, Mexico, Venezuela and Russia. He helped discover and appraise several large oil and gas fields.

Late in his career, he worked on unconventional shale oil and gas petrophysics and developed many unique techniques for evaluating these difficult reservoirs. In cooperation with Professor Mike Lovell (University of Leicester in the U.K.) he developed a one-week course in shale reservoir petrophysics. Andy has a B.S. in Geology from the University of Kansas.

DISCLAIMER

The material, opinions and positions presented in this book, *Politics and Climate Change: A History,* are those of the author, Andy May, and were developed as a result of significant research on the subject. The publisher and editor, American Freedom Publications LLC, make no representations or warranties of any kind and assume no liabilities of any kind with respect to the accuracy or completeness of the contents of this book.

The publisher and editor shall not be held liable or responsible to any person or entity with respect to any loss or incidental or consequential damages caused, or alleged to have been caused, directly or indirectly, by the information contained herein.

President Dwight David Eisenhower, January 17, 1961:

"In this revolution, research has become central, it also becomes more formalized, complex, and costly. A steadily increasing share is conducted for, by, or at the direction of, the federal government.

The prospect of domination of the nation's scholars by Federal employment, project allocation, and the power of money is ever present and is gravely to be regarded.

Yet in holding scientific discovery in respect, as we should, we must also be alert to the equal and opposite danger that public policy could itself become the captive of a scientific-technological elite."

President Eisenhower correctly predicted the future. We have reached the time he feared. Public policy is the captive of a scientific-technological elite. The elite are, in turn, controlled by federal bureaucrats and politicians. Both his fears were realized simultaneously, and a vicious circle of government/scientist co-dependency has developed. Government officials want predicted catastrophes to frighten the public into giving up freedom for security and scientists want a continuous supply of research dollars for themselves and their work. We've provided numerous examples of both problems in this book.

Andy May

AMERICAN FREEDOM
PUBLICATIONS